D1615934

California Farmland

Ever since California was settled by the Spanish beginning in 1749, a significant amount of the land in private ownership has consisted of large individual holdings. This study focuses on large agricultural holdings–2,000 or more acres–and provides reasons why a pattern of large landholding developed in California that was different from that which developed in other parts of the country. The author identifies the varying factors that shaped this tendency–the types of crops cultivated, the development of special markets, the supply of labor, the need for huge water projects–and examines in detail why particular uses of land made large holdings profitable and feasible.

California Farmland
A History of Large Agricultural Landholdings

ELLEN LIEBMAN

ROWMAN & ALLANHELD

ROWMAN & ALLANHELD

Published in the United States of America in 1983
by Rowman & Allanheld
(A division of Littlefield, Adams & Company)
81 Adams Drive, Totowa, New Jersey 07512

Library of Congress Cataloging in Publication Data

Liebman, Ellen, 1950-
    California farmland.

    Bibliography: p.
    Includes index.
    1. Farms, Large—California—History. 2. Land use,
Rural—California—History. 3. Land tenure—California
—History. 4. Agriculture—Economic aspects—California
—History. I. Title.
HD1471.U52C24   1983   333.33'5'09794   82-20759
ISBN 0-86598-107-8

83 84 85/ 10 9 8 7 6 5 4 3 2 1

Printed in the United States of America

For Dudley and Amie

Contents

List of Tables and Maps   ix

Acknowledgments   xi

Introduction   1

Chapter 1: From Spanish to American Control (pre-1870)   6
    The Spanish and Mexican Periods   6
    The Influence of the Ranchos   8
    The Early American Period: 1846-1870   13
    State Land Disposal up to 1870   20
    Summary and Conclusions   24
    Notes   26

Chapter 2: Complex Trends in Landownership (1870-1918)   29
    Introduction   29
    Public Land Disposal   30
    Agricultural Developments Associated with Large Holdings   43
    Intensive Cultivation and the Subdivision of Large Holdings   51
    Marketing Developments   56
    Irrigation   60
    Labor   63
    Nonagricultural Land Uses Associated with Large Holdings   67
    Summary of Landownership, 1870-1918   73
    Summary and Conclusions   79
    Notes   81

Chapter 3: Intensive Agriculture and the Consolidation of Landholdings (1918-1945)   85
    Introduction   85
    Changes in Production   86

Farm Real Estate Credit   *94*
Rise of Farm Organizations   *98*
Marketing and Prices   *100*
Water   *104*
Labor   *110*
Summary of Landownership, 1918-1945   *119*
Summary and Conclusions   *122*
Notes   *125*

Chapter 4: The Dominance of Agriculture by Large Owners
(post-World War II)   129
Introduction   *129*
Changes in Cropping Patterns   *130*
Agribusiness   *144*
Water Development   *147*
Labor Developments   *160*
Who Owns the Land?   *169*
Summary and Conclusions   *171*
Notes   *174*

Chapter 5: Conclusions on the Development of Large Agricultural
Landholdings   177
Pre-American Period   *177*
First American Period   *178*
Second American Period   *180*
General Summary of Landownership   *182*
General Summary   *183*

Appendix A: Description of the Study Used to Create
Appendix B   184

Appendix B: Large Landholdings in California —
Late 1970s   188

Bibliography   209

Index   220

List of Tables and Maps

Tables

1.1 Land Owned and Land in Cultivation in the Four Leading Cattle Counties, 1872   15

1.2 Wheat Production and Exports, 1854-1870   17

1.3 Largest Landholdings, 1871   23

1.4 Size Distribution of Landholdings, 1872   24

1.5 Number of Holdings by Size and County, 1872   25

2.1 Disposal of Federal Land in California   30

2.2 Size of Federal Land Grants in California to the Railroads   39

2.3 Miller and Lux Landholdings in the San Joaquin Valley by County, 1916   44

2.4 Some Large Delta Landholding Companies, 1918   50

2.5 Tenure of Some Large Delta Tracts, 1910   50

2.6 Values of Extensive and Intensive Crops, 1869-1919   52

2.7 Number of Bearing Trees and Vineyards in Southern California, 1890-1910   54

2.8 Irrigated Acreage in California, 1870-1919   60

2.9 Large Tracts Sold by the Railroads in California   69

2.10 Large Landholdings in California, 1916/17   76

2.11 Comparison of Concentration of Landownership in the Central Valley, 1872 and 1916/17   77

2.12 Comparison of Concentration of Landownership in Southern California, 1872 and 1916/17   78

3.1 Some Large Cotton Holdings, 1946, Tulare Lake Basin and Upper Westside of the San Joaquin Valley   90

3.2 Large Landholdings of Processors and Shippers   92

3.3 Oil Company Landholdings, 1946   94

3.4 Farm Mortgage Debt and Forced Sales, 1926-1939   95

3.5   Agricultural Conservation Payments to Some Large Landholders, 1939   103
3.6   Large Landowners, 1945/46   120-21
4.1   Harvested Acreage in Five Major Producing Regions, 1945 and 1974   131
4.2   Dairy and Beef Cattle Numbers, 1947 and 1980   131
4.3   Decrease in Assessed Land Value for Six Large Landowners, 1976   133
4.4   Land Holdings Used for Cattle   135
4.5   Some Large Landholdings Used for Cotton Production   138
4.6   Some Large Landholdings Used for Rice Production   139
4.7   Some Large Sugar Beet Producers   140
4.8   Some Large Landholdings Containing Large Orchards or Vineyards   143
4.9   Some Large Landholdings in the Kern Country Water Agency   152
4.10 Private Parties in the Sacramento Water Contractors Association   155
4.11 1960 Percentage of Mexicans in Labor Force and Acreage Harvested for Bracero-dominated Crops, 1960-1966   164
4.12 Price Fluctuations for Winter Lettuce, 1962-1967   165
4.13 Size Distribution of Large Landholdings   170
4.14 County Breakdown of Acreage in Large Landholdings   172

Maps

1.1   Subregions of California   4
1.2   Counties of California   5
1.3   Mexican Land Grants   10
1.4   Major Agricultural Areas   11
2.1   Railroads in California, 1888   38
2.2   Outline Map of California Oil Fields and Districts   74
4.1   California State Water Project   149
4.2   Central Valley Project   153

Acknowledgments

A number of people have been extremely helpful in preparing this book. Dick Walker's careful editing and close reading of the various drafts has been much appreciated. Bill Friedland's enthusiasm for this study was extremely refreshing and encouraging; not to mention helpful. Much of Chapter 4 would not have been possible without Don Villarejo's generosity. Don allowed me to use the files compiled by the Institute for Rural Studies (Davis, California) in the course of preparing *Getting Bigger* and other publications. The librarians of the Giannini Foundation Library cannot be left unmentioned. Not only were they extremely helpful, often going out of their way to locate something for me, but they made Dudley welcome. Dud is particularly indebted to Phyllis for her thoughtful attention. I did not use the Water Resources Library as extensively as the Giannini, but again mention should be made of both the librarians' helpfulness and warmth towards Dudley. Both libraries are extremely pleasant places to work. Typesetting the book would have been extremely difficult without the help of John Hevelin. I am especially grateful to him for allowing me to use his -MJ macro package.

Introduction

Ever since California was settled by the Spanish, a significant amount of the land in private ownership has consisted of large individual holdings. Excoriation has been the common response to the existence of such landholdings. Thus, it should be stated at the outset that what is presented here is not intended as a polemic against (or for) large landholdings. The material collected here has not been gathered with an eye to that subject. My concern has been to write a history of large agricultural landholdings in California that would both describe the large landownership situation over time and would explain how and why these patterns arose.

Before undertaking such an enterprise, it is essential to state what is meant by a large agricultural landholding. What is meant by agricultural holdings should be self-evident. However, some land that was in nonagricultural uses in the nineteenth century came into agricultural use in the twentieth century. In order to provide an adequate discussion of the present, it is necessary, when dealing with earlier times, to include such holdings. Otherwise, large holdings used for timber, minerals, or whatever are excluded from consideration. I have defined a large landholding as a holding embracing 2,000 or more acres. There is always something unsatisfactory in such a choice. Certainly, 2,000 acres of orchards does in some sense seem larger than 2,000 acres of grazing land and, similarly, a 2,000-acre orchard seems larger for the nineteenth century than for the present. Nonetheless, for a historical study to make useful comparisons, it is desirable to keep to a uniform measure throughout and for all uses (which often change while the ownership units remain the same). Furthermore, 2,000 acres can be regarded as large for most uses in any time period. Finally, this choice of size limit enables one to make the most of available information about landownership.

Agricultural production does not occur uniformly throughout the state. Hence, large agricultural landholdings do not appear in every corner of the state. They occur mainly along the central coast, southern California, and in the Central and Imperial Valleys. Even within these agricultural areas my focus has been the Central Valley. Other areas have not fallen into total neglect, but coverage has been weaker, simply because there is less information available about them. Readers unfamiliar with California geography will find Maps 1.1 and 1.2 helpful in locating geographic regions and features of California (Map 1.1) and California counties (Map 1.2).

I have considered two aspects of agricultural land ownership in explaining the existence of large agricultural landholdings. First, and most important, is the ability to use the land profitably. This is one fundamental reason for the creation and continued existence of large landholdings. Thus, I place great emphasis on land use, considering why particular uses were profitable and feasible for large holdings. The factors that I have found to be most important in determining the profitability and feasibility of a given agricultural use have been the existence of suitable markets and marketing techniques for the product, the presence of the requisite labor force, the availability of irrigation water, and access to credit. The relative importance of each of these varies over uses and over time, but they are all always germane. Also important is the effect large owners have had on developments in all these areas; that is, landownership helps create the conditions necessary for its continuation. Second is the role of investment and speculation. Agricultural land has a value as a commodity that is distinct from its agricultural value. Speculation and investment activity have significantly affected agricultural development in California and have been responsible for a not insignificant amount of land concentration.

The presentation is a mixture of chronological and thematic approaches. Chronologically, it moves through four sequential periods. The first period runs from the Indians through 1870. The second and longest period goes from 1870 to the end of World War I. The third period carries us to the end of World War II and the fourth period ends in June 1981. These periods were chosen for their abilities both to stand as a unit and to have endpoints coinciding with existing studies of landownership. Within each period the discussion moves among different thematic developments such as land disposal, the rise of certain crops, creation of a labor force, irrigation, and so on.

To give the reader some orientation towards what follows, the basic findings will be summarized. A major theme running throughout this study is that landownership has been an extremely complex phenomena. Until the end of World War I tendencies towards concentration and disaggregation vied for dominance; each had areas of prevalence. Since then disaggregation has become insignificant. These patterns reflect closely changes in agricultural production; other factors have been of secondary importance. In all periods large landholdings have encompassed a vast and, despite any countervailing tendencies, ever-increasing acreage.

A word should be said about sources. Because the concern here is with landownership, the U.S. Census of Agriculture is useless. It is not uncommon to see discussions of landownership predicated on census data, but this is a grievous error as the census only deals with operating units. There is a surprising amount of landownership data available in sundry places, particularly state reports, congressional hearings, standard financial manuals, newspaper articles, and landownership maps. What is lacking is a good general history of California agriculture. Unfortunately, I had to construct such a history for myself as I went along in order to be able to discuss profitability of different uses in a sensible manner. To some degree this study fills in this gap, but much material has been excised in the interests of keeping to the subject at hand.

Map 1.1 California Regions

COUNTIES OF CALIFORNIA

0   100 MILES

Map 1.2 California Counties

1

From Spanish to American Control (pre-1870)

The Spanish and Mexican Periods

In California, both the history of landownership and the history of agriculture have their origins with the Spanish settlement that began in 1769. Before that time, the land was under the control of the native Indians who had virtually no agriculture and no concept of landownership comparable to our own. The only tenure they recognized was that of either occupancy or regular use; hence their recognition of claims to villages and hunting grounds.[1] Subsequent inhabitants of California felt that the Indians had certain rights to the lands they occupied, although the Spanish, the Mexicans, and the Americans all considered that absolute title was vested in themselves. The rights conferred on the Indians by their occupancy were of a theoretical nature only, however, being largely ignored in practice by each of the three ruling powers.

Spanish settlement began in 1769 when a mission was founded on the present-day site of San Diego. Under Spanish rule the Indians were to be prepared to take over some of their own lands. This preparation was one justification for the mission system about which the Spanish settlement of California centered. At its peak, this system comprised a string of twenty-one missions from San Diego to Sonoma, four *presidios* (garrisons) and the *pueblos* (villages) of Los Angeles and San Jose. Under this system, the missions did not own the lands they controlled; ownership remained with the Crown. Instead, the missions were viewed as holding the land in trust for the Indians, who were to assume this trust when the missions' goal of civilizing (that is, Christianizing) them had been met. When this occurred it was intended that the missions would be secularized and made into pueblos in which both Indian and Spanish settlers would reside and own land. This development of pueblos was the crux of the Spanish settlement plan for

6

California. The pueblos were to serve first as foci for settlement and, later, as centers of commercial activity.[2]

Since growth was to proceed from the pueblos, Spain was not particularly eager to make private grants outside of pueblo (or future pueblo) areas. In fact, it was not until 1784 that several veterans of the Spanish army of occupation became the recipients of the first concessions. During the entire Spanish period approximately thirty such grants were issued.* Not all of these passed on to the recipients' heirs; some reverted to the Crown on the possessor's death. The change from Spanish to Mexican rule in 1822 had no immediate effect on landownership. Spanish grants were respected, and the policy of making few concessions continued. Between twelve and fifteen grants were made before secularization of the missions in 1834.[4] That so few grants were made in these twelve years was, no doubt, in large part due to the fact that the missions already controlled "the major part of the most desirable lands."[5] The mission lands had become "desirable" because in attempting to develop a food supply for themselves, the presidios, and the Indian neophytes, the missions demonstrated that California land had agricultural value.

The agriculture that was developed to meet these food needs involved livestock, grain and bean crops, viticulture, and some horticulture made possible by the "fairly extensive irrigation system" most of the missions possessed.[6] This development was not just devoted to subsistence. With so much essentially free labor available, the fathers were able to expand their herds and engage in the production of hides and tallow. Beginning around the 1820s, these two items formed the basis of a profitable trade. At the same time, private citizens, attracted by the trade, began agitation for secularization of the missions. This finally took place in 1834. After secularization, the mission lands were available for private ownership and the era of *ranchos* was inaugurated. The *rancheros* devoted themselves to livestock production more exclusively than did the missions. Although they took over almost all the mission lands, some gardens remained under the control of the fathers. The demonstration of the possibility of cultivation, especially of fruits, grapes, olives, figs, and citrus, along with the original stocking of the ranges constituted the agricultural bequest of the missions.[7]

In the years following secularization, private grants were made generously. From 1834 to 1846 over 500 ranchos were granted to private individuals. These individuals included a number of non-Mexicans who arrived in the 1840s and became eligible for landownership upon converting to Catholicism and adopting Mexican nationality. Since most of the coastal land was already taken by the 1840s, these foreigners tended to receive grants in the then less desirable Sacramento and San Joaquin Valleys (less desirable because of the Indian menace of which Fremont complains as late as 1852 and also because of their inaccessibility).[8] The most conspicuous

---

*As Robinson points out: "No complete list of Spanish land concessions is available."[3]

characteristic of these grants was their size. Most of them were between one and eleven leagues or between 4,426 and 48,686 acres in size (in theory eleven leagues was the maximum size, but there were exceptions like the 96,000-acre El Tejon and Simi ranchos). This was less extravagant than it appears to us today because the ranchos allowed the rancheros to utilize "the ranges and valleys in the only way possible when neither settlers, capital nor markets were available for an intensive agriculture."[9] Furthermore, because of aridity "a large area was needed to furnish year round grazing for the number of cattle that could be handled as a single herd."[10]

Although largeness of the landholding was a necessary condition for this extensive use of the land, it was not sufficient. The care of the animals and preparation, however minimal, of the hides and tallow, called for much more labor than the rancheros could have provided on their own, had they been so inclined. But the hide and tallow trade was not capable of providing substantial wages for the laborers it required. This is apparent from the fact that it only provided the rancheros with a modest life. It was not until the Gold Rush generated demand for beef that the rancheros showed signs of wealth.[11] Thus, the rancheros followed the mission fathers in using the Indians to supply virtually free labor. That they were able to do this was an inevitable concomitant of secularization since the goal of secularization was to make available to private citizens the wealth of the missions. This wealth had its basis both in the lands and the Indian laborers already "domesticated by the mission system."[12] Secularization explicitly transferred the land; the Indians were shifted to new "employers" in only a mildly roundabout way:

> Theoretically, at least, on secularization the great mission holdings of livestock and stores of food were distributed among the Indians. Adult children as they were, incapable without leadership of any form of regulated living, these riches were soon dissipated . . . and large numbers of them became victims of a peonage system under which they were actually bought and sold as farm hands and in some cases treated little better than farm animals.[13]

The Influence of the Ranchos

The reign of the rancheros over their lands and Indians was untrammeled until the American takeover of California in 1846. The legal aspects of this transfer of California, in particular, the treatment of property rights established under previous rulers were determined by the Treaty of Guadalupe-Hidalgo (1848). Articles VIII and IX of the treaty "specifically promised full and complete protection of all property rights of Mexicans."[14] Just what these rights were, however, was far from clear. The Mexican titles were often poorly documented. Many grants, for example, had vague boundaries or were not in compliance with the laws under which they were made. A similar situation had prevailed in parts of the Louisiana Purchase and, as in that case, Congress, by the Land Act of 1851, created a land commission to investigate land titles. Under the terms of this act, the burden of proof rested on the claimant.

The procedures involved included the right to appeal the commission's decision, and all but 19 of the 813 claims presented were carried to higher authorities. Litigation was seemingly endless; the average length of time to settle a title was seventeen years and final settlement of all the claims was not completed until 1890. In the end, out of the original 813 claims covering about 14 million acres (approximately 14 percent of the total area of California), 588 were accepted as valid. These covered 8,850,143 acres (roughly, 9 percent of the total area of California.).[15] Although these included claims that were not ranchos, like those for missions and pueblos, over 500 were for ranchos and made up most of the area involved. Their extent can be seen in Map 1.3.

The concern here is with the influence these grants had on the size of future agricultural holdings. Such an influence could be exerted either directly, setting ownership patterns in the areas covered by the grants, or indirectly, by affecting development in the rest of the state. In the latter case, the processes of land disposal and settlement and the types of land use that developed would show some response to the existence of the grants. Map 1.4 shows the present-day agricultural regions in California. It is clear from a comparison of it with the rancho map (Map 1.3) that much of this area must be devoid of any direct influence from the grants.

Even in the areas once covered by the grants, it is generally felt that they did not leave a lasting mark. Most often referred to in this regard is R. H. Allen's "The Influence of Spanish and Mexican Land Grants in the Agricultural History of California". Allen studied the fates in four counties (Monterey, Ventura, Contra Costa, and Sacramento) of thirty-seven grants, all of which were greater than 10,000 acres in size. In 1930 there were at least fifteen large holdings still in existence (his data are not complete up to 1930 for all of the grants), of a minimum of 2,000 acres in size. He found that these were generally on land not suited to intensive agriculture. That is, intensive agriculture was associated with the break up of large holdings. The grants do not seem to have been an obstacle or even a factor in the future agricultural developments in the areas they involved.

In 1943 Frank Adams found twenty land grants still fully intact, twelve more than two-thirds intact, and six between one-third and two-thirds intact. At best, this list would involve 1,083,215 acres or 12.8 percent of the confirmed acreage.* In fact, however, this oft-quoted list is not complete. It does not include, for example, the Rancho San Marcos, 35,573 acres in Santa Barbara County, reported intact in 1960. Also not mentioned are the 8,801-acre Rancho Sespe of Ventura County, of which 4,200 acres were still intact in 1964, the 1,100-acre El Escorpion in Los Angeles County held as a single parcel until 1958, and the 48,834-acre Suey grant, over two-thirds of

---

*Computation based on the size of the grants as given in Beck and Haase (1974).

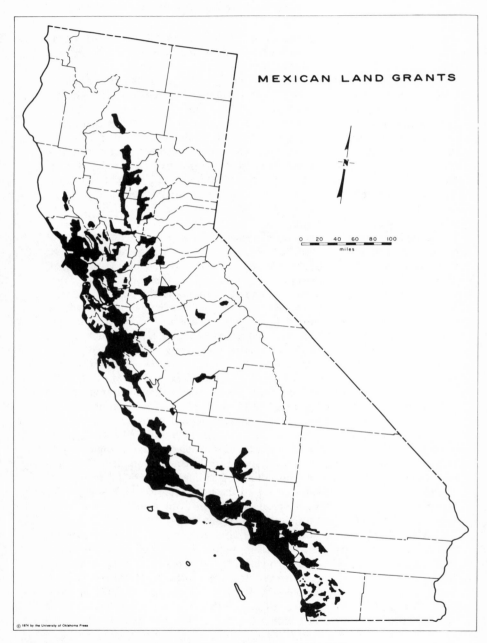

MEXICAN LAND GRANTS

0 20 40 60 80 100
miles

© 1974 by the University of Oklahoma Press

Source: *Historical Atlas of California*, by Warren A. Beck and Ynez D. Haase.
Copyright 1974 by the University of Oklahoma Press.

Map 1.3

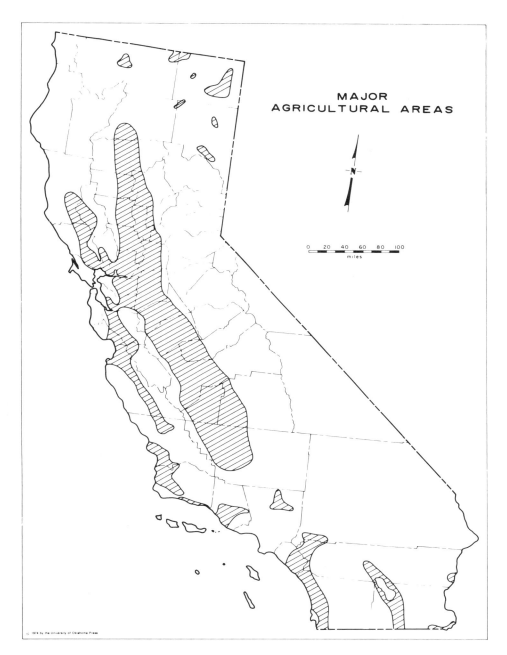

MAJOR
AGRICULTURAL AREAS

N

0 20 40 60 80 100
miles

Source: *Historical Atlas of California*, by Warren A. Beck and Ynez D. Haase.
Copyright 1974 by the University of Oklahoma Press.

Map 1.4

which has been part of the Newhall Ranch since 1883.[16] But even if several hundred thousand acres were left out (and this seems a generous concession) the staying power of the grants would not be impressive. Furthermore, this conclusion rests on forty-year-old data, accumulated before many of the grants succumbed to urbanization and before the largest completely intact grant (Santa Margarita y Los Flores, 133,441 acres in San Diego County) was converted into Camp Pendleton and lost to agriculture.

It is apparent that if we are to assign the grants a significant role in determining the future size of holdings, it will have to be through their indirect effects. It is possible that Mexican ranching established a precedent for future land use, one for which large holdings would be essential. While it is true that Spanish cattle first stocked the coastal ranges, these were inferior to American cattle, and by 1860 the market for them had fallen out. By the 1870s the range cattle industry in California had been established inland and on the basis of American cattle, most of which had been brought in from the Great Plains. Thus, the roots of California ranching lie in Texas, "the cradle of the ranch cattle industry of the United States".[17] The late E. J. Wickson, authority on California agriculture, described the situation in this way:

> Although historically there were foundations laid for animal industries by the Spanish occupants, the superstructures rest only remotely on these foundations, for they have now deeply passed from view beneath the achievements of the Americans who developed in Central California herds and flocks on the basis first of the British and later of the Hollandish breeds.[18]

A last possible grant influence arose from the claim settlement procedures determined by the Land Act of 1851. These procedures were chosen after a battle in Congress and have been viewed with disfavor by a number of historians.[19] In the main this criticism is not due to which titles were confirmed. As Paul Gates points out: "Few equitable rights were lost and some questionable titles were confirmed."[20] The criticism has been directed to the costly effects of the length of time needed for settlement of title disputes and the corresponding expense of the litigation involved. The very fact that land titles were clouded made real estate a doubtful collateral, which, in turn, contributed to the extraordinarily high interest rates that prevailed during these years. These high rates were a cause of the ruin of many rancheros. The burden of litigation costs, compounded by the effects of the drought of 1863-1864 and the loss of the market for Spanish cattle, was overwhelming under the then-prevailing usurious conditions. Thus, for legitimate owners, the result was hardly in keeping with the spirit of the Treaty of Guadalupe-Hidalgo. Far from having their property rights safeguarded, owners were frequently ruined in their attempts to establish that they were entitled to such rights. Victory was often pyrrhic, occurring after the land was lost to the original owner.[21]

Under these circumstances, original owners were easily displaced. This generated a great deal of speculation and also helped to foster the hopes of squatters. Squatting was further abetted by the difficulty in segregating public land from grants. This could not be accomplished until (at least most) titles were settled, and it was not until 1868 that this segregation of public land was substantially completed. It is likely that this led to some slowdown in settlement and land acquisition beyond the range of the grants. Unfortunately, it is impossible to separate the uncertainty effect from the lack of interest in other land that prevailed until agriculture developed and transportation improved. When such developments were in the offing, around the time the segregation of public lands was completed, lands not included in the grants were acquired with alacrity. Thus, while only 1.5 million acres of federal lands were entered* by private parties by June 30, 1867, the year in which the Southern Pacific route was filed, an additional 3.7 million acres were entered in the next three years.[22] It does not appear that any retarding effect the grants exerted on the spread of landownership beyond their range was of great import. At best, thanks to the additional time, one might expect the development of good policies and a sound administration for land disposal. This was hardly the case, as will be shown below.

The Early American Period: 1846 to 1870

From the discussion of the Spanish-Mexican land grants, it is clear that the roots of land concentration in California must be sought elsewhere; in particular in the processes of disposing of the federal and state lands. As indicated, these did not enter their prime until after the late 1860s. Yet even in these early years concentration was a common result. Henry George was decrying land engrossment in California in 1871 in *Our Land and Land Policy*, and he was hardly the first to complain.

It is not surprising that land appeared attractive in these years. The importance of mining should not blind us to the agriculture developing as early as the 1850s. In fact, after 1854, gold production declined and the character of mining changed; the next decade marked the transition from individual to company mining.[23] In these years many miners left mining for agriculture, which was first practiced simply to meet the food needs of the mining population, and by the late 1850s as a commercial endeavor in its own right.

Livestock Industries

One major agricultural development was the destruction of the ranchero cattle industry and its replacement by the type of ranching practiced in the

---

*Note that not all land entered was finally patented. The two terms are not synonymous.

Great Plains. The cattle drives in the 1850s brought in many American cattle, much superior to the existing Spanish stock. The Americans established their own ranches with these cattle; these tended to be further north and inland than those of the rancheros, both to be nearer the northern markets (the north was the population center) and because it was necessary to go where the lands were not already stocked. In 1869 some of the inland counties (including Tulare and Merced) were leaders in cattle production. The cattle industry grew throughout the 1850s, and by 1861 there were 900,000 cattle in the state. The drought of 1863-1864 hit the industry hard, and in 1869 the number of cattle had fallen to 787,000. [24]

The sheep industry originated in the 1850s. This is not to say that the Spanish and Mexicans did not have sheep, but there could not have been very many of them as only 123,094 were reported in the state in 1855. By 1861 there were 1.1 million sheep and in 1869 this had grown to 2.9 million. The sheep, like the new breed of cattle, had been driven overland into California. From 1852 through 1857 (after which the Apache Indians made the drives impossible), 551,000 sheep came from New Mexico to California. In 1854 the first pure-bred wool producers were imported from Vermont. Most of these sheep were located in northern California because of the northern markets for mutton and also to be close to the sea transport necessary for the wool industry. [25]

Sheep boomed in southern California in the 1860s. Previously, many rancheros were faring poorly because of American competition in the cattle industry. Nonetheless, their ranchos remained largely intact for there were no alternative uses for them. The rancheros could not usually afford to make changes in their use, nor would anyone else want to develop the irrigation necessary for cultivation when there were no markets and no transportation. Restocking the area was unattractive since the northern ranges were meeting local demand. The drought of 1863-1864, which completed the bankruptcy of many rancheros, came at an opportune time to precipitate a major change. The disruption of the cotton trade during the Civil War had brought about an increase in the price of wool, and wool production became increasingly desirable. What happened was that:

> Soon after the opening of the Civil War, a number of the largest wool growers in Monterey, Santa Cruz and adjacent counties sought to extend their operations farther south and either lease or purchase some of the large cattle ranchos near Los Angeles. The drought of the mid-sixties played directly into the hands of these outsiders and by the close of the Civil War the sheep industry was firmly established in a number of southern counties. James Irvine and Flint, Bixby and Company were among the largest of the landowners who chose to put sheep instead of cattle on their newly acquired ranges. [26]

After the Civil War, the wool tariff of 1867, secured in part by the action of California wool growers, enabled wool production to remain profitable. [27] Without this factor, financially embarrassed ranchos may well have littered a stagnant market until the land developed other attractions. The drought of

1876-1877 did destroy the sheep industry in southern California, but by then the area was ripe for more intensive agriculture, so many of the remaining sheep moved inland.

The livestock industry had two effects on large landholdings. Insofar as the existing large ranchos continued to be used for stock animals, they were kept at least partially intact, sometimes by the original Mexican owners but usually by new American owners. Among the largest holdings existing in 1872 (those over 100,000 acres in size), three were of this variety: Edward Beale's Tejon Ranch, estimated as 200,000-300,000 acres; the Bixby, Flint and Company holding, estimated as between 150,000 and 200,000 acres; and the 120,000 acres owned by John Foster.[28] There were many more such holdings of smaller size. It can also be inferred that the move to the interior valleys was accompanied by acquisition of large holdings from the public domain, which were used for stock. Since this move occurred concurrently with development of plans for the railroad, it would be folly to attribute all land acquisition in the valleys to stockmen. But, as can be seen in Table 1.1,

TABLE 1.1
Land Owned and Land in Cultivation in
Four Leading Cattle Counties, 1872

County	Land in Cultivation in 1872	Land Owned in 1872
Fresno	20,000	1,357,475
Kern	18,000	657,694
Merced	98,000*	938,392
Tulare	32,882	388,771

Source: California State Surveyor General *Biennial Report* for 1871-1873 for acres in cultivation, and California State Board of Equalization (1874) for the acres owned.

Note: The land in cultivation for Merced County is for 1870; later reports were clearly the product of an imaginative person.

there was a gross disproportion in 1872 between acreage owned and acreage in cultivation in four leading cattle counties. Anticipation of future cultivation can only go so far in explaining the amount of land owned, and it is impossible not to accept that most of this land was owned for stock production.

Wheat and Barley Production

The increasing importance of cultivation during the 1850s and 1860s is illustrated by the question of fencing. In 1850 the Trespass Act, which placed the responsibility for fencing on the farmer, was passed. In 1872, after years of bitter complaints, the responsibility was finally shifted to the stockman. The rise of field crops, especially wheat and barley, first gave farming pre-eminence. Between 1850 and 1870, the production of wheat and barley rose about a thousandfold. The two crops were put to different uses. Barley was not generally for human consumption, except through its contribution to malt liquors. Its dominant use was as animal feed for pack animals; hundreds of thousands of which were necessary to supply and work the mining fields. Wheat was primarily milled for flour. Wheat was the preferred crop because of its higher price.

The earliest production of both crops took place in the Bay Area, Santa Cruz, and Sacramento Counties. By 1870 the counties in the Sacramento Valley and northern San Joaquin Valley were among the leading grain producing counties. Production was centered in northern California because of limitations on the ability to transport the crop to markets or major ports. Coastal areas could make use of sea transport and interior valleys used the rivers. In these years the Sacramento River was navigable to Red Bluff and the San Joaquin River to Stockton. Thus, in the San Joaquin Valley production was limited to the region between the present cities of Stockton, Manteca, and Escalon, which had easy access to river boats running to San Francisco and the mining areas.[29] The arrival of the railroad in the 1870s permitted the spread of cultivation down the valley.

Both wheat and barley were so prolific that surpluses developed early; it was only in the early 1850s that local users had to rely on imports. The first wheat exports were made in 1854 to New York, Australia, and Great Britain, but were not very significant in size.[30] Surpluses were not a serious problem until the end of the 1850s at which time large-scale exporting was initiated. This can be seen in the figures presented in Table 1.2.

Wheat production was essentially constant from 1854 until 1859. Then it took a huge jump, which is reflected in a corresponding leap in the export figures. Exports continued to increase, except during the drought of 1863-1864.

Factors Responsible for the Development of Grain Production

It is worthwhile to consider the factors that encouraged Californians to expand their grain production. First was the emergence of new markets. The wheat trade centered on Britain to the point that Liverpool prices determined those in San Francisco during the 1860s. There was good reason for this extensive trade with Britain. The virtual repeal there of the Corn Laws in 1846 meant that Britain was increasing reliance on imported wheat because, as transport costs decreased, her farmers were increasingly unable to compete. California produced "a hard, dry, unusually white wheat that

TABLE 1.2
Wheat Production and Exports, 1854-1870

Year	Production (centals)	Exports (centals)
1854	1,281,160	214,610
1855	1,325,540	425,046
1856	1,462,120	134,139
1857	1,057,700	22,169
1858	1,517,400	57,228
1859	2,403,820	556,105
1860	3,570,280	2,120,246
1861	3,000,780	1,136,256
1862	3,527,720	1,427,342
1863	3,542,880	1,441,172
1864	1,885,320	295,114
1865	4,062,320	1,794,424
1866	7,239,900	5,099,284
1867	7,226,340	5,051,473
1868	8,476,000	5,753,012
1869	8,700,000	5,926,908
1870	7,107,240	4,167,413

Source: Davis (1894), pp. 602, 608.

was highly prized by the British and Irish millers who frequented the Liverpool Corn Exchange."[31] This wheat also did not rot on board ship. Britain provided a fairly certain market during the 1860s because of poor European crop yields. During the Civil War California had a further advantage in that "the activities of Confederate raiding ships forced California merchants to buy most of their supply of manufactured goods in Europe and the export of wheat not only facilitated payment but also served as a return cargo for British ships."[32] Even in later years of normal European harvests, Britain could be anticipated to be a good market.

The attractiveness of grain was enhanced by the fact that California presented an extremely favorable environment for its production: good soils, lack of trees to clear, and no need to worry about rains ruining a harvest. Grain would grow well, at least in the early years, with only a shallow plowing. High yields were achieved almost effortlessly; thirty or more bushels per acre was common (this was to fall after years of poor farming practices including shallow plowing, no fallow, and no rotation).

Furthermore, grain, unlike its competitors—livestock and fruits—did not call for a heavy initial investment. To stock the range or plant the trees entailed a waiting period before profits would be realized—several years in the case of orchards. The cloudiness of many titles made this sort of fixed investment unattractive, and excessive interest rates were a major obstacle to raising capital. Cattle ranching had a further disadvantage in that a year of drought could destroy a large initial investment; the example of 1863-1864 probably discouraged many. Fruits were also burdened with what were then unsolvable problems in transport and marketing due to their perishability and lack of a large local market. Vegetables suffered from these same problems, besides probably having even a smaller local market. Also, large-scale fruit production really depended on the development of irrigation and called for skill in cultivation. A problem with wheat, however, was a shortage of labor to harvest the prolific crop.

In the 1850s labor was supplied by discouraged miners or Indians. Miners did not start drifting back from the mines until the early 1850s, and many would leave again to rush off to Comstock in 1859. They were not a group to rely upon for agricultural labor. The Indians were available as virtual slaves thanks to a series of laws California passed from 1850 to 1855. Not only were the Indians denied the right to testify in court* (repealed in 1872) and allowed to be indentured for a long term of years for only subsistence in return, but

> any Indian merely upon the word of a citizen might be brought into court and declared a vagrant. Thereafter he might be put up at auction and his services sold to the highest bidder for a period not to exceed 4 months. No compensation, of course, was given, although the owner was expected to support the Indian. This act obviously made it possible for a native to be held not only as a peon but as an actual slave, for any unemployed Indian could be proved a vagrant. [34]

The importance of Indian labor on the grain farms of northern California is hard to assess however. Bidwell's use of Indians is a well-known example in the Sacramento area, and there are mentions of Indian labor elsewhere in northern California. Nonetheless, since the Indian population decreased from about 85,000 in 1850 to 28,000 in 1859 and 23,000 in 1870, one may guess that the relative importance of Indian labor also decreased significantly during these years. [35]

It is hard to determine whether the lack of agricultural labor in the 1850s was due to an absolute shortage of laborers or, as is more likely, simply to a shortage of sufficiently cheap labor. In 1859 California Agricultural Society pointed out that wages had remined at the same level for the past four years (by the year at $30 per month and during harvest at $2 per day). Nor did the situation improve with the growth of the population. Ten years later the Agricultural Society reported that "Our most enterprising men frequently fail in their undertakings, simply from the fact that they cannot command sufficient labor at *reasonable rates* to carry through to a successful conclusion their enterprises [emphasis added]" [36]

The labor problem is exemplified by the Central Pacific Railroad's importation of ten thousand Chinese laborers. In fact, the Central Pacific

---

*The Spanish view was quite different. They allowed Indians to testify in court and at worst the Indian was viewed as a "child before the law." [33]

probably drained workers from agriculture as it was competing for the same laborers (and working for the railroad might well have been more appealing than being an agricultural laborer, whether or not the wages were better, since the work was steadier). Nonetheless, during these years some Chinese were working in agriculture.[37]

The desire to plant as much wheat as possible was not to be obstructed by the labor shortage. Conditions were eminently suitable for mechanization: "the nature of the soil and the superficial character of the seedbed preparation made for the utilization of gang plows almost from the beginning of the extensive cultivation of wheat."[38] The dryness of the harvest season allowed use of the header for harvesting (combine harvesters were toyed with from 1854 on, but did not achieve full development and popularity until the 1880s). These developments allowed large mechanized farms, devoted exclusively to grain, to appear in the 1860s — farms which were the first of this type in the world.*[39]

It should be emphasized that mechanization developed concurrently with the formation of large holdings. Mechanization arose as a response to the labor shortages hampering expansion of cultivation. That large-scale production became feasible was a direct effect of the Californian attempt to overcome an unfavorable labor situation.

The legacy of the grain boom for large land holdings is generally positive but not altogether unambiguous. Stanislaus, Solano, San Joaquin, and Santa Clara counties were leading wheat producers that were not noted for livestock production. Table 1.5 (see page 25) shows the presence of a number of large holdings in these counties as well as a substantial number of smaller holdings, between 100 and 500 acres. Both large and small-scale production were evidently possible. Grain cultivation helped keep some ranchos intact and helped subdivide others. Similarly, it was responsible for the acquisition of holdings of all sizes from the public domain. One point is nonetheless clear: to the degree that production came to be associated with large holdings, it owed more to the ability of prospective owners to take advantage of the land disposal system than to mechanization. Cheap labor played almost no role at this time.

One last development that affected grain production was the building of the transcontinental railroad. Prior to its construction, there were about sixty-five miles of narrow gauge railroads in California. The Central Pacific started building in 1864; by 1868 through traffic over the Sierra was established and the line was completed in 1869. This opened up markets for those near the rail, i.e., in the Sacramento Valley and east towards the Sierra Nevada. For the San Joaquin Valley, the Southern Pacific was the important rail. In 1867 its intended route was made known, and in 1870 the

---

*It is also possible that this desire to plant as much as possible for maximum profits was a special characteristic of the California population of ex-miners. This has been suggested by Fuller and Higgins for example.[40] The idea is that a population more interested in family-style farming would not have been so inclined towards large units.

line was authorized and work begun.[41] This meant that where transportation limitations had previously kept the land in grazing, grain would be possible. It also meant that the land served by the railroad would be eagerly acquired.

Speculation

The general sense of California's agricultural potential (in particular, the promise of wheat cultivation) made land an attractive investment. Speculators avidly acquired land and, as will be seen in the next section, state land disposal policies were especially favorable to their activities. Speculative activity during this period is most fruitfully considered along with the speculative activity that occurred in the 1870s and 1880s. Hence, a detailed discussion of this topic is deferred until Chapter 2.

State Land Disposal up to 1870

Both the federal and state governments had land to dispose of in California. Until the late 1860s disposal was largely of state land. For this reason, state land disposal will be discussed in this chapter and federal land disposal, over 86 percent of which occurred after 1870, will be discussed in detail in the next chapter. We may note in passing, however, that until 1870 the majority of the 5.2 million acres of federal land acquired by private parties was acquired by cash sales under policies conducive to the acquisition of large holdings.

Land disposed of by the state derived from four grants of land to California from the federal government. In total, 8,824,000 acres were involved.* The grants were made under the following acts:†

1. An 1841 act of Congress granted 500,000 acres for the purpose of internal improvements to each of the existing public land states and to such new states as might later be admitted to the Union. Hence, upon admittance in 1850, California became entitled to such a grant.

2. An 1850 act of Congress granted to California and eleven other states all the swamp and overflowed lands within their borders; 2,193,000 acres were granted under this act.

3. An 1853 act of Congress conferred upon the state the sixteenth and thirty-sixth sections (or indemnity where the land was not available) in each township for purposes of public schools (this amounted to 5,730,000 acres) along with seventy-two sections (46,040 acres) for the use of a seminary of learning and ten sections (6,400 acres) for the purpose of erecting public buildings.

---

*Note that the salt marsh and tide lands within the state borders were also owned by the state. These did not derive from a federal grant but were the state's by virtue of its sovereignty. Their disposal was provided for in the nineteenth century and banned in the twentieth century when oil production became significant in the tidelands.

†This summary of the acts follows Appendix A in Dana and Krueger (1958).

4. The Morill Act of 1862 donated to each state 30,000 acres of nonmineral land for each member of Congress in order to establish a college for agriculture and the mechanic arts. Under this act California received 150,000 acres.

The disposal of the lands granted under the first three acts was handled by the state while the disposal of the agricultural college land was provided for by the Regents of the University of California beginning in 1868. The first disposals were of the 500,000-acre grant under an act of 1852. Numerous laws governing the other lands followed beginning in 1855, and these were endlessly modified through 1868 when a consolidation act was passed (This act itself was also subject to changes in subsequent years, but state policy remained substantially the same through the rest of the nineteenth century.). Until 1858 there was no state administrative agency for land sales; local officials, acting without supervision, handled the sales and frequently the state Surveyor-General was ignorant of the results. In 1858 an act was passed establishing an agency which was "hardly imposing, for it consisted of the Surveyor-General, who was made Register *ex-officio* and allotted $500 additional yearly salary and an extra clerk."[42] The 1852 act established several invidious policies that were to be retained through all the metamorphoses of the land laws. The most notorious was to permit holders of warrants for any of the lands to locate them on unsurveyed land.* This policy was in contradiction with federal policy and was in fact declared illegal in 1863. By that time titles were utterly confused because the federal government would grant land already granted by the state. In 1866 this problem was obviated by a federal law that confirmed the titles granted by the state in cases of dual grants.

Another unfortunate California policy begun in 1852 was the credit system of sales which enabled purchasers to gain control over areas without putting much down. Similarly, since state law did not empower the Land Office to force prosecution of applications for title, by paying a $5 filing fee the applicant clouded the title and impeded others from applying for the land in question; George claimed in 1871 that 1.2 million acres were monopolized in this manner.[43]

Prior to 1868 various restrictions existed on amounts of land in the different grants which a single individual could obtain. Besides codifying the laws relating to land disposal, the 1868 consolidation act accomplished little besides dropping any such restrictions; all the above mentioned shortcomings were retained. Interestingly, an 1870 amendment to the act that included a provision to limit lieu land to 320 acres per person was signed by the governor without the provision. It had been eliminated by forgery and was not restored until 1872.

---

*One result of this policy was that, unlike in other states where the state first located swamp lands and the purchaser selected from these, in California the purchaser determined what was swamp.

The sale of the 150,000 acre Morrill Act grant was conducted in much the same manner as that of the other grants; there was no limit on the size of the holding and credit sales were permitted. Although sales began in 1868, the agricultural college scrip did not come into greatest demand until after 1871, when Congress conferred special privileges on the scrip which made it useful for entering on otherwise unobtainable or hard to obtain land.*

Considerable scandal and fraud were associated with state land disposal, particularly of the swamp lands and school lieu. The legislature must bear much of the direct responsibility. As an 1876 Report of the Assembly Committee on Land Monopoly pointed out:

> It seems that up to this time ingenuity has not been able to invent a fraud that the Legislature was not willing to legalize and while your committee have prepared and herewith present for the consideration of the House, two bills intended to effect some reform in the disposition of the public lands, they have no great confidence in their effecting any good unless the Legislature discontinues their practice of passing curative Acts, ratifying such disobedience of the laws as speculators may find necessary for their purposes.[45]

Legislative activity was not the only shortcoming in California's land disposal:

> Ineptitude as well as outright corruption characterized the functioning of the State Land Office. A Surveyor-General and two clerks were not enough staff to handle the distribution of eight million acres of public lands. Often important speculators held these positions themselves and they did not find it difficult to influence low-salaried state employees when opportunities arose.[46]

The Surveyor-Generals from 1862 to 1875 were particularly corrupt and all were involved in land speculation. In fact, it was in part the activities of state Surveyor-General Gardner that prompted the 1876 report.

Large holdings were easily acquired from the state's lands. For example, between 1868 and 1871 alone, there were 28 purchases of swamp and overflowed land larger than 5,000 acres in size. These comprised 452,154.68 acres or an average of 16148.38 acres. In 1876 it was reported that 53 purchases of more than 2,000 acres of school land accounted for 545,537 acres. Although 569 patentees accounted for 147,870 acres of the Morrill Act grant, 25 patents were greater than 1,000 acres in size and accounted for 70,300 acres. Of these, 5 patentees held 29,420 acres. Dummy entrymen were a popular way to amass such holdings. B. M. Maudlin, for example, acquired 132,000 acres of swamp and overflowed land in this way and the firm of Mullen and Hyde was notorious for such practices.[47]

---

*This "involved two congressional measures that allowed the state to enter its acreage on unsurveyed land in lots as small as 40 acres, to enter the reserved double-minimum-priced land within the grants to railroads by paying $1.25 an acre extra, and allowed the holders of the scrip to have thirty days after a tract was surveyed during which time only holders of the scrip could make entries."[44]

Land concentration was brought to Kern County by an act of 1857 that "granted to a group of entrepreneurs—W. F. Montgomery, Joseph Montgomery, A. J. Downer, F. W. Sampson and their associates—the right to reclaim 500,000 acres of swamp and overflowed lands by means of constructing navigable canals linking Kern Lake, Buena Vista Lake, Tulare Lake and the San Joaquin River" and they were to receive all odd sections in the reclaimed tract—as much as 200,000 acres.[48] This project was taken over by Baker in 1863. By 1873 his lands (90,000 acres) were in the hands of Livermore and Redington, later to become part of the Kern County Land Company.[49]

It seems that the thrust of the state's policies and practices was to create an engrossers' paradise. Although "corruption" superficially explains how this came to be, probably much of the impetus derived from the fact that in California, as elsewhere, the leading political lights were the leading economic lights. This overlap was felt in other areas besides land disposal, but further discussion lies outside the scope of this study.

The total effect of these state land disposals, combined with the federal disposals and the remaining intact ranchos, was dramatic. It can best be derived from two sources: Henry George's *Our Land and Land Policy* published in 1871, and the *Report* for the year 1872 of the State Board of Equalization. George's attack on U.S. land policies was in large part motivated by the evils of land monopoly that he saw around him in California. He gave a list, shown in Table 1.3, of the most egregious large

TABLE 1.3
Largest Landholdings, 1871

Owner	Acreage (approximate)
Charles McLaughlin	300,000
William Chapman	350,000
Edward Beale	300,000
Miller and Lux	450,000
J. F. Houghton	300,000
Bixby, Flint and Co.	150,000
Roberts and Co.	120,000
Issac Friedlander	100,000
S. R. Throckmorton	146,000
John Foster	120,000
Thomas Fowler	200,000
Murphy family	150,000
Philadelphia Petroleum Co.	200,000

Source: George (1871), p. 26.

holdings. McLaughlin, Chapman, Houghton, and Friedlander were notorious land speculators; the others used (or attempted to use) their land productively.

The State Board of Equalization compiled, from the county assessors' reports of 1872, the size distribution of landholdings in California shown in Table 1.4. It was also indicated in a report of the State Legislature's Committees on Swamp and Overflowed Lands and Land Monopoly that the 122 largest holdings included 67 holdings of an average of 73,000 acres. This means that 122 individuals controlled a minimum of 6 million acres; Carr gives 8,685,439 as the exact figure for the acreage encompassed by the 516 largest holdings.[50] Table 1.5 gives the county breakdown of the above distribution. It shows that a great deal of the concentration in land ownership occurred in the old rancho areas and most of the rest in the Sacramento and San Joaquin Valleys where the agriculture of the day was moving.*

Summary and Conclusions

This chapter spans the Spanish-Mexican eras and the first two decades of California's statehood. By the time of the American takeover, a system of large land grants run as ranchos by cheap (virtually free) Indian labor had been established. Tempting as it is to see foundations for the present situation in this system, it is a temptation to be resisted.

TABLE 1.4
Size Distribution of Landholdings, 1872

Number of holdings	Size (in acres)
122	20,000 and upwards
158	10,000 to 20,000
236	5,000 to 10,000
104	4,000 to 5,000
189	3,000 to 4,000
363	2,000 to 3,000
1,126	1,000 to 2,000
2,383	500 to 1,000
23,315	100 to 500

Source: California State Board of Equalization (1874), pp. 22-23.

---

*The problem of large holdings was actually pervasive in California for all forms of exploitation of the land: agriculture, timber, and minerals. Both Henry George's figures and those of the Board of Equalization embrace all these kinds of holdings. Thus, although the board reports refers to the holdings as "farms," this is not correct. There is no way to sequester the purely agricultural land holdings.

TABLE 1.5
Number of Holdings by Size and County, 1872

County	100 to 499 acres	500 to 1,999 acres	2,000 to 4,999 acres	5,000 to 9,999 acres	10,000 to 19,999 acres	20,000 or more acres
Alameda	738	89	10	6	0	1
Alpine	16	0	0	0	0	0
Amador	479	12	1	0	0	1
Butte	817	80	6	3	2	2
Calaveras	522	19	0	1	0	0
Colusa	609	156	32	14	9	6
Contra Costa	572	67	9	4	2	1
Del Norte	96	14	2	0	0	1
El Dorado	608	18	2	0	0	0
Fresno	371	196	43	22	12	12
Humboldt	496	72	7	3	2	1
Inyo	182	4	0	0	0	0
Kern	320	21	6	1	6	4
Klamath	92	0	2	0	0	0
Lake	437	29	7	1	0	0
Lassen	278	11	1	0	0	0
Los Angeles	537	95	36	19	8	10
Marin	175	93	11	7	7	0
Mariposa	296	26	5	1	0	1
Mendocino	888	203	28	0	4	3
Merced	400	153	34	17	12	6
Mono	91	8	1	1	0	0
Monterey	940	79	27	19	16	8
Napa	620	108	16	3	1	0
Nevada	371	19	2	0	0	1
Placer	448	57	3	3	4	1
Plumas	272	21	2	1	0	0
Sacramento	983	139	20	4	4	1
San Bernardino	134	32	10	8	4	4
San Diego	436	41	29	8	10	6
San Joaquin	1,268	184	28	9	5	2
San Luis Obispo	492	71	16	20	14	13
San Mateo	316	89	19	1	1	0
Santa Barbara	467	44	24	9	14	22
Santa Clara	805	106	14	6	1	6
Santa Cruz	435	41	9	3	1	0
Shasta	165	20	0	0	0	1
Sierra	135	7	1	0	0	0
Siskiyou	418	43	5	3	0	2
Solano	771	133	30	8	3	0
Sonoma	1,101	213	31	5	3	1
Stanislaus	694	186	30	9	5	2
Sutter	600	105	10	1	0	2
Tehama	300	60	16	3	3	0
Trinity	60	1	0	0	0	0
Tulare	303	98	32	8	1	1
Tuolumne	517	39	1	0	0	0
Yolo	756	137	30	5	4	0
Yuba	488	72	8	0	0	0

Source: California State Board of Equalization (1874), pp. 22-23.

Although some present-day large landholdings were originally Spanish-Mexican land grants, the present landholding situation is not a result of the grants. The land grants had little influence on later land monopoly. For the most part they were not located in future major agricultural areas (and hence could not be the basis of land concentration in these areas). Their survival record was unimpressive. Those that did survive were usually in extensive uses, while more intensive use brought about their break up. In 1943 most of the ranchos were found to be broken up.

The Spanish and Mexican agriculture had little influence on later agricultural development. The missions' broad agriculture included grains, citrus, grapes, olives, and small-scale irrigation. This was discontinued after secularization of their holdings, as the rancheros were interested only in livestock. These activities did have a slight effect on the Americans as decaying mission gardens were their first source of fresh fruits and vegetables. Furthermore they gave the Americans a sense of California's agricultural potential. The livestock industry of the ranchos was, in turn, completely revamped with American cattle and techniques brought from the Great Plains and the Southwest. It was even relocated inland from the coastal areas, which became devoted to sheep (also new American breeds). The trade in hides and tallow ceased to be important after 1850. Grain, which had been a minor crop before 1850, grew to premier status under the Americans by 1860.

Use of the original Spanish labor source, the Indians, briefly carried over into the American period. In fact, a number of measures that permitted something quite akin to their enslavement were passed in the 1850s. But Americans were seemingly more interested in killing the Indians than in using them for labor, and the Indian population declined dramatically during these years. It is to the Chinese that we should look for the real foundations of cheap labor, but they did not become important as agricultural laborers until the 1870s. In this period (1850-1870), large agricultural land holdings grew despite a labor shortage, not because of cheap labor.

American public land disposal did not begin until the late 1850s, and throughout this era interest centered on state lands. Here was a new source of concentration that soon eclipsed Spanish-Mexican land grants in importance. In this case the inclination to monopolize was enhanced by a sense of California's agricultural potential, a sense fostered by successful grain cultivation and a profitable overseas grain trade during the 1860s. Thus, by 1870 land monopoly was extensive and widely deplored (Henry George found much of the inspiration for his work in the California situation). The situation is well summarized by the fact that 516 persons had holdings over 5,000 acres in size which covered 8.7 million acres.

Notes

1. Adams (1946), p. 4; Robinson (1948), p. 6.
2. Staniford (1975), pp. 47-50.

3. Robinson (1948), p. 55.

4. Reversion of Spanish grants in Staniford (1975), pp. 47-50; number of grants from Cleland (1941), p. 27;

5. Adams (1946), p. 23.

6. Brown and Shaw (1944), p. 47.

7. Hide and tallow trade in Cook (1976), p. 41; gardens in Wickson (1923), pp. 66-67.

8. Smith (1939), p. 76.

9. Adams (1946), p. 27.

10. Allen (1935), p. 127.

11. Nordhoff (1973), p. 153.

12. Fuller (1934), p. 50.

13. Brown and Shaw (1944), p. 70.

14. Robinson (1948), p. 100.

15. Ibid., and Nash (1964), p. 207; Gates (1968), p. 115.

16. Adams (1944); San Marcos from Tompkins (1960), p. 274; Newhall, from Krebs (1972), p. 3097; Sespe from Steiner (1964); El Escorpion from Nelson et al. (1964), p. 11.

17. Dale (1930), p. 76.

18. Wickson (1923), p. 215.

19. For example, Cleland (1941), p. 70 and Caughey (1953), pp. 317-18.

20. Gates (1975), p. 159.

21. Caughey (1953), pp. 317-18. Eldridge (nd), pp. 457-58 describes interest rates in detail; Robinson (1948), pp. 129-31 for other information.

22. Derived from United States General Land Office Report for each of the years 1868-1873.

23. Chiu (1963), p. x.

24. Allen (1935), p. 131 for cattle drives of the 1850s; California State Surveyor General, Annual Report for 1861; California State Surveyor General, Biennial Report for 1869-1871 (The overall numbers and indications of leading counties in these reports agree with the United States Census of Agriculture for 1860 and 1870 as reported in Burcham (1957), pp. 256-257. These are the only series of statistical information available at the county level for this period. They differ markedly at times and both clearly have their inaccuracies. However, where there is agreement it is reasonable to assume accuracy. I chose the Surveyor-General figures as they seemed more complete.).

25. Number of sheep in state from California State Surveyor-General Report for 1855, 1861 and California State Surveyor-General Biennial Report for 1869-1871; Allen (1935), p. 18 for sheep drives; Wickson (1923), p. 253 for 1854.

26. Cleland (1952), p. 66.

27. Wickson (1923), p. 253.

28. George (1871), p. 29.

29. The same pattern of development is shown by the United States Census of Agriculture for 1850, 1860, and 1870 (reported in California State Board of Agriculture (1912), pp. 107, 121), California State Surveyor General, Annual Report for 1855, 1856, 1861, and California State Surveyor General Biennial Report for 1869-1871. See note 24 for the reason for using both sources. Transportation considerations and information from Brown and Shaw (1944), pp. 94, 270.

30. Davis (1894), pp. 604-7.

31. Paul (1958), p. 394.

32. Ibid., p. 393.

33. Cook (1976), p. 309.

34. Ibid., p. 258.

35. Ibid., pp. 256, 464, 465.

36. California State Agricultural Society (1859), p. 347 for wages; California State Agricultural Society (1869), p. 6 for quote.

37. United States Immigration Commission (1911a), p. 655.
38. Rogin (1931), p. 42.
39. Ibid., pp. 105-6.
40. Fuller (1934), p. 87; Higgins (1958), p. 21.
41. California State Surveyor General (1866), *Biennial Report*, for mileage; Robinson (1948), p. 155 for authorization of the line.
42. Nash (1964), p. 129.
43. George (1871), p. 21.
44. Gates (1975), p. 169.
45. California Assembly, Special Committee on Land Monopoly, (1877), pp. 6-7.
46. Nash (1964), p. 133.
47. California Legislature, Joint Committee on Public and State Lands (1872), pp. 62-64 for swamp land; school lands from California State Land Commission (1877), pp. 14-18; Morrill Act land from Bratten (1967), pp. 82-86; dummy entries from Nash (1964), p. 133; and Gates (1975), p. 167.
48. Cooper (1954), pp. 16-17.
49. Ibid., p. 87.
50. California Legislature, Joint Committee on Swamp and Overflowed Lands and Land Monopoly (1874), p. 194; Carr (1875), p. 294.

2

Complex Trends in
Landownership (1870-1918)

Introduction

As we have seen, by 1870 much of the privately owned land in California was in large holdings. In the years through World War I further accumulation of large holdings occurred. Concurrently, many such holdings were being subdivided. This was especially characteristic of areas in which small-scale farming, usually irrigated and almost invariably involving specialty crops, was feasible. The rate of subdivision was certainly inadequate to vanquish land monopoly, but it did have a significant impact on the pattern and extent of large holdings. The apparent persistence of large land holdings, as suggested by expostulations against them that marked the beginning and end of this era, masks shifts in locus. Concentration of land ownership is a dynamic and complex phenomenon.

The rest of this chapter is divided into nine sections. The first of these describes federal land disposal, indicating how easy it was to acquire large holdings from the public domain. This is followed by a section dealing with the activities associated with large holdings, that is, the livestock industries and extensive cultivation, and also adduces examples of large holdings so used. Next come four sections concerned with intensive cultivation. A great deal of space is devoted to this topic because it is necessary to do two things: explain why intensive cultivation led to the breakup of large holdings, and describe in detail the developments in marketing, irrigation, and labor responsible for intensive cultivation, thus providing a basis for discussion of these factors in later chapters. Each of these subjects is discussed in a separate section. The seventh section considers nonagricultural land uses of importance; namely speculation and investment, and petroleum exploitation. This is followed by a comparison of the extent of land in large holdings at the beginning and end of the era.

Last are conclusions and a chapter summary.

Public Land Disposal

State and federal largess was the typical source of new large holdings.* The disposal of land after 1870 followed the patterns established in the previous twenty years. State land disposal has already been discussed. The 1876 hearings adverted to in Chapter 1 were the last of a series of such hearings occurring in the 1870s. After two decades the inadequacies of state policy could no longer be ignored, nor could they, judging from the negligible effect of all the hearings and general brouhaha, be influenced by public disapprobation. The reports of the state Surveyor-General show that state land sales continued rather steadily through the century.[1] But the quantities of land involved were small compared to what the federal government disposed of; not only was there simply less state land available but the most desirable state land had already had been taken. By the end of the 1870s interest and attention had shifted completely to the federal domain.

Some thirty-eight percent of the land in the state passed into private ownership under the direct aegis of federal policies. Table 2.1 gives a breakdown of this acreage by method of disposal.

Land disposal did not occur at an even rate between 1870 and 1918. The peak periods of entering federal land occurred from 1883 to 1892, 1903 to 1906, and 1909 to 1915 (note that not all acreage entered went to patent). Over one million acres were entered in almost every one of these years.[2]

TABLE 2.1
Disposal of Federal Land in California

Method	Acreage
Cash Sales	8,631,000
Homestead	11,433,000
Desert Land Act entries	1,108,000
Timber and Stone Act entries	2,899,000
Scrip, lieu, etc.	2,400,000
Mineral entries	583,000
Timber Culture Act entries	142,000
Railroads	11,588,000
TOTAL	38,784,000

Source: Dana and Krueger (1958), p. 43

---

*Aggregation of small holdings and recombination of existing large holdings (usually railroad land or ranchos) also occurred to some degree. Instances will be indicated in later sections.

The terms of the laws under which this distribution was made will be summarized below, and their potential to lead to the formation of large holdings will be indicated (The order of presentation follows that of Table 2.1).*

Cash Sales

Cash sales of public lands were initiated in the United States in 1800. Until 1820 credit could be obtained from the federal government. At first all sales occurred at auction or, for lands unsold at auction, privately, for the minimum price of $1.25 per acre. Only nonmineral, unreserved, surveyed lands could be purchased. The Preemption Act (1841) provided that *bona fide* settlers could settle upon and purchase at $1.25 an acre up to 160 acres of surveyed, nonmineral, unoccupied, and unreserved public land. This act was extended to California in 1853 and cash sales began in California in that year. The Graduation Act (1854) reduced the minimum price for land, making it a function of the length of time the land had been available for purchase. In 1862 the terms of the Preemption Act were extended to unsurveyed land. This meant that squatters anywhere on the public domain, on land that did not turn out to be mineral or reserved when surveyed, had the first option to buy. In California preemption was the major source of cash sales; public auction sales were never used extensively.[3] Both of these types of sale were repealed in 1891, effectively ending cash sales except in isolated cases.

Although "all assignments and transfers of the preemption right prior to the issuance of the patent were null and void" and the claimant had to swear to continuous residence (including making improvements), large holdings much in excess of 160 acres were easily accumulated under the law.[4] This was done by using dummy entrymen who judiciously lied about their compliance with the law. An example is an 1875 timber deal of S. A. D. Puter in Humboldt County. Puter built cabins, of sorts, on his "dummy's" claims but

> There were no other signs of habitation or cultivation whatsoever, the building of the cabin being the only improvement made on a preemption or homestead claim in those days. . . .[and furthermore] The entrymen hardly ever slept over night there, although they made final proof within 8 or 10 months from the date of filing, wherein they alleged a continuous residence.[5]

Puter sold his tract to a Eureka capitalist for $800 to $1,200 per claim, thus making a tidy profit while the land remained in a single holding with an owner who had nothing whatsoever to do with its alienation from the

*Unless otherwise indicated, the information about the terms of the laws comes from a summary of all the federal and state laws relating to land which is found in the appendices in Dana and Krueger (1958).

government. Similar techniques were employed with agricultural land. It is impossible to determine how much land was thus acquired.

Homestead Acts

The original Homestead Act (1862) which replaced the Graduation Act, provided that *bona fide* settlers could obtain 160 acres from the public domain for free after five years residence, or, after six months residence, the land could be purchased directly for $1.25 per acre—a procedure referred to as commutation. Only unreserved, unoccupied, nonmineral, surveyed land could be homesteaded. Between 1862 and 1880 preemptors had an advantage over homesteaders as the right of preemption attached from the date of actual settlement while the right of homestead dated from entry at the local land office. Thus, preemptors were able to displace homesteaders. In 1878 preemptions became commutable to homesteads (i.e., unsurveyed land could be homesteaded) and in 1880 the right to a homestead was pushed back to the date of settlement.[6] The bulk of the homestead entries in California were made under the 1862 law and these modifications.

However, three additional homestead laws were passed in the twentieth century that played a small role in public land disposal in California. The Forest Homestead Act (1906) opened for homestead entry lands in national forests, chiefly valuable for agriculture, that could be occupied without injury to the forest. Commutation was not permitted. Altogether, only about 344,000 acres were opened to entry in California. The act was not a stunning success. In 1921 it was estimated that about 50 percent of the homesteads established under it in the state were abandoned.[7] In 1912 the Enlarged Homestead Act (1909) was extended to California. This act made it possible to acquire 320 acres under certain conditions. Commutation was not permitted. Last was the Stockraising Homestead Act (1916). This act permitted entry on 640 acres of nonirrigable land suitable only for extended use. This law was most popular in the Midwest and had little impact in California.

As with the Preemption Act, the Homestead Act was abused by the use of dummy entrymen. Entrymen misrepresented their intentions and compliance with the law's requirements and then sold off, after waiting the necessary six months, to engrossers. Once again the amount of land involved in such frauds cannot be determined. On a national level the percentage of homesteads commuted increased from 4 percent of the total number of homesteads claimed prior to 1880 to 23 percent of those claimed between 1881 and 1904.[8] Not all commutations were turned over to speculators nor do these numbers necessarily reflect the California experience, although there is no reason to think they misrepresent it. In California this probably became a significantly used route to large ownership after 1880.

(3) *Desert Land Act*

The Desert Land Act (1877):

> provided for the sale in eleven western states and territories of 640 acres of nontimbered, nonmineral land, unfit for cultivation without irrigation to any settler who would irrigate it within 3 years after filing. A payment of $0.25 per acre was to be made at the time of filing and $1 per acre at time of final proof.[9]

The terms of the law do not suggest any real reason for this legislation. The same lands could be entered by preemption or homesteading and it is not likely that anyone believed that this law would bring irrigation to them; or, if it did, that anyone would need 640 acres of irrigated land. The actual rationale for the law is described in this summary by the San Francisco Chronicle of a 300-page investigation of the act:

> ... the Desert Land Act of Congress was simply a ring job and was made the medium for a colossal steal by the ring, to the prejudice of thousands of honest, *bona fide* settlers, against whom it was so used as to prevent them enjoying the benefits and spirit of the Act. By arrangement and collusion, the thing was so managed as to furnish from Washington to the Ring here [in San Francisco] instant information of the Executive approval of the Act, and in less time, by weeks, than it requires to officially communicate the necessary orders to give proper operation to an Act of Congress on this coast, the Ring land-grabbers had been allowed by the officers of the Visalia Land Office to list and locate an immense area of the desert tracts.[10]

This "ring" consisted of a number of well-known California land speculators. California Senator A. A. Sargent, one of the authors of the bill, was involved with members of the "ring."[11]

The act functioned as intended—as an aid to land monopolists. Large holdings were amassed by the use of dummy entrymen. Ben Ali Haggin, for example, used at least 286 dummies to acquire 183,000 acres of land.[12] Also, because of the $0.25 down payment and three-year payment period, stockmen and speculators were able to control thousands of acres for a nominal amount, barring entry and use by others. Depending on their intentions, they could sell this interest or complete payment.

The act was tightened up in 1891 as part of the General Revision Act (1891). The maximum entry was lowered to 320 acres and actual plans for irrigation had to be filed. One dollar per acre was to be expended in each of the first three years on the irrigation project and four years were given to prove and pay. This did not really change things; the amount of water necessary for "irrigation" still remained vague and the terms were basically unenforceable.

Timberlands

The general issue of timbered lands is not of direct interest here. While it is true that timberlands are often used for grazing, this is a sideline for the owners. That is, timber holdings, large though they often are, do not fall within the purview of large agricultural holdings. Their alienation is discussed here because it indicates the mood of the times about land disposal. Until the Timber and Stone Act (1878), there was no legal way to acquire timberlands not potentially valuable for agriculture. However, homesteaders and preemptors were not barred from timberlands, and a few misstatements by entrymen could make the land theirs under those acts. Puter's above mentioned activities in Humboldt County exemplify this sort of misuse of the Preemption Act.

The Timber and Stone Act provided that one person could purchase 160 acres of surveyed, nonmineral land, chiefly valuable for timber or stone and unfit for cultivation, at a price of not less that $2.50 per acre. It was repealed in 1955. Dummy entrymen, as ever, were the way to amass large holdings under this law. The first big frauds to occur on the Pacific Coast under the law were in 1882-1883 in Humboldt County. The California Redwood Company hired dummies to enter on land in the northern part of the county and then sold this land to a Scottish syndicate. An investigation led to suspension and later cancellation of 150 to 200 of these entries.[13] Wholesale abuse of the act came later when:

> Recognizing the handwriting on the wall following the passage of the Forest Reserve Act [in 1891] timberland locators went to work in real earnest in California in land acquisition. Gangs of men were gathered from the cheap lodging houses of the cities and taken on excursions to areas where the big trees grew.[14]

Timberland scandals in 1902 represented the culmination of the activity initiated in the wake of the Forest Reserve Act. However, another culprit in 1902 was the Forest Lieu Land Act. Misuse of the Placer Mining Act also occurred. Thomas Walker amassed over 500,000 acres in northern California using all these stratagems. Others who operated in a similar manner with only slightly less success were Curtis, Collins and Holbrook Company of San Francisco, Wheeler Brothers of New York, and the Diamond Match Company.[15]

Scrip and Lieu

This category includes military bounty warrants, agricultural college scrip, Valentine scrip, Sioux Indian scrip, and Forest Lieu Land Act lieu. From 1846 to 1856 four military bounty bills were passed. The cumulative action of these was to provide grants of one quarter section, in the form of assignable warrants, to any soldier, or his heirs, who had served a minimum of nine days in any war after 1790, or in the Revolutionary War.[16] It was a small matter for speculators to buy these warrants cheaply from soldiers in the East and either sell them dearly in the West or use the warrants and then sell the land dearly. This was the fate most of the warrants met. Nothing illegal was involved in such transactions.

The Morrill Act (1862) granted to each state 30,000 acres of nonmineral public land for each congressman to which it was entitled under the 1860 census. The proceeds of the land sales (at a minimum of $1.25 per acre) were to be used to establish colleges of agriculture and the mechanical arts. California received 150,000 acres (whose disposal was discussed in Chapter 1) under this act. States without public lands were given an equivalent amount of scrip, purchasers of which were to take up not more than one million acres in any one state. This scrip was eagerly purchased by speculators and used in the western states. Noteworthy acquisitions made in California with this scrip include 210,000 acres by William Chapman, 142,000 acres by Issac Friedlander, and 79,000 acres by Miller and Lux. [17]

Valentine scrip and Sioux Indian scrip were created to meet some special circumstances—Valentine scrip arose in the course of settling the claim for Arroyo de San Antonia in Sonoma County, and Sioux half-breed scrip had originally been intended for half-breeds in Minnesota. Neither existed in large quantities, but because they had the fewest limitations in their application, they were much sought after and used for special acquisitions (and not only in California). For example, Lloyd Tevis used Valentine scrip to enter on land containing flowing springs, and William Chapman used Sioux scrip to obtain valuable timberland. [18]

The Forest Lieu Land Act (1897) permitted those who either owned or had an unperfected *bona fide* claim within the limits of a forest reservation to exchange this tract for a tract of vacant land no greater in size that was open to settlement. This act was mainly used, as previously indicated, to obtain timberland. Typically, already logged over and worthless land was exchanged for valuable forest lands. The act was so clearly a speculator's dream that it only lasted until 1905. A curious use in California was as a vehicle for obtaining petroleum land in Kern County in 1900. Because mineral claims were filed at the United States Land Office and scrip claims at the county recorder's office, interests clashed, conflicting decisions were rendered and the cases dragged on for years, leaving titles clouded well into the twentieth century. [19]

Mineral Lands

The first act providing for the sale of mineral lands was in 1866. Under this act lode mines could be purchased at $5.00 per acre if the claimant had occupied them according to local mining rules and had expended $1,000 in labor and improvements. In 1870 it became possible to purchase placer mines. Under the Placer Mining Act (1870), placer mines could be purchased at $2.50 per acre in tracts not greater than 160 acres. In 1872 the amount a single individual could claim for a single discovery was reduced to a maximum of 20 acres, while it remained 160 acres for an association of individuals. Because lands were only classified as mineral upon discovery of minerals within them, it might seem that the act would not encourage concentration. However, in the Mother Lode area this was not an onerous condition, and H. H. Yard, with others, was able to acquire 100,000 acres of valuable timberland in Butte and Plumas Counties by making massive dummy entries under it.[20]

With petroleum a proven discovery was difficult and expensive to make, and many preferred to acquire possible oil-bearing land under other laws and then explore (or resell) at their leisure—hence the above described use of the Forest Lieu Act in Kern County. Yet even in these circumstances large petroleum holdings resulted from placer mining entries. In Kern County twenty-five persons each accumulated in excess of 2,000 acres of petroleum land, and several families had aggregate holdings of more than 2,000 acres.[21]

Timber Culture Act

The Timber Culture Act (1873) was not particularly important, either in California or the nation as a whole. It donated 160 acres to persons who met certain requirements with respect to tree planting. It was repealed in 1891. No large holdings can be attributed to it.

Railroads*

During the years 1850 to 1871, the federal government enacted a number of laws granting lands to aid railroad construction. An act of 1850 made the Illinois Central Railroad the first recipient of such a grant. This grant, and a number of other early grants, was actually made to the state containing the railroad. The state, in turn, was to dispose of the land in such a way as to promote the construction of the rail. Later grants, particularly those in the Far West, were made directly to the railroad corporation. In California all railroad grants were of the latter type and were made to either the (old) Western Pacific Railroad, Central Pacific Railroad, California and Oregon Railroad, or Southern Pacific Railroad.† In 1870 the Western Pacific and

---

*This section relies almost entirely on Kincaid (1923). Since his dissertation lacks page numbers, specific references would be impossible to give; hence the hiatus. Unless otherwise noted, all factual information and quotes comes from this source.

†Strictly speaking, this is inaccurate. In 1866 a grant was made to the state for the Stockton and Copperopolis Railroad Company, and in 1867 a grant was made directly to the Placerville and Sacramento Valley Railroad. Each of these grants was forfeited by an act of Congress in 1874 and played no real role in California land ownership history.

California and Oregon Railroads were merged into the Central Pacific Railroad and carried with them their land grants. In 1884 the Central Pacific merged with the Southern Pacific, which thus became the possessor of all remaining land in all the grants issued to railroads in California. Map 2.1 shows the location of these railroad lines (note that the California and Oregon Railroad line is the line going north through Sacramento and Redding).

The terms of the Central Pacific land grant were fixed by the Union Pacific Railroad Act (1862), as amended in 1864. This act applied to the line from San Francisco, connecting with the Union Pacific. Other lines built by the Central Pacific, such as the one from Lathrop to Goshen in the San Joaquin Valley, did not receive any land grants. The act provided that the Central Pacific receive ten sections per mile on each side of the road. The sections were to be alternate, odd-numbered and within twenty miles of the side of the road. Any land that was sold, preempted, or otherwise reserved (as, for example, mineral lands—a category that did not include iron or coal-bearing lands) or otherwise disposed of (for example as homestead claims) was excepted from the grant. No provision was made for indemnity land. That is, there was no lieu land for tracts lost to the grant by the above exceptions. The minimum price for government lands within the grant was $1.25 per acre (raised to $2.50 in 1868). Furthermore, any land that had not been "sold or disposed of" by the company within three years of completion of the railroad was to be subject to settlement at $1.25 per acre (also raised in 1868 to $2.50). An 1865 act of Congress permitted the the Central Pacific to assign the part of its grant between San Francisco and Sacramento to the Western Pacific Railroad, which built the railroad connecting those two cities. In effect the Western Pacific also received a land grant under the Pacific Railroad Act as its land was governed by and derived from that act.

By an act of 1866, the California and Oregon Railroad received ten, odd-numbered, alternate sections per mile on each side of the road with the same exceptions as the Central Pacific. The grant covered a line from Sacramento to the Oregon border. This grant differed from that to the Central Pacific in two ways: (1) government land within the grant had a minimum price of $2.50 per acre, and (2) a strip of land stretching within ten miles of of each side of the original grant was provided for indemnity. The indemnity tract nearest the original grant had to be chosen.

The Southern Pacific Railroad received its land in two batches.* By section 18 of the 1866 act for the Atlantic and Pacific Railroad Company, the Southern Pacific was to receive land, under the same terms as the Atlantic and Pacific, for its line from San Francisco connecting with the Atlantic and Pacific. Section 23 of the 1871 act granting land to the Texas Pacific Railroad Company granted the Southern Pacific land for its line

---

*The information about the Southern Pacific grants in this paragraph comes from Froberg (1917). Again lack of pagination prevents greater specificity.

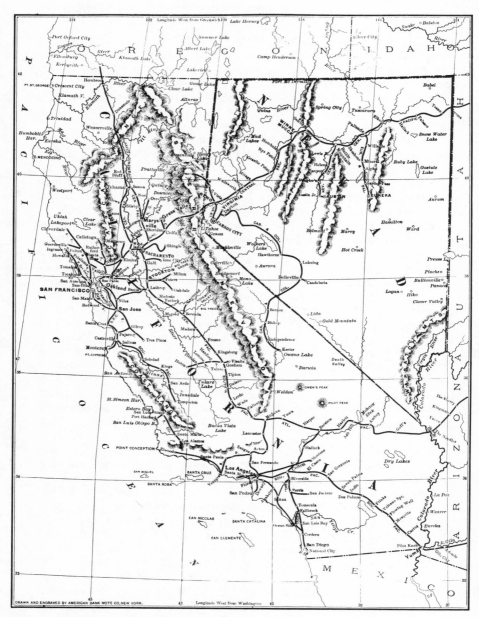

Source: *Poor's Manual of Railroads, 1888.*

Note: The line going north to Oregon was originally the California and Oregon Railroad.

Map 2.1 Railroads in California, 1888

connecting San Francisco with the Texas Pacific. However, the conditions of this grant were not those applying to the Texas Pacific, but those of the 1866 Atlantic and Pacific act. Thus, all Southern Pacific land grants were governed by the terms of the 1866 act. These were the usual ten, odd-numbered, alternate sections per mile on each side of the road with the same stipulations and exceptions as the Central Pacific grant. Government sections originally had a minimum price of $1.25 per acre, but this was later increased by an act of Congress to $2.50 per acre. Indemnity land was provided for in the same manner as for the California and Oregon; however, the nearest tract did not have to be chosen. The line was to be completed by 1878.

The Southern Pacific did not construct a new line to San Francisco. Since it was controlled by the same group as the Central Pacific, it only built the necessary extensions from the Central Pacific line. Thus, the first grant covered the Southern Pacific lines from San Jose to Tres Pinos (50.26 miles), Huron to Mojave (112 miles), and Mojave to Needles (263.60 miles). The second grant covered the branch line from Mojave to Yuma (346.97 miles).

The acreage involved in each of the grants and the acreage ultimately patented under them is shown in Table 2.2.

TABLE 2.2
Size of Federal Land Grants in
California to the Railroads

Railroad	Superficial Estimate of Grant Acreage	Estimated Acreage of Grant	Total Acreage Patented
Central Pacific	1,843,200	1,339,449	978,091
Western Pacific	1,576,498	1,349,758	464,130
California and Oregon	3,891,200	3,266,728	3,237,347
Southern Pacific (main line)	7,520,256	4,968,096	4,656,425
Southern Pacific (branch line)	4,441,088	4,094,050	2,251,539

Source: McAllister (1939), p. 434.

The implementation of these land grants was not happy. It led to a confusion deleterious to the interests of settlers who wished to acquire the federal land mixed in with the grants. The whole issue of the withdrawals was fraught with problems. Because of the fact that the land involved was, for the most part, unsurveyed (hence even and odd sections could not be distinguished), all land in a wide swathe around the road had to be withdrawn in order to protect the railroads' odd-numbered sections. For the Central Pacific, which had no indemnity land, this swathe was twenty five miles on each side of the road.* The California and Oregon and Southern Pacific had forty miles withdrawn on each side—twenty miles for the grant itself and twenty for the indemnity land.

Before the withdrawals could be ended, the rail line had to be definitely located or fixed. Only at that point could surveys be initiated because they used the railroad line as a baseline. The law unfortunately did not define how or when the line was definitely fixed. This issue was not trivial because adverse claims to the land that could effect its exception from the grant had to be made before the date of definite location. It was not until an 1885 decision that this situation was finally clarified. In the case of the Central Pacific Railroad, the decision resulted in a change from July 18, 1868 to October 20, 1868 thus permitting a greater number of adverse claims to be made. The delays from first withdrawal to the fixing of the line were substantial. For the Central Pacific the withdrawals were made in 1862 and 1864. The first fifty miles were located by March 1864, the next fifty-nine in 1866, and the rest in California by November 1867. For the Western Pacific and the California and Oregon the last twenty miles were not definitely located until January 1870 and August 1874, respectively. The Southern Pacific made its last location, after its 1878 deadline for completion, in 1883. Surveying could begin as each twenty-mile section was definitely located. This process was not completed until the twentieth century. One reason for this dilatoriness was that the Land Commissioner was unable to pay a high enough rate to attract surveyors.

After the line was fixed and the land surveyed, the railroad selected a list of lands it wanted. This list was sent to the Land Office to be checked for availability. Once approved and put on a selected list, a patent would be granted to the company upon payment of survey, selection and conveyance fees. Until payment of the fees, the land was in a state of conveyance but not actually conveyed. In this state the company could lease, mortgage, and otherwise use it but it was not subject to taxation or liable to sale until patented. Delays arose both in making selections and in patenting. Because the government did not necessarily survey the most marketable lands first and the companies preferred not to select land they were not as yet interested in, selection became bottlenecked. Even after selection and approval, if the company did not foresee sales, it would put off paying the fees so as not to be burdened with taxes. Of these two only the delay in selection really affected ownership patterns by leaving titles clouded on odd-numbered sections. The effect of the avoidance of taxes was to increase

---

*The Central Pacific withdrawal included five extra miles, not to allow for indemnity, but because it was not exactly clear where the external boundary of the grant would fall after the road was definitely located and in this way the railroad's interest was safeguarded.

the burden on actual settlers. Though heartily castigated, the companies could not be forced to pay the fees.* The delay between selection and patenting was worst during the 1880s. In that decade over 2.3 million acres were selected, yet only about 100,000 acres were patented. However, in the next decade some 4.3 million acres were patented while only 2.65 million acres were selected. During the twentieth century, selection and patenting proceeded apace. [22]

The discussion so far applies only to lands directly granted in the various acts. The situation was even more complex for indemnity land. Prior to 1879 it too was viewed as railroad land and was withdrawn along with the directly granted land and held until definite location. After an 1879 decision, it was held that the companies' title to the lands was acquired by selection and not by definite location. But at that point the company was still protected by the withdrawal. The Guildford-Miller decision (1887) of the Land Commission pointed out that indemnity withdrawals were illegal and invalid by the terms of the original grants for several rails, including the California and Oregon, and Southern Pacific. In the same year a revocation order was made on such withdrawals. In California this involved the 5 million acres withdrawn for the Southern Pacific and the 1,650,000 acres withdrawn for the California and Oregon. Thus, after 1887 the protection of withdrawal was lost to the railroads. This, combined with the 1879 decision, meant that the railroads could lose the indemnity to a settler if he/she established a valid claim before the railroad's selection had been approved. Much land remained to be selected after 1887, and it can be safely assumed that this decision had a significant impact on the railroads and was a great help to settlers.

Decisions in several other contentious areas also affected railroad interests. The first concerned the recapture clause of the land grants, which indicated that if the railroad was not completed within a specified time the land reverted to the public domain. The Supreme Court decided in *Schulenberg* vs. *Harrison* (1874) that such clauses created a condition subsequent and forfeiture had to be enforced by a congressional or judicial declaration. Otherwise, the railroad could take up the land whenever it finished building, regardless of the time limit. Until the Railroad Land Grant Forfeiture Act (1890), each forfeiture involved a separate act. The major beneficiary of this decision in California was the California and Oregon, which did not complete its line within its time period but which was never the subject of a forfeiture act and so retained all its land upon its tardy completion. The Central Pacific and Western Pacific completed their lines within their time period. The Southern Pacific lost land by a special act of Congress (in 1875) affecting the Texas Pacific and by the General Forefeiture Act. The latter involved the never-completed Tres Pinos to

---

*Apparently, they also stood outside the tax laws. After changes in the tax structure made in the 1878 state constitution, the railroad refused to pay taxes for more than what they felt was reasonable *viz.* the amount they paid under the old constitution.

Alcalde line.

A second contentious area was the clause that land not sold or disposed of within three years of completion of the railroad line should be opened to settlement at the minimum price of $2.50 per acre. This clause was defeated by the Supreme Court decision in *Matt* vs. *Union Pacific* (1879) in which a mortgage was regarded as a valid disposition. Hence mortgaging lands would void the clause of all efficacy and so all the railroads mortgaged their land (as mentioned above, this could be done before patenting).

A final problem area was mineral lands. Mineral lands were not to pass to any of the railroads by the terms of the granting acts. The Land Office policy of using the patent date as the date when mineral character had to be shown instead of the date of definite location was approved by the Supreme Court in 1894. In 1914 the definition of mineral character was eased, thus keeping more land out of the railroads' hands. The Southern Pacific was the affected rail. The Central Pacific grant ran through the Mother Lode and the character of these lands was established early and with a minimum of controversy. However, the Southern Pacific grant involved a great deal of land on the west side of the San Joaquin Valley later shown to be oil bearing, and a number of fraud suits were brought against the company in the 1920s resulting in the forfeiture of 259,000 acres of this land.[23]

Conclusions about Land Disposal

This section has established that the laws governing federal land disposal were extremely compatible with the accumulation of large holdings. Virtually all of the legislation applying to disposal to private individuals could be and was abused to this end. Also, land donations to the railroads not only gave away outright huge areas to a few corporate owners, but, in the process of doing so, blocked disposal of equally vast realms for a number of years. These two circumstances combined to create a situation that was extremely unpromising for the legitimate settler whose access to much of the public domain was either limited or mediated by a middleman. That this occurred is not surprising. The federal government had to serve a number of interests when disposing of its land, and the incompatibilities between settlers, business, and speculators meant that compromise was inevitable. Regardless of which group's interests were articulated in law, all were served to some degree.

These same laws applied to the rest of the United States and comparable railroad land grants were made throughout the West. Yet elsewhere small farmers came to predominate, while in California (and the Southwestern states) landownership remained highly concentrated. The rest of this chapter seeks to make this phenomenon comprehensible.

Agricultural Developments Associated with Large Holdings

During this era the agricultural uses associated with large holdings were livestock, grain cultivation, and the cultivation of some row crops. This section will establish that these uses were indeed common for large holdings.

Livestock

Growth in the livestock industries between 1870 and 1918 can be attributed to cattle and not sheep. Cattle numbers generally increased and there were 2 million in 1920 as compared with 600,000 in 1870. Sheep numbers followed a different pattern. They peaked in 1877 at approximately 6 million and within a decade had fallen to 2.5 million, several hundred thousand less than in 1870. There was little fluctuation from this level through 1920.[24]

Both industries experienced some changes in location. The beef cattle industry showed perceptible movement to the northeast counties and into the Central Valley, resulting in concentration in the central and southern coastal counties and the contiguous inland counties. Sheep moved to the inland valleys, the northeast, and to the northern coast. These relocations were a response to the spread of cultivation that followed the arrival of the railroad to the inland valleys. The original impetus was the repeal in 1872 of the Trespass Act (1850). This forced stockmen to take ownership of land and move to less arable areas.[25] Thus, animals began to predominate in the topographically rougher foothills and coastal counties and in the arid southern portion of the San Joaquin Valley.

In the San Joaquin Valley and central and southern coastal regions, many large grazing holdings were accumulated. In southern California the predominance of Americans in the grazing industries led to changes in grazing holdings. Large grazing holdings already existed in southern California in the form of Mexican grants. Some of these simply changed owners and continued with the same contours. The largest of these was the Santa Margarita Rancho in San Diego County. Its 133,000 acres were part of the 200,000 acres owned by the Pico family, which in 1917 were owned by James O'Neill and James Flood and operated as a stock ranch. Often new aggregations were formed, and such aggregations comprised most of the largest enduring grants. James Irvine's 100,000-acre ranch formed by 1886 from three ranchos, and Newhall's 143,000-acre ranch, put together by 1880 out of six different ranchos, are still well known. Actually, a large proportion of the large holdings in southern California were still used for stock in 1917. A study of large landholdings in eight southern California counties (Imperial, Los Angeles, Orange, Riverside, Santa Barbara, San Bernardino, San Diego, and Ventura) found that in 1917 only 29 percent of the 2.3 million acres in holdings larger than 2,000 acres was classified as tillable.* The percentage of tillable land was particularly low in Santa Barbara, San Diego, and Ventura Counties (12, 17 and 15 percent respectively), which bespeaks old ranchos still used for grazing.[26]

Along the central coast, the most well-known holding was Hearst's holding, divided between San Luis Obispo and Monterey Counties. George Hearst began acquiring land in 1865 when he purchased the 48,806-acre Piedra Blanca Rancho in San Luis Obispo County. Soon thereafter he purchased the 13,184-acre Santa Rosa Rancho and the 4,469-acre San Simeon Rancho, both also in San Luis Obispo County. Other ranchos and much land from the public domain were added to this holding. By 1900 the Hearst holding comprised some 240,000 acres in Monterey and San Luis Obispo Counties, and there was additional land in Tulare, Marin, Fresno, Butte, Sacramento, and San Mateo Counties.[27]

Located inland were the Miller and Lux holdings, second in extent only to the lands of the Southern Pacific Railroad. At the time of Miller's death in 1916 (Lux died in 1887 leaving Miller in complete control of the company), these consisted of about 1.25 million acres in California.[28] Of this, 920,274 acres were in the San Joaquin Valley, divided among the counties as shown in Table 2.3.

TABLE 2.3
Miller and Lux Landholdings
in the San Joaquin Valley
by County, 1916

County	Acreage
Merced	247,743
Fresno	268,092
Kern	186,400
Madera	148,039
Tulare & Stanislaus	70,000

Source: Lawrence (1933), p. 51.

The rest of the land was scattered through thirteen other counties, including San Mateo, Santa Clara, Monterey, San Louis Obispo, and San Benito. There were two foci, one in the northern San Joaquin Valley in Fresno, Madera, and Merced Counties, and one in Kern County in the southern San Joaquin Valley. The former area was where Miller began acquisitions with the purchase in 1857 of 8,835 acres of the Rancho Sanjón

*This ignores Southern Pacific holdings which account for another 2.6 million acres of which only 15 percent was tillable. This land is left out because so much of it was beyond any sort of use and was simply desert.

de Santa Rita. The rest of that grant and all or parts of fourteen others also became Miller and Lux property. These grants, along with substantial parts of the public domain, made Miller and Lux the largest landowners in those three counties. In the Kern County area, the kernel of their land was 60,000 acres along the Kern River, acquired as swamp and overflowed land. Additions were made from the public domain. In acquiring federal lands, Miller often used agricultural scrip (for 79,000 acres) and also followed the tiresomely familiar, but ever popular, routine of dummy homestead and preemption entries. In Merced County, for example, between 1863 and 1887, 287 plots, over half of which were 160 acres, were deeded over to Miller and Lux. Miller is also said to have filed on six townships (138,240 acres) in a single day at the Visalia Land Office.[29]

Remarkably enough, Miller "did not buy land merely to own it, or as a speculation, but he bought it principally to produce his animal stock in trade."[30] Hence, only insubstantial quantities were sold before his death in 1916. Financial difficulties arose after that date, and by 1923 land offices and agents were established throughout the state to facilitate the sales. The lack of interest in speculation is further indicated by the fact that all the irrigation works controlled by Miller and Lux, except the San Joaquin and Kings River Canal Company, served their lands exclusively and most of that water was used for wild pasture.[31]

The Tejon Ranch in Kern County is a well-known cattle empire. Edward Beale acquired four ranchos, beginning in 1865 with the purchase of the 48,299-acre La Liebre grant. Later in the same year, the 26,626-acre Los Alamos y Agua Caliente and the 97,612-acre El Tejon were purchased—both contiguous to La Liebre. Somewhat later he acquired the 22,178 acre Rancho Castac. In total this made 192,000 acres. By 1891 Beale had 265,215 acres. Twenty years later 278,000 acres were sold to the Chandler interests. Since there were no other grants in the area, some 73,000 acres must have come from the public domain. Beale used this land, until his death in 1893, as a cattle ranch. From his death until it was sold to the Chandler interests in 1912, his son Truxton continued to run it as a cattle ranch. Throughout these years only a single attempt was made to diversify. This resulted in the planting of 100 acres of trees, vines, and alfalfa in the 1880s, which were to languish in subsequent decades. For the first twenty years or so of their ownership, the Chandler group continued using the ranch basically for cattle; there was some citrus development and a notable failure with the ostrich industry (ostrich feathers were used in women's clothing during the late nineteenth century and early twentieth century; fashions changed in the 1920s and the industry fell apart).[32]

Grain

Much of the land accumulated in the 1870s and 1880s was indicative of the spread of wheat cultivation to the inland valleys, newly tied into national and international markets by rail transportation. In 1870 wheat seemed like a sure thing: a firm export trade was well established, prices were high, and actual cultivation was rather simple. Only the vagaries of rainfall, especially in the more southerly parts, made wheat an uncertain enterprise. So promising did wheat appear, that as soon as the railroad opened up land to markets, it succumbed to its cultivation. This was especially dramatic in the San Joaquin Valley where cultivation was freed from the constraints imposed by transportation on the San Joaquin River, which at best was navigable to Stockton. As the railroad moved south from Lathrop, reaching Goshen in 1872, Bakersfield in 1874, and the end of the valley in 1876, wheat kept pace. Thus, in 1870, the same year the line reached Modesto, the first trainload of grain left that city by rail for Oakland.[33] Merced had been reached in 1871 and, writing in the next year, Nordhoff said, "between Stockton and Merced lie about six hundred square miles of wheat."[34]

Wheat production, already occurring on a large scale, continued to develop in that direction. Mechanization became increasingly sophisticated. In the 1870s harvesting was still performed with headers, complemented by the recently ascendant steam threshers. At the same time, experimentation was going on with combined header-threshers — perhaps inspired by memories of the Hiram Moore machine brought from Michigan in the 1840s and briefly and successfully operated in the 1850s.[35] A combine harvester was finally developed by 1880 and was widely adopted in that decade, a step that has been described as "constituting the logical ultimate step in the evolution of large-scale methods in harvesting wheat under particularly favorable conditions."[36] Although steam tractor driven combines were available in the 1890s, they did not generally displace the horse-drawn combines. This awaited the development of the gasoline-driven tractor. Larger, improved gang plows and broadcast seeders were developed concurrently with these advances in harvesting.

Mechanization was most feasible for large-scale production. With it large farms were able to outcompete small ones. In fact, after wheat prices began their decline in the 1880s, the large farms were the ones best able to operate at a profit.[37] This large-scale advantage is apparent from the fate of the bonanza wheat farms. This is discussed in detail in the next section. It suffices here to point out that when such large farms were subdivided, it was not for use as small grain farms but as more intensively cultivated, usually irrigated, units.

The success of such large-scale operations encouraged the accumulation of large properties. Unfortunately, there is no information available that would permit estimation of the extent to which this occurred. Instead, a number of instances will be adduced to give some sense of the scope of such accumulation. In the Salinas and San Benito Valleys, where agricultural land was already in large holdings derived from Mexican grants, wheat cultivation had little to do with accumulation. At best it permitted the survival of the grants; more often it was a first step in subdividing the large ranchos previously devoted to livestock.[38]

In the Sacramento Valley outsized wheat farms were derived both from Mexican grants and the public domain. The most famous bonanza operation in the state belonged to Dr. Glenn in what was then Colusa County (now divided into Colusa and Glenn Counties). Perhaps the largest wheat farm in the state, its fame is probably due as much to the fact that its workings were described in detail in the *Cereal Report* included in the 1880 United States Census of Agriculture as to its size. Between 1867 and 1874 Glenn accumulated over 55,000 acres of land, over half of which was derived from parts of the Larkins Children and Jacinto Grants. The rest was probably public land. Most of this land was devoted to wheat and farmed in seven to nine farms run by foremen who oversaw approximately 700 laborers. Two other Mexican grants used in large part for grain in the Sacramento Valley were Bidwell's 23,000-acre Rancho Chico and Gehrke's 18,000-acre holding derived from the grant to Peter Lassen. An example of a large Sacramento Valley wheat farm not on a Mexican grant was on Joseph Cone's holdings in Tehama County. Between 1869 and 1894 Cone accumulated 100,000 acres, a significant portion of which came to be in wheat. Two other such examples were the Colina Walsh Estate of 17,000 acres and the 20,000 acres owned by I. F. Moulton, which were largely in wheat.[39]

Most holdings acquired in the San Joaquin Valley derived from the public domain. Information about grain bonanzas in this area tends to be more generic than specific. Nordhoff said, referring to his travels by train in 1874 through

Wheat, wheat, wheat and nothing but wheat is what you see on your journey as far as the eye can reach over the plain in every direction. Fields of two, three and four thousand acres make but small farms; here is a man who "has in" 20,000 acres; here one with 40,000 acres and another will some still more preposterous amount—all in wheat.[40]

Vander said of nineteenth-century wheat production in Fresno County that:

The wheat ranches were of a great size operated necessarily on a gigantic scale and corresponding cost. One thousand to three thousand acre grain fields were not uncommon.[41]

Two particular cases encompassed by these generalities were John Mitchell, who owned 42,000 acres planted with wheat in the area between the Tuolumne and Merced Rivers, and Clovis Cole who had a 10,000-acre wheat farm in Fresno County.[42]

None of the large holdings mentioned so far were formed after the late 1890s. The Tulare Lake area is a significant exception to this pattern. When reclamation came to the region at the end of the nineteenth century, the lake bed was converted into bonanza wheat farms. In 1905 one such farm, 18,000 acres in size, was claimed to be the largest in the world.[43] The threat of flooding is one reason for the bonanzas, as the permanent settlement that goes with smaller farms was impossible.

In the rest of the state the decline in wheat prices, begun in the 1880s and reaching its nadir in 1893, led to land being acquired for other purposes. During the twentieth century as other uses become common, wheat acreage declined. Over two million fewer acres were harvested to wheat in 1918 than in 1900 (506,000 acres as compared to 2,800,000 acres). Barley acreage was relatively constant from the early 1870s until the mid-1880s, but as wheat prices went down it became more attractive and acreage began to increase. After 1900 barley acreage increased by approximately 400,000 acres (going from 890,000 in 1900 to 1,320,000 acres in 1918).[44] Because barley production was quite similar to that of wheat, in particular being as subject to mechanization, it is likely that some large wheat holdings turned to it.

The commercial production of rice began in 1912 in Butte County. The acreage devoted to rice increased rapidly: in 1915, 32,000 acres were planted to it; in 1916, 65,000 acres; in 1917, 82,320 acres; and in 1918, 129,375 acres, largely in Glenn, Colusa, Butte, and Yolo Counties. Along with this rapid increase in acreage went price increases: from $1.98 per 100 pounds in 1912 to $4.95 in 1918. With a yield averaging 3,500 pounds per acre this meant returns far beyond those from other grains. Fortunately for owners of grain land in the valley, rice did best on the adobe soils that previously were unusable for anything but wheat. Because rice culture necessitated a fallow after several years, most rice farmers rented land. Rentals were for $15 to $25 per acre or one-quarter to one-third share of the crop. A switch to rice kept some large holdings intact. Some even produced rice on the same large scale that had been used with wheat. These included the Fair, Moulton, and Spaulding ranches with 5,000, 1,500, and 2,500 acres in rice, respectively. The Dodge Company both produced on a large scale (3,700 acres) and followed the more obvious path of renting out 4,436 acres in small parcels for rice production.[45]

Row Crops

Row crops were also associated, although to a lesser degree than grain, with large land holdings in this era. The most important crops in this regard were sugar beets and beans. The Sacramento-San Joaquin delta, noted for large holdings, produced a melange of row crops, particularly beans and potatoes. Probably the most important feature of row-crop production, which enabled it to be conducted on large holdings, was that the producers were typically tenant farmers.

Sugar beets came early to California in the 1850s but did not fare well. The history of the early sugar beet refiners is one of failure. Successful refining companies did not appear until the 1890s. One feature of these companies was their tendency to own large amounts of land—mostly to ensure that there would be a sufficient supply of sugar beets to keep the factory busy. Three such refining companies were the Spreckels Company, the Alameda Sugar Company, and the Union Sugar Company. In 1897, concurrent with the building of a factory in the Salinas Valley, the Spreckels Sugar Company began acquiring land in the valley. In 1911 they owned

20,000 acres, much of which was owned long beyond the end of this era. Some of this land was farmed directly by the company and the rest was farmed by tenants (an arrangement which prevailed until 1927 when the company completely ceased to farm and all its land became tenant operated). The Alameda Sugar Company originally owned 2,500 acres in Alameda County. In 1918 it no longer owned the Alameda County land, but instead owned 10,379 acres in Sutter County on which it raised sugar beets. The Union Sugar Company owned land in Santa Barbara County, which amounted to 11,000 acres in 1918.[46]

Dry beans became a leading crop during the twentieth century. Acreage harvested increased from 46,000 acres in 1900 to 158,000 acres in 1910 and 472,000 acres in 1920. One leading producing area was southern California, particularly San Luis Obispo, Ventura, and Los Angeles Counties. The Irvine ranch began to grow beans in the 1890s and had 1,800 acres planted to them in 1896, farmed largely under shares. By 1911 the ranch had 14,000 acres of beans grown under shares.[47]

The Sacramento-San Joaquin delta was another important bean area, in addition to producing other row crops and some vegetables. Land was first acquired in the delta under the workings of the state's disposal of its swamp and overflowed lands. Most of the land was acquired in the 1860s and 1870s. The latter decade was when reclamation really began to make progress; 92,000 acres were reclaimed between 1870 and 1880, and activity was intense during the next four decades. By 1920 some 417,000 acres were reclaimed.[48] As was indicated above (Chapter 1) disposal of this land led to considerable concentration of ownership. In the delta, this left much of the land in the hands of reclamation companies. Through World War I, the major occurrences in delta landownership were the changing contours of the aggregations owned by reclamation companies. Table 2.4 lists some of these large landholding companies in 1918.

The ability to make a satisfactory profit by leasing land was an attraction of delta land for large owners. Edwin Cox reported in 1916 that "being able to secure ample returns on their actual investment by leasing to foreigners, the majority of owners in the delta district, when interviewed by the writer, denied any desire to sell to purchasers of small tracts."[49] This was exactly what the United States Immigration Commission had found six years earlier. The Immigration Commission's report gave information about the leasing of some large delta tracts. This is summarized in Table 2.5.

Clearly, the actual scale of the farming unit was not well reflected in the size of the ownership unit. The success of this tenant farming depended on two things: the availability of tenants, and the existence of a crop regime valuable enough to warrant high rents (or yield high rents under sharecropping). A number of immigrant groups became tenants. Asiatics, Portuguese, and Italians predominated. Although members of these groups would have preferred to own their own farms, establishing oneself as a small farmer in California called for a fair amount of capital and these newcomers often lacked such resources. Furthermore, the Chinese were

TABLE 2.4
Some Large Delta Landholding Companies, 1918

Name	Acreage
California Delta Farms	39,337
Holland Land Company	25,000
Rindge Land and Navigation Company	21,300
Sargent Canal Ranch	3,388
Staten Island Land Company	9,260
Venice Island Company	3,843
H. W. Wolf & Sons	2,200
TOTAL	104,328

Source: *Walker's Manual of Pacific Coast Securities* for the years 1918 and 1920.

TABLE 2.5
Tenure of Some Large Delta Tracts, 1910

Tract	Acreage	No. of Owners	No. of Tenants
Staten Island	9,230	1	36
Lower Sherman Island	4,000	1	10
Venice Island	2,275	1	14
Woodward Island	2,060	1	12
Orwood Tract	2,464	1	5
Clayton Tract	2,600	1	5
Byron Tract	8,300	2	6
Lower Jones*			
Upper Jones*	18,455	1	29
Rindge Tract*			

Source: United States Immigration Commission (1911a), Part 25, Vol. 2, pp. 328, 330.
Note: These three tracts are combined due to information on page 237 of Thompson (1955). Rindge Land and Navigation of Table 2.4 owned them all.

legally prohibited from owning land after 1886.

Barley was the leading delta crop by acreage, but it was far surpassed in value by the field beans and potatoes with which it was grown in rotation. Between 1900 and 1918 the average farm value per acre of barley grown ranged from $10.66 to $29.90, averaging $18.99. The average farm value per acre of potatoes during these same years ranged between $55.12 and $217.50, averaging $105.66. Beans brought in $50 to $62 per acre.[50] Furthermore, because of the fertility of the peat soils of the delta, all of these crops sustained much higher yields than in the other areas of California where they were grown. Thus, it is no surprise that delta owners were able to obtain a very good return by renting out their land.

Intensive Cultivation and the Subdivision of Large Holdings

Throughout this entire period, 1870-1918, large holdings were being broken up. This phenomena was associated with the land being put to more intensive agricultural use (and occasionally urban uses) that usually entailed the planting of orchards and vineyards, typically under irrigation. By 1919 fruit production could be found throughout the state. Citrus orchards were concentrated in southern California, although oranges were also grown in the eastern San Joaquin Valley (the piedmont region). Southern California also contained most of the walnut orchards in the state. Deciduous orchards were more common in northern California than in southern California. The Sacramento Valley, Bay Area, and Central Coast led in almonds, apricots, pears, plums, and prunes. The San Joaquin Valley led in peaches and produced most of the state's grapes.[51]

Vegetables were not produced on a very extensive scale until the twentieth century. As late as 1920, only 165,000 acres were devoted to vegetables—as compared with 1,392,000 acres in bearing orchards and vineyards.[52] Vegetable production was not necessarily associated with subdivision or small holdings. We saw this above in discussing the delta.

Table 2.6 shows the values of extensive crops (grains and other field crops) and intensive crops (fruits and vegetables) from 1869 to 1919. The 1890s are clearly a turning point, which, because of the time it takes orchards and vineyards to come to fruit, indicates their development during the 1880s. The 1880s and 1890s were decades of declining grain prices, and the switch to intensive crops was a response to this decline. An obvious strategy for owners of large grain farms would have been to convert their land to orchards. And, indeed, the agricultural economist Varden Fuller claims that during the nineteenth century a "not-insignificant proportion" of large grain and livestock holdings were converted into huge fruit farms. Fuller thought this happened because landowners had access to a sufficient amount of cheap labor to work the land themselves.[53]

It is contended here, contrary to Fuller, that during the nineteenth century large-scale conversion for intensive uses was rare. The costs of conversion were high and the crops were not sufficiently profitable. Fuller did not substantiate his claim and it would be impossible to do so. Examples of large fruit farms do exist but they are not common. Nearly every time an orchard or vineyard larger than 1,000 acres in size is mentioned in the literature of the period it is claimed to be, if not the largest in the state or world, maybe the second largest. Thus, the 3,000-acre Paige and Morton fruit farm in Tulare County, of which 1,500 acres were said to be planted in 1891, was claimed, in that same year to have "borne the reputation of the largest orchard in the state." In this it was not alone. In 1890, the 1,200-

TABLE 2.6
Values of Extensive and Intensive Crops, 1869-1919

	Value of Crop (000)		Percent of Total	
Year	Extensive	Intensive	Extensive	Intensive
1869	$35,007	$2,444	93.4	6.6
1879	69,304	2,814	96.1	3.9
1889	62,602	6,852*	90.0	10.0
1899	53,111	40,442	56.7	43.3
1909	70,246	68,887	50.5	49.5
1919	204,692	346,249	36.6	63.4

Source: Fuller (1934), p. 330
Note: The U.S. Census of Agriculture, the source for the rest of the table has no value for orchard crops for 1889 but $1,420,565 is given for the value of market garden and small fruits sold. In the report of the State Board of Equalization for 1890, the value of the fruit crop was said to be $2,715,787. This is surely too low as a number of counties were not reported. An estimate was made by doubling this amount and adding it to the market garden value (with which it overlaps) from the census.

acre orchard of Hatch and Rock in Butte County was also termed "the largest orchard in the state of California." In the same year the Natomas Company vineyard of 1,500 to 2,000 acres in Sacramento County was called the "second largest in the world." The Nadeau vineyard of more than 2,000 acres located midway between Los Angeles and Anaheim was referred to as the "most extensive vineyard in California," second to the 3,575 acre Stanford vineyard in Tehama County which was "the largest in the world". Los Angeles County also had "the largest olive grove in the world," 2,000 acres in Sylmar.

Even in later years the same size scale was applied. Thus, in 1918 the Fancher Ranch of 3,900 acres in Merced county, was "the world's largest canning peach orchard." In the same year the 3,547 acre Italian Vineyard Company's vineyard at Guasti in San Bernardino County and the 3,631-acre Wakhole vineyard in Fresno County (2,500 acres of which were planted and bearing) were amongst the "largest . . . in the world." Also, a 1,620-acre raisin vineyard in Merced County was "believed to be the largest raisin vineyard in the world." In 1934 the Limoneira Company's 1,850 acres was one of the "largest citrus farms in the state," while in 1931 the Mills orchard of 1,760 acres was one of the "largest citrus orchards" in the United States. In 1940 world leaders in citrus ran larger: Sunny Hills Ranch near Fullerton had 2,000 acres and the Irvine ranch had 3,000 acres so planted.[54] Apparently, a size of several hundred acres was sufficient to constitute a large orchard or vineyard and several thousand acres was huge.

Furthermore, some of the more enduring holdings did not even begin conversion until marketing procedures improved in the twentieth century. Thus, it was not until 1906 that the Irvine ranch began planting citrus, and the Newhall Land Company and the Tejon Ranch did not do so until 1912. [55] These examples only involve the owners converting a small part of their land to an orchard. In other words, there is no evidence to support the contention that large holdings were converted to orchards. Known instances of large orchards are described in such a manner as to indicate their rarity. Wholesale conversion could not have taken place on many holdings over 2,000 acres in size and on none of those constituting 10,000 acres or more.

The strength of the relationship between subdivision and intensive agriculture is well evidenced by Fresno County. Successful subdivision (or colonization as it was often called; the distinction is rather obscure) first occurred in 1875, and by 1891 the county contained over thirty distinct subdivisions, besides a great deal of land simply in small holdings. A 1907 landownership map showed over sixty subdivisions, but more significantly some fourteen townships, all in the Piedmont area where most orchard and vineyard development occurred, were completely given over to small holdings. The early activity is reflected in the fact that in 1873 the real estate deeds of the county filled 7 volumes, while in 1889 they occupied 163 volumes; a fact that was reported at the time as an indication of the influence of irrigation on the transfer of real estate. The same association was noted in 1914 during a soil survey of the Fresno area. Irrigation was essential for fruit culture in Fresno and increased subdivision was followed by tremendous jumps in the numbers of trees and vines. For example, the number of bearing vineyards rose from 16,000 in 1890 to 25 million in 1900 and 41 million in 1910. The number of bearing peaches and nectarines increased from 112,000 in 1890 to 924,000 in 1900 and 2,277,000 in 1910. [56]

Southern California presents an additional example of the correlation between subdivision and the planting of trees and vines. A land boom was set off by the rate war between the Southern Pacific and the Santa Fe after the latter's rails reached Los Angeles in 1885. On March 6, 1887, a flurry of price cutting was climaxed by the Southern Pacific actually setting passenger fares between Kansas City and Los Angeles at $1.00. [57] Fares soon rose, but for at least a year they remained extremely low. The low fares led to a flood of immigrants to southern California and a land boom.

The boom had its greatest impact in the developing urban areas, especially Los Angeles and Pasadena. But most of the southern California low land was affected to some degree. As towns were formed, development of agricultural land also increased.* Thus, in 1886 South Riverside was formed as a colony on 12,000 acres of the Yorba ranch in Temescal Valley. Outside of San Bernardino, George Bonebrake acquired 50,000 acres in

---

*In both cases, formation of new towns or creation of agricultural subdivisions, large holdings were being broken up—usually old Mexican grants.

1887, and later in that year a company he headed, the Semi-Tropic Land and Water Company, laid out a number of settlements in that area. In the San Fernando Valley part of one large holding was subdivided in 1888. This was 12,000 acres of the 60,000 acres that the Los Angeles Farm and Milling Company had acquired in 1880 from the San Francisco Homestead Association, which itself had originally purchased the land from former Mexican governor Pío Pico in 1869. The 1888 subdivision was under the supervision of Isaac Lankenshein.[58]

Table 2.7 shows the number of bearing lemon and orange trees and grapevines in 1890, 1900, and 1910 in the seven southern California counties of Los Angeles, Orange, Riverside, San Bernardino, San Diego, Santa Barbara, and Ventura. Notice how the number of trees and vineyards increased dramatically after the boom and subsequent subdivision (it takes four to five years from planting before the trees or vines come into bearing).

TABLE 2.7
Number of Bearing Trees and Vineyards
in Southern California, 1890-1910

	1890	1900	1910
Lemons	77,000	1,429,000	875,000
Oranges	1,117,000	4,598,000	5,368,000
Grapevines	36,000	7,586,000	14,338,000

Source: California State Agricultural Society (1911), pp. 162-69.

There was some subdivision in the Sacramento Valley in the nineteenth century, but the brunt of it occurred in the first few decades of the twentieth century. Despite the difference in timing, there was again the association between irrigation, intensive agriculture, and subdivision. The situation in the valley was described in this way in 1919:

> While extensive irrigation of the valley plains has been discussed and irrigation works have been partially completed at great expense, progress in irrigation and intensive agriculture has been blocked by engineering difficulties, litigation, and the indifference and opposition of the land owners themselves, who here, where grain can still be produced at a small profit, prefer in many cases to continue the direction of uncertain farming operations over an estate of many thousand acres rather than to take up the management of a smaller irrigated farm.[59]

Causes Of Subdivision

Of course, not all wheat and livestock holdings were subdivided. Even when irrigated some were maintained, being used for irrigated pasture, alfalfa and even some grains. But when conversion to orchards occurred, the holding was subdivided. The basic reason why this occurred is that fruit prices did not warrant the high costs conversion entailed.

How expensive was conversion? An 1885 estimate of the cost of planting and bringing to bearing a 10-acre citrus orchard in Los Angeles County put the cost at $230 per acres. This would be $460,000 for 2,000 acres. Based on 1912 estimates of the cost of converting one acre into a bearing orchard, it can be estimated that to convert 2,000 acres into a bearing citrus orchard would have run $778,000. Conversion into a deciduous orchard or vineyard would have cost $110,000 if unirrigated and $212,000 if irrigated.[60]

The 1912 estimates were presented as conservative. This is corroborated by their general agreement with figures produced in 1904 by the California Promotion Committee, whose interest in encouraging settlement no doubt, made their estimates unduly optimistic. Note also that the estimates do not include the cost of clearing the land and, in general, making it ready for plowing. The costs of preparing the land for irrigation (leveling and grading the land, and putting in a water distribution system) are not included in the 1885 estimate. The 1912 estimate includes $10 per acre for grading the land and $25 per acre for flumes for water distribution. The former is almost certainly too low. In that same year, J.C. Forkner spent $21 per acre to level 12,000 acres outside of Fresno in preparation for planting them to an irrigated fig orchard (which was sold off as small farms). In the State Land Settlement Colony at Delhi, leveling for irrigation was found to cost $32.94 per acre in 1921.[61] Another cost not counted in the estimates is the interest on money borrowed to pay for the conversion. Clearly, the cost of converting a large landholding in extensive use to and orchard would be expensive; the estimates presented here are probably less than the actual cost would have been.

Furthermore, managing a large-scale orchard is completely different than managing a large grain or livestock enterprise. Conversion would call for a great deal of knowledge on the part of the owner. Thus, many owners sold their land; it was the most profitable thing to do. Typically, they did not subdivide it themselves. Instead, a speculator came in, bought the land, developed a water supply, did some conversion, and subdivided and resold at a much higher price than he paid for the land.

These developers had no interest in large-scale agricultural production but only in the profits from land sales. One might think that poor fruit markets would be a drawback but large advertising campaigns and widely publicized stories of enormous profits to be made with fruits inflated land values and attracted settlers.[62] Many of these new small farmers failed; they also suffered from low prices and had the additional burden of high land payments. Others, however, succeeded and through their efforts helped improve the marketing of their crops, thus establishing conditions favorable to large-scale production. Some large owners, such as Newhall and Irvine, began to convert part of their land into large orchards, but this sort of conversion was not attractive until the second decade of the twentieth century, when marketing problems were finally overcome for many of the crops.

When price problems were "solved," large owners could convert profitably. In fact, after World War I, conversion was not even necessary to realize the potential of large-scale production because enough land had been developed for smaller-scale production to permit the consolidation of a number of smaller, intensively used holdings, which in the aggregate constituted a large amount of land (albeit scattered). Two such holdings, that of the Earl Fruit Company and that of Calpak, included acquisitions from 1915 and 1918 respectively.[63]

Intensive cultivation did not only require good markets for the crops, adequate supplies of water and labor were also necessary. The next three sections consider in detail the developments in each of these areas.

Marketing Developments

The problem of prices originated in the fact that the local market for fruits and vegetables was quickly sated, almost as soon as production became significant, so that growers had to rely on markets in outside areas, mostly the eastern United States. Yet there they were faced with competition from eastern growers in which they were hampered by spoilage, transportation costs, lack of organized marketing, and a general lack of demand for California products. Several developments of the late nineteenth century helped to solve these problems and pave the way for the later national dominance of California agriculture. First, the transcontinental railroad sped delivery and lowered shipping costs. Second, growers began to organize into marketing associations that not only packed and marketed the fruits but established standards for the products they handled. Trade names became attached to their products and these were heavily advertised. Third, the development of dried fruit and canning industries eased the seasonal glut problem and also helped to open up new markets for fruits and vegetables. Marketing improvements via these means were crucial to the development of intensive cultivation and hence to subdividing California's landholdings.

Northern California was the first part of the state to have transcontinental rail connections. This occurred in 1869. The next year shipment of deciduous fruits and grapes began and their commercial production was able to begin in earnest.* Southern California's first transcontinental connection

---

*The San Joaquin Valley had rail connections by the valley line several years later. Since the grape industry was not well established until late in the 1870s, and citrus and deciduous fruit production came even later to that area, this was of no import. That is, the presence of the railroad was necessary but not sufficient for the development of orchard crops.

came in 1876 when the Southern Pacific Valley line, connecting through Sacramento line to the east, reached Los Angeles. In 1877 W. Wolfskill sent the first carload of citrus to St. Louis. Commercial production in southern California received its principal impetus from the completion of the southern line of the Southern Pacific to New Orleans in 1881 and particularly in the arrival of the Santa Fe Railroad four years later. In the 1890s the refrigerated railway car, which had first appeared in 1889, had a revolutionary impact of the marketing of fresh fruits. [64]

From the start railroad rates came under criticism. In fact the first formal organization of growers, the California Fruit Growers and Dealers Association, formed in 1869, devoted its attention to this problem. The Association's only known accomplishment was to bring about some reduction so that

> The California Farmer reported [in 1870] that the Railroad Directors "now offer to take *fruit* on their regular trains at the reduced rate of $500 per car, and will *prepare cars* to carry it safe — or they will send it on express trains at $950 per car. . . .This we esteem liberal and we hope it will be justly regarded." [65]

These rates must have prevailed for some time. They were what Wolfskill paid for his 1877 citrus shipment. [66] In 1885 the Southern Pacific offered special rates if the growers supplied fifteen cars daily.

A number of marketing organizations began to be formed as fruit production expanded. In northern California deciduous growers formed the California Fruit Union (which lasted nine years) in 1885, and several other associations appeared in the next few years. Southern California citrus growers formed the Orange Growers Protection Union in 1885 (lasting until 1893), which stood alone until a flurry of organizational activity in the early 1890s. None of these organizations endured, but they were followed by more successful ones that benefitted from their experience and still exist today. [67]

Rail rates were but one concern of these associations. Dissatisfaction was rife over the marketing procedures followed by the shippers and brokers. These were haphazard at best and often led to either glutted or bare markets. In the 1870s and 1880s California fruit was easy to market in the East, but this success soon led to extensive plantings and overproduction. Successful marketing became difficult. Rahno MacCurdy describes the situation for the citrus growers and it probably applied to all fruits:

> At first the system of dealer purchase, imperfect though it was, returned profits to both grower and dealer, but as the supply increased business proved less remunerative and more uncertain. Also, there was no understanding between buyers as to distribution among the eastern markets and glutting and undersupply followed. With the resultant instability of the market, the buyer, had he wished to, could not pay the maximum prices for the fruit that would have been possible with a market in which all interested factors had confidence. [68]

The early organizations did succeed to some degree in ameliorating conditions but they were inadequate to the task after the depression of 1893. The early 1890s had been particularly poor for citrus even before the depression and were referred to as red ink years.* Deciduous fruits and grapes were not in such bad shape until after the depression (when, for example, raisin prices fell from $.05 per pound to $.0075 per pound). Perhaps because of their greater need, the citrus growers were the first to establish (in 1895) an enduring association—the Southern California Fruit Exchange.[70] The Exchange served as a model for the other fruit associations. Its basic structure has remained the same to the present. Foremost, it is composed of a number of local packing units, mostly cooperative associations (some of which preceded its existence). These local associations both harvest the fruit of the members and prepare it (pack, grade, clean, and so on) for market. Thus, members do not have to deal directly with any sort of agricultural laborers. The local associations are organized into district exchanges which are themselves federated to form the overall exchange. This overall structure handles marketing, advertising, selling, etc. It is controlled by the local units through the district exchanges. The growers pay a certain percentage of what they receive for each box marketed through the exchange.

The Southern California Fruit Exchange experienced difficulties in 1903 and 1904 due to demoralized markets. In these two years, it combined forces with the California Citrus Union, an organization of commercial shippers, to form a selling organization called the California Fruit Agency. Although this move was somewhat successful in terms of dealing with the immediate market problem, it was an unstable combination as the two members' interests did not meld. It was dissolved in 1904. In 1905 the Southern California Fruit Exchange was renamed the California Fruit Growers Exchange. The overproduction problem was the first to be dealt with "(1) by better methods of distribution and (2) by the creation of dependable marketable qualities in the product through the establishment of standard grades and improved handling practices."[71]

In 1907 advertising campaigns were begun to enlarge the market for California citrus fruit. Iowa was the test area. It was there that the Sunkist trademark of the Exchange was first introduced. Interestingly, the Southern Pacific matched funds spent by the Exchange on this advertising campaign.[72] By the end of the decade, the citrus industry was, thanks to the Exchange, in good shape and prospects were bright. It is not surprising that Irvine began citrus plantings in 1911.

Deciduous fruit growers did not establish a comparable organization until the California Fruit Exchange, a cooperative marketing association

---

*Citrus growers in California had a stroke of luck in the 1894-1895 Florida freeze which pretty much destroyed the industry in Florida, their only domestic competitor. Florida production did not surpass California until 1943; prior to the freeze, Florida was by far the larger producer.[69]

following the pattern of the Southern California Fruit Growers Exchange, was established in 1903.* Since few local associations existed in 1901, these had to be created; in these early years this activity was largely concentrated north of Fresno. The local associations only handled packing, grading and other preparation for shipment; they did not arrange for picking. The California Fruit Exchange itself, as with the Southern California Fruit Growers Exchange, also handled marketing, advertising and selling. In fact, except for 1903 and 1904 when the Southern California Fruit Growers Exchange was selling through the California Fruit Agency, the California Fruit Exchange sold through the citrus growers' agents. In the years 1903 and 1904, the California Fruit Exchange joined the California Fruit Distributors, a group of independent shippers. This latter organization, which endured from 1902 to 1927, at first handled 80 percent of the shipments from California. By 1917 it was down to less than 50 percent and in 1927, the year it discontinued operations, it handled about 20 percent of the shipments. Much of this reflected a switch in control to the California Fruit Exchange. By the second decade of the century the markets for deciduous fruits were in good shape, mostly because of the various marketing organizations.[73]

The deciduous and citrus fruit exchanges were the most important marketing associations formed in these years. Raisin growers began to organize with some success in the California Raisin Growers Association, which exited from 1898 to 1903, but a long-lasting organization was not formed until 1912. Nut growers organized marketing associations in 1910 (almonds) and 1912 (walnuts). Other fruit and vegetable associations were formed in the next few decade; most followed the pattern set out by the citrus and deciduous exchanges formed in this era. In 1915 there was a total of 197 cooperative marketing and purchasing associations in California, including all the local organizations.[74]

Even with the cooperative marketing agencies, surpluses could still be a problem, and good years for production could be bad years for profits. Fortunately, not all fruits and vegetables had to be sold fresh. Grapes, apples, plums, pears, peaches, and apricots could all be dried. Raisins, produced in the United States only in California, were probably the most successful of the dried fruits. Despite low prices at times, production increased steadily. For deciduous fruits and vegetables, canning was a savior. California's first cannery was built in 1860. In 1870 the total pack produced was 36,000 cases. A decade later 221,000 cases were in the total and by 1890 1.5 million cases were produced. In the 1889 Census Report canned and preserved fruits and vegetables were valued at $6 million. In 1914 this had increased to $61 million and in the next six years it surged to $220 million.[75]

---

*It was originally named the California Fresh Fruit Exchange and was renamed the California Fruit Exchange in 1903.

Irrigation

Overcoming marketing difficulties was crucial to the success of intensive cultivation, but production itself could not have been feasible without sufficient irrigation development and the availability of an adequate labor force. Irrigation development in California was particularly difficult because California was burdened with two disparate systems of water rights: that based on common law and that based on appropriation. The problems this presented with respect to ground water were resolved in 1903, but a viable compromise with respect to surface rights was not obtained until the state constitution was amended in 1929. At that point the criteria of reasonable use was fully established as the way to mediate difficulties in water rights. One result of these confusions was pointed out in 1900 (and could well have been said in any of the fifty years):

> At present, it is notorious that anyone attempting to utilize the streams of California for any purpose has to add to the ordinary or legitimate risks and expenses of his enterprise, a large and continuing outlay for litigation to maintain his right to water.[76]

Nonetheless, as Table 2.8 shows, irrigation developed rapidly.

Virtually all of this was by private possessors of surface or ground water rights. As late as 1919, 85 percent of irrigation was privately undertaken. Nonetheless, governmental involvement in irrigation development was significant. This did not include the oft-cited federal efforts to encourage irrigation, however. The Carey Act (1897), whereby the federal government offered each state 1 million acres to sell to finance irrigation projects, was never used in California. The landmark Reclamation Act (1902), which "authorized the federal government to construct irrigation projects to make arid land fertile," was not applied in California until after 1918 and so will not be discussed in this section.

TABLE 2.8
Irrigated Acreage in California, 1870-1919

Year	Acreage
1870	60,000
1880	350,000
1889	1,004,233
1899	1,446,114
1909	2,664,104
1919	4,219,040

Source: Harding (1960), p. 80.

The state was involved in two important ways. After 1911 all commercial venders of water were subject, as public utilities, to rate and other forms of regulation by the State Railroad Commission, and there was increasing involvement in water planning, as evidenced by the 1914 adoption of the water commission plan.

Most important, the state provided for the development of irrigation districts. The motivation for this was to ease costs for the small owner and give him greater control over irrigation—instead of it being totally in the hands of the developer of the water supply. The idea of the irrigation district was based on the theory that land and the water to irrigate it should be held jointly. This would be achieved by all landowners calling for the formation of an irrigation district. The district itself would own the water rights in trust for the landowners, who would be able to obtain water from the district in which they resided. This idea had a long history in California, and a number of rather useless laws, under which nothing was accomplished, were passed between 1872 and 1887 to provide for the creation of irrigation districts.[77] The 1887 Wright District Act was the first vaguely workable law. Under it:

> Provision was made for the ordering of an election for the organization of districts on petition of fifty or a majority of the freeholders of the proposed district. Lands included in any district were to be susceptible of irrigation from a common source. County supervisors were given power to grant or deny petitions from freeholders desiring to form districts. They could order the necessary election and amend boundaries. District directors . . . were elected from divisions into which the districts were divided. Upon the adoption of plans and the making of an estimate of cost by an engineer, bonds were issued and their sale was permitted at not less than 90 percent of their face value. In voting on the formation of the district and on the issuance of bonds no property qualification was prescribed.[78]

The important feature is that all landowners, regardless of size of holding, had an equal vote in the proceedings. One large owner could be overruled by a number of small owners, as the law intended. The law was not particularly successful, however. Chicanery ensued with the bond issues; sometimes the burden of taxation due to low cost estimates became so great that districts attempted to default on their obligations. The act was repealed in 1897 and replaced with the Wright-Bridgeford Act. In doing this "the legislature of 1897 had the impression that it was imposing conditions so severe that further district organization was not likely to recur for some time. This proved to be the case for twelve years. . . ."[79] Under this act the irrigation districts came under state regulation. Over thirty districts were formed under the 1887 act, and by 1900 few were in successful operation. Only seven survived well into the twentieth century. After 1909, when activity began under the 1897 law, a number of new districts were formed so that in 1918 forty-four were in operation.[80]

Irrigation development was not wholly, or even chiefly, of benefit to intensive cultivation and subdivision of large holdings. Surprisingly, perhaps, the acreage devoted to intensive crops, even as late as 1919, only comprised 1,557,000 acres (165,000 of which were harvested to vegetables). Had all the intensive crops been irrigated, their acreage would not, in any given year, have accounted for more than 37 percent of the total irrigated acreage in the state.*

Actually, the major proportion of irrigated land was dedicated to extensive use, cereal crops, and especially forage and pasture. This remains the case today. Certainly, small farms grew these crops; alfalfa was even recommended for small farmers as a crop until orchards came into bearing. But typically they were grown on large holdings, especially forage and pasture. Wild grass pasture was particularly well-suited for large owners as it could be irrigated through very primitive means. All that was necessary was to contrive to overflow the land for a while. Thus, Miller and Lux used all of their water in Kern County for alfalfa, grain, and pasture, and of 116,500 acres irrigated in 1910, the Kern County Land Company had all but 5,000 acres in such extensive crops. In other counties, such as Merced and Madera, Miller and Lux also devoted most of their water to pasture. The Herminghaus land in Madera County, famous for its involvement in a 1926 case about riparian rights, was another large holding used for wild grass pasture.[81] The bonanza grain farms in Tulare Lake bed were also irrigated. In short, irrigation was predominantly associated with holdings, often large, in extensive use.

Large owners also had an advantage as reliance on ground water increased in the twentieth century. In 1919 it accounted for 20.5 percent (868,050 acres) of the irrigated acreage, an increase of 6.4 percent (500,000 acres) from 1909. In 1919 the costs per acre foot of water from pumped wells were 2.5 to 3 times as much as that for surface water.[82] Although this suggests that such water would have to be put to more intensive, or at least most profitable uses, it implies nothing about the scale of the user. In the next chapter the rise of more profitable crops, suitable to large-scale production will be discussed. Because practically all of the well development was by individuals or partnerships, in later years when wells had to go deeper and became increasingly expensive to build, ground water use began to favor large-scale producers.

Irrigation must therefore be assessed as a factor that, while frequently contributing to the conditions that made intensive cultivation possible and hence encouraging the break-up of large holdings, also helped sustain many large operations.

---

*It was common in northern California to grow deciduous fruits, nuts and grapevines without irrigation.

Labor

Labor developments in this period are important for two reasons. First, intensive cultivation could not have occurred without the presence of a cheap labor force. Second, when the time came for large owners to grow more valuable crops, they relied heavily on hired labor. The origins of a suitable labor pool, of mobile workers accepting low wages, can be found in the nineteenth century when intensive cultivation was first developing. The role of cheap labor went far beyond actual cultivation. It was essential for the construction of railroads, irrigation and reclamation projects, as well as the canning and packing industries.

The Chinese formed the first substantial pool of cheap labor. In the mid-1860s the Central Pacific Railroad hired about ten thousand Chinese — mostly ex-miners, and thousands of contract laborers brought to the United States from China. When the railroad was completed these men were forced to find new employment. This often turned out to be other construction work. By composing a large portion of the Southern Pacific labor force, performing most of the reclamation work in the Sacramento delta and in general being involved in irrigation and reclamation projects, the Chinese performed work essential to the development of California agriculture. But their most important contribution to agriculture came from their labor on the farms. Although numerically they never dominated the agricultural labor force, because of specialization in orchard and vegetable crops they acquired a significance disproportionate to their numbers. This influence was not confined to any one portion of the state, though in the early 1870s Indians and Mexicans were of greater importance in southern California. For example, the Anaheim colony "relied primarily upon Mexican and Indian labor" and "about San Bernardino" the farm laborers in 1872 were "chiefly Indians." However, the Chinese also appeared on southern California ranches as early as 1864, became as important in southern California as in northern California by the end of the decade, and by the 1880s were well established in orchards and vineyards throughout the state. [83]

The importance of the Chinese to the success of the new orchards and vineyards was remarked upon by growers. Thus, in 1877, the Reverend William Brier, a northern California fruit grower told a Senate committee investigating Chinese immigration that "At the present prices of fruit, we could not raise it without Chinese labor." [84] Nine years later, L. J. Rose, a fruit grower near San Gabriel, told the State Horticultural Society that "If it had not been for the labor of [the Chinese] fruit growing and the wine industry would not be where they are now." [85] The advantages of Chinese labor are well described by Nordhoff:

> It is a fact, however, that they do a great deal of work white men will not do out here; they do not stand idle, but take the first job that is offered them. And the result is that they are used all over the State, more and more, because they chiefly, of the laboring population, will

work steadily and keep their engagements.

Moreover, the admirable organization of the Chinese labor is an irresistible convenience to the farmer, vineyardist, and other employer. "How do you arrange to get your Chinese?" I asked a man in the country who was employing more than a hundred in several gangs. He replied "I have only to go or send to a Chinese employment office in San Francisco, and say that I need so many men for such work and at such pay. Directly up come the men, with a foreman of their own, with whom alone I have to deal. I tell only him what I want done; I settle with him alone; I complain to him, and hold him alone responsible. He understands English; and this system simplifies things amazingly. If I employed white men I should have to instruct, reprove, watch, and pay each one separately; and of a hundred, a quarter, at least, would be dropping out day after day for one cause or another. Moreover, with my Chinese comes up a cook for every twenty men, whom I pay, and provisions of their own which they buy. Thus I have nobody to feed and care for. They do it themselves."[86]

Furthermore, according to the 1885-86 report of the California State Bureau of Labor Statistics, the Chinese accepted lower wages than non-Chinese agricultural laborers. These characteristics then distinguished the Chinese: willingness to do work others spurned, being organized in such a manner that saved the employer from having to deal directly with many individuals, being available for work as needed all over the state, and accepting lower wages. These same characteristics appear in all other groups that were to labor in California agriculture. They are a combination that maximizes labor availability while minimizing costs.

That a group with such characteristics was essential for the establishment and practice of intensive agriculture is apparent from the results of a study Ping Chiu made in which he found that "of the vineyards and orchards of Southern California listed in the 1880 manuscript census, labor costs amounted to from one quarter to one fifth of the total estimated income with two . . . exceptions."[87]

The ratio was much less for grain farms, which had the advantage of partial mechanization. Little could be done to avoid human labor in the orchards and vineyards. Small farms, especially orchards and vineyards, were dependent upon seasonal labor at harvest time.* The Chinese never played much of a role on grain farms: work with teams was pretty much reserved for whites and the Chinese were limited to helping with binding and threshing during harvest time labor shortages.[89]

Since the large grain farmers were not dependent upon the Chinese and there were not very many large orchards and vineyards, it would seem implausible that the Chinese agricultural laborers had much to do with the

---

*Fisher claimed that in 1953 even ten acre fruit farms needed such labor.[88] If this were the case in more technologically advanced days, it must have been even more so in the nineteenth century.

existence of large agricultural holdings. It was the smaller farmers who had the principal interest in Chinese labor. William Brier, quoted above, owned only fifty acres in fruit, yet employed eight men, seven of whom were the Chinese he found essential. During the anti-Chinese agitation in 1886, a resolution against the agitators was signed by fifty-eight Vacaville farmers "most of whom had less than 50 acres," who were interested in protecting their "property and laborers."[90] That some large owners, like Hollister, favored Chinese immigration does not seem a satisfactory reason to believe that their ability to retain their land was dependent upon the presence of the Chinese, especially given that other large owners, like Senator A. A. Sargent, were vehemently opposed to Chinese labor.[91]

The Chinese slowly dropped out of the labor force after immigration of Chinese laborers was barred by the restriction act in 1882. The Geary Act of 1888 and the McCreary Act of 1893 further restricted Chinese immigration and rights. The original restriction was the culmination of several decades of almost continuous fulmination. This anti-Chinese agitation, although frequently attributed to a general lowering of wages that competition between whites and Chinese was supposed to have engendered, was more likely due to prejudice based on racial and cultural differences. It was not until the 1890s, when there was a general labor surplus, that the relationship became more competitive than complementary.[92]

The adequacy of the labor force in the 1890s was further assured by the entrance of the Japanese. The Japanese first appeared as fruit pickers at Vacaville near the end of the 1880s and in the next decades they became a major source of labor on farms throughout the state. Their importance increased dramatically in the first decade of the twentieth century, and by 1909 (two years after their exclusion by the Gentlemen's Agreement) it was said that "the Japanese are at present the predominate race of hand workers in most districts."[93]

The United States Immigration Commission described their rise to predominance in the following way:

> In some instances the Japanese have been employed where a new industry was being introduced, as, for example, the growing of sugar beets in certain sections of the State; in others they have taken the places vacated by the Chinese, who were diminishing in number; while in other cases they have displaced the Chinese or white men by underbidding or by their superior organization. In most of the localities in which Chinese were employed at the time the Japanese came to the community—as about Vacaville, Fresno, and on the Sacramento River—they were soon extensively displaced by the Japanese, who had the same organization, were younger, more adaptable, and more agreeable, and who, when they did not work for a lower wage, did more work. In a few instances where white men had been employed to replace the Chinese, who became scarce and difficult to secure, the white men were displaced by the Japanese. . . . Thus the dominant position of the Japanese has been gained as a result of the decreasing number of Chinese, and because

they were cheap laborers. The emphasis, however, must be placed upon the first facts rather than upon the fact that the Japanese have been cheaper laborers than the other races available for employment in most parts of the State.[94]

The commission found that the Japanese received lower wages than whites, on the order of $.30 a day. Considering that the maximum average wage per day reported by the commission for any category of farm laborers was $1.89, this is a significant wage differential.[95]

That Japanese labor filled the same place the Chinese had previously occupied in small-scale intensive agriculture suggests that, like the Chinese, their presence facilitated the break-up of large holdings. In addition they did not remain only seasonal laborers. Some also became land owners, provoking a great deal of ire which lead to the passage of the Alien Land Act of 1913. In 1918 they owned 526 farms, totalling 30,305 acres. This is an average of 57.6 acres.[96] They were not large owners. The San Joaquin and Sacramento River delta area was one of the few parts of California with both a high level of tenancy and a high degree of land concentration in these years. Both the Japanese and Chinese (the latter much less so) were two of the groups involved as tenants and insofar as this tenancy abetted large holdings, they contributed to the maintenance of such holdings in the delta.

Two other nationalities that contributed to the cheap labor pool were East Indians and Mexicans. The Immigration Commission found their wages to also be significantly lower than those of whites; in fact, their average wages were lower than those of the Japanese by $.10 to $.20 per day in 1910. Both these groups only entered agricultural labor in any numbers during the first decade of the twentieth century. The East Indians were reported as making their northern California debut in orchard, vegetable farms, and vineyards in 1908, and appeared on the same class of farms in southern California in 1909. Their numbers were never more than 5,000. By 1920 only approximately 2,600 were still in California and this was fast decreasing. Mexicans had not yet attained large numbers in agriculture. Increased immigration during the 1900-1910 decade was, as in the case of the Chinese before them, chiefly for such things as construction, railroads, mining and related industries, and only lastly for seasonal farmwork in Texas, Colorado, and California.[97]

Just prior to World War I there was an abundance of agricultural labor due to industrial unemployment. Whites were apparently drawn into agriculture in unprecedented numbers. The presence of whites in the fields is best attested to by the famous Wheatland Riots of 1913. It has been pointed out that conditions existing on the Durst farm were no worse than in previous years, but that the protest against them was evoked by the presence of a class of people not accustomed to farm labor conditions.[98] A similar phenomena was to be observed in the 1930s.

During World War I Mexicans began to achieve some importance in agriculture; highlighted by the fact that:

On May 22, 1917, the United States Secretary of Labor issued an order instructing immigration officials on the Mexican border to disregard the literacy test, the contract-labor section, and the head-tax provision of the immigration law with reference to the coming of Mexican people who were to engage as workmen in agricultural pursuits. [99]

This order remained in force until 1921. It did not result in a large influx. In 1919, for example, only 9,998 Mexicans entered this country under its aegis. [100] But it adumbrated the increasing reliance on Mexicans that was to come about in the 1920s.

Nonagricultural Land Uses Associated with Large Holdings

Land Investment

A great deal of agricultural land was acquired simply for its resale value. Many of the holdings involved were quite large. Some of these even endured, turning out to be more valuable as large-scale agricultural enterprises. The nature of land investment varied from the purely speculative venture to the legitimate business. No matter where the enterprise fell on this spectrum, the basic intent remained the same. Land was acquired with an anticipation of an increase in value—due to the arrival of the railroad and/or the development of irrigation or reclamation projects, or simply because population pressure would increase demand. Frequently, the investor was also involved in a development project. If at some point the anticipation was realized, the land was resold, usually to small farmers. This often did not occur until the land passed through the hands of a series of owners, wreaking havoc on many hopefuls. Carrying costs could be met by leasing the land for grazing or, conditions permitting, higher agricultural uses. Tax avoidance was also practiced.

The largest example of a land investment verging on the speculative was the railroad land grant. Extending through almost every county in California, it included much worthless land, but by and large it was probably an excessive reward for private initiative. Land sales, timber and stumpage sales, and land leases were lucrative. McAllister went through all the annual reports of the Central Pacific and Southern Pacific Railroads and collected the yearly income from land sales, timber and stumpage sales, leases and pasturage. The amount brought in from land sales was not corrected to cover surrendered contracts, but some reports included this information. It can be concluded that by 1918 these sources had brought the Central Pacific a total of at least $18.5 million and the Southern Pacific a total of at least $19.3 million. The average price per acre reported in annual reports of the Southern Pacific and Central Pacific companies indicates that the railroad did not extract an exorbitant rate for its land. Nonetheless, this average price rarely dipped below the government price of $2.50 per acre and most often was between $3 and $10 per acre. [101] Presumably, it was kept down by competition with the government and from the practical need to encourage the settlement necessary to create business for the railroad.

Most of the land sold by the railroad was sold to smaller farmers, but there were no limits on amounts purchasable. Table 2.9 shows the size and price of the largest tracts sold by the railroad.

In all of the counties there were numerous sales, which ranged from 1,000 acres up to the maxima listed in Table 2.9. Many of these were to land speculators, the most interesting of which are the ones to Charles McLaughlin. It was commonly believed, as Leland Stanford stated in his testimony before the Pacific Railway Commission, that McLaughlin obtained the land grant that was assigned to the Western Pacific Railroad Company. This is almost true. McAllister went through county records for all the deeds of sale from the railroads and concluded that the Central Pacific Railroad Company actually received the grant, or a large part of it. But, as Table 2.9 shows, McLaughlin obtained the land (328,000 acres out of 458,000 acres in the grant) by "purchases" (totalling $1,134 of which $1,000 was for 240 acres) from the Western Pacific and Central Pacific Railroads. This business with the token payments is somewhat bewildering and McAllister says that "it cannot be determined clearly whether or not he [McLaughlin] bought and sold land as an individual businessman or whether he acted as a special agent for the Company." [102] Nor is it clear why others were so blessed with $1.00 and $5.00 payments. However, except for these instances, the prices paid for large amounts of land were of the same magnitude per acre as those paid for smaller parcels.

Throughout this period, in fact until 1949, the Southern Pacific was selling its land. Despite eighty years of land sales, the Southern Pacific still remains the state's largest private landowner with approximately 2.4 million acres to its name. Most of this is not agricultural land; it is timberland, mineral land, desert, or railroad rights of way. [103]

The most fabulous instances of land speculation occurred in the late 1860s and 1870s. Hundreds of thousands of acres were accumulated from public land—ephemeral empires that dissipated as soon as the owner skimmed off the profit derived from standing between the landseeker and the government. One-third of the list of largest owners of 1872 referred to in Chapter 1 consists of such fleeting holdings (McLaughlin, Chapman, Friedlander, and Houghton). These were only the most outstanding instances. Activities on this scale were not easily realized later in the century when much of the land that could be anticipated to become of value to farmers was already in private hands and was no longer cheaply acquired by abuse of the laws governing land disposal.

A good example of this style of speculation is afforded by a stunt pulled by Friedlander and Chapman, who often acted together, in Fresno County in 1869. Thanks to land office connections, they were able to use scrip to acquire all of the alluvial land along the Chowchilla and Fresno Rivers and the Cottonwood Creek bottom, while the founders of the Alabama Colony

TABLE 2.9
Large Tracts Sold by the Railroads in California

CENTRAL PACIFIC

County	Year	Purchaser	Acreage	Price
Alameda	1868-1878	McLaughlin	78,640	$37*
	1868	Slicer	8,551	na
	1873-1907	Mary Crocker	7,796	16*
	1874	Carr	22,040	3*
Placer	1869-1883	Towle	8,701	22,516
Placer	1871-1875	Contract Finance Co.	12,063	30,532
	1872	S.A. Boutwell	7,143	16,789
	1874-1886	E.S. Brickell & Co.	10,612	17,545
	1893	W.E. Brown	9,384	23,341
	1900	Power Estate Co.	6,699	33,489
Sacramento	1871-1882	McLaughlin	64,623	31*
San Joaquin	1870-1880	McLaughlin	133,223	1,066*
	1870	P.G. Weaver	2,240	1
	1870	Slicer	2,244	9*
	1872	McFarlin	2,553	1
Stanislaus	1873-1881	McLaughlin	51,575	19*

SOUTHERN PACIFIC

County	Year	Purchaser	Acreage	Price
Fresno	1886	Tim Page	17,218	$68,953
Kern	1871	Issac Gates	54,300	1
	1878-1886	J.B. Haggin	33,866	108,084
Kings	1896	Fresno Canal & Irrig Co.	4,446	24,072
Los Angeles	1884-1893	M.L. Wicks	6,704	16,809
	1902	J.H. Cook	6,307	28,379
Riverside	1902	T.H. Thompson	15,077	67,846
	1902	F.A. Gribb	18,461	83,072
	1902	Thomas Walker	32,515	144,448
San Benito	1904	T.H. French	2,067	4,428
San Bernardino	1902	J.H. Cook	10,049	45,218
	1902	T.H. Thompson	24,925	112,165
Santa Clara	1889	Wm. Howard	18,529	47,090
	1892	Horace Wilson	8,658	12,227
Stanislaus	1886	Wm. Howard	18,529	47,090
	1905	Henry Morris	30,834	19,051
Tulare	1880	J. Clark	4,204	14,078

Source: McAllister (1959), pp. 255, 256, 260, 286-87.
Note: The purchase prices marked with an asterisk (*) are sums of a number of $1 or $5 purchases (the $1,066 for McLaughlin consists of $1,000 for 240 acres and $66 for the rest).

were off inspecting some of those very same lands. The colony (which failed by 1875) acquired what it wanted, only it paid $2.50 an acre, or twice the government price to Friedlander and Chapman.[104]

A more enduring style of land investment was also initiated in the 1870s. This was the irrigation or reclamation company that also dealt in real estate. Irrigation development began on a significant scale in the 1870s, accelerating in intensity through and beyond the era. The first such company was the Kings River Canal and Irrigation Company, incorporated in 1871 with the grandiose purposes of:

> The construction of canals in the State of California leading from the San Joaquin River and Kings River and their tributaries; also from Tulare Lake and streams flowing thereinto, and other waters, for the transportation of passengers and freights, and for the purpose of irrigation and water power, and for the conveyance of water for mining and manufacturing purposes. Also, the supply of cities and towns in the State of California and the inhabitants of cities and towns, with pure and fresh water. Also the buying and selling of real estate.[105]

This company has been described as "one of the financial bubbles that arose through the speculative genius of William C. Ralston."[106] Although parts were completed by 1874, the original structure was a failure, the bubble burst and Henry Miller acquired the remains of the works and the company.

Sometimes a company lost its original intent to eventually subdivide and sell. The best known and largest of these is the Kern County Land Company. The company itself was organized in 1890 to operate the holdings Haggin, Carr and Tevis had accumulated over the preceding two decades in Kern County. As indicated above, they were the most flagrant abusers of the Desert Land Act, and probably every other method of land acquisition was also used by them. The railroad was the source of their first holding, the Issac Gates tract (see Table 2.9), purchased in 1871 for $1, and another 34,000 acres were later purchased by Haggin directly from the Southern Pacific. These Southern Pacific deals were probably facilitated by the fact that both Carr and Tevis were Southern Pacific officials. The even numbered government sections, necessary to make these holdings solid blocks, along with other government lands, were acquired by the usual chicanery: buying out preemptors, commuted homesteads, and so forth. Beale had left one Mexican grant in Kern County, San Emidio (17,000 acres) and this they purchased in 1878. In 1879 they divided up the Livermore, Redington and Chester holdings (remnants of the Montgomery Patent) with Miller. By buying up water rights, they were also able to drive out settlers who needed the water. They then bought up their land at low prices. At its peak, around 1900, the holding comprised over 500,000 acres, most of which had been acquired by 1890.[107]

Although the Kern County Land Company remained, until fairly recently, basically a cattle ranch, it nonetheless appears to have been acquired as a speculative venture. Margaret Cooper points out that:

various current [1950] official and unofficial statements made by or about the Kern County Land Company stated that the original purpose . . . was to acquire land on which to establish a vast cattle ranch. . . .

These statements contrast with pronouncements issued by Haggin and Carr while they were gathering in their vast domain. Then they reiterated time and again the promise that they were accumulating land only in order to improve it, to construct an irrigation system and after demonstrating the productivity of the land, to sell the land to small farmers.[108]

Furthermore, although Carr seems to have been against land sales, selling out to Haggin when S. W. Ferguson, a real estate promoter, was hired to take charge of colonization, colonization was attempted around 1890 when four colonies were established: Rosedale (2,000 acres), Lerdo (11,000 acres), Union Avenue (13,000 acres), and Mountain View (9,000 acres). The average lot sold was twenty acres for $60 to $120 per acre with long terms available. Many bought in. Colonization failed for a number of reasons. Although production was successful, it exceeded local needs and no transportation was available. The irrigation was poorly done, causing water logging and alkali accumulation. Probably most important were the depressed economic conditions of the mid-1890s. Whatever the fate of these schemes, between 1900 and 1925, 125,000 acres were sold.[109] Unlike Miller and Lux, the Kern County Land Company sold water to others and did not develop its water resources just for itself. The Kern County Land Company appears to have been a speculative acquisition that turned out to be maintained more usefully as a single unit.*

Oil

The first commercial activity related to oil in California involved the use of asphalt from the pits at La Goleta (1855) in Santa Barbara County and La Brea (1856) near Los Angeles.† Attention then began to be paid to the oil seepages scattered through the state. The first oil well in California was drilled in Humboldt County, near present-day Petrolia, in 1861. This well was unproductive, but successful wells soon followed and Humboldt County had a small oil boom in the mid-1860s. At about the same time southern California and the San Joaquin Valley also experienced brief booms. Conway and White began to acquire Mexican grants in Ventura County in 1861.

In 1864 they hired Benjamin Silliman, a noted geologist, who was in California for other reasons, to inspect their property. He inspected the Ex-

---

*Haggin's 44,000 acre Rancho del Paso in the Sacramento Valley seems to have been a similar case. An original attempt at subdivision, made in the 1870s, failed and Haggin turned it into a breeding ranch for racehorses. It was not sold off until the first decade of the twentieth century.[110]

†Noncommercial use goes back to the aboriginal Indians.

Mission San Buenaventura and Ojai grants and was given a sample of crude ostensibly from these lands. Silliman then proceeded to acclaim the area loudly, publishing reports that created an oil rush and whose contentiousness later ruined his reputation.* This rush centered in Santa Barbara and Ventura Counties. The most active participant was Tom Scott, who acquired all or part of eight ranchos in Ventura County (three of these were never involved with oil); a total of 187,000 acres was acquired on behalf of his Philadelphia and California Petroleum Company (later, California Petroleum Company). Oil was found but it was too heavy to use. Hence the company made no money from petroleum in these years and after 1867 much of the land was sold off with Scott retaining petroleum rights. [112]

In the San Joaquin Valley, there had been interest in oil since the early 1860s. An 1864 discovery of oil seepages on the eastern slope of the coastal ranges had set off a short boom in Fresno County and by 1865 at least four oil companies were organized and were working near the sites of present day Coalinga, Reward and McKittrick. [113] For the next two decades there was intermittent activity in or around the sites of the present San Joaquin producing areas.

Early oil development was not easy. California crude generally was much heavier than that of the eastern United States and known refining techniques were unable to cope with it. It was not until the 1870s that any advances began to be made in handling California crude. Had there been a great demand for petroleum products, the low quality of California products would not have been such a drawback. However, until fuel oil became popular in the 1890s, the market for petroleum products was mostly limited to illuminants (kerosene) and greases. California greases and kerosene were of very low quality and except during shortages of eastern products, they sold very poorly. Development was further stifled by the inaccessibility of most producing areas. The railroad, for example, did not reach the Coalinga area until 1887. Nonetheless, oil continued to generate excitement, companies were formed, and exploration went on, culminating in the big discoveries in Los Angeles in 1895, at Coalinga in 1896, and the Kern River, Midway, Sunset, and Mckittrick in the next decade (see Map 2.2 for the location of the oil fields). No other major discoveries were made until the ones in Los Angeles in 1922.

The oil fields were located either in the southern San Joaquin Valley, on land that largely remained in the public domain at the time of oil discovery because of its dismal quality, or in the southern coastal counties, usually on Mexican grants. As discussed above, many laws were used to acquire mineral lands from the public domain and it was pointed out that sizeable holdings could be realized even under placer mining law. Public domain land ceased to be available after the 1909 withdrawal of oil land from sale and entry. This withdrawal affected 2,871,000 acres in California. These

---

*Silliman's sample seems to have doctored and his reports ill-advised, at best. [111]

were scattered through much of the existing fields, but the principal impact was on the Midway-Sunset area on the west side of Kern County.[114] Leasing then became the only option for using public lands. The old ranchos remained available for purchase, however.

Multitudes of oil companies were formed after 1890. Most faded and the others tended to coalesce. Often the individual holdings were small, but as they were absorbed into one of the several companies that came to dominate the industry, these holdings of small companies became part of very large accumulations. In 1918 the concentration of the industry was not yet complete. Oil companies controlled, by lease, much more land than they owned and these leases were quite valuable. They also sometimes owned only the mineral rights in land. Included among the large oil holdings existing in 1918 (only lands owned in fee are counted here) were the 38,048 acres the Associated Oil Company possessed in various fields in the southern San Joaquin Valley. The Honolulu Consolidated Oil Company owned 3,856 acres also in the valley fields. The Central Oil Company held 2,250 acres in southern California in 1918, Pan American Petroleum owned 10,000 acres in Santa Barbara County, and the Union Oil Company owned 30,893 acres in eight counties including 19,000 acres in Ventura County which were remnants from the Scott purchases of the 1860s.[115]

Unfortunately, information is lacking about such major holdings as those of the Southern Pacific Railroad Company, and those of two predecessors of Standard Oil of California, the Pacific Oil Company and Standard Oil Company (California). These three companies had an interesting relationship. Until 1920 the Southern Pacific oil lands were leased. It is apparent how profitable this was since in 1917, 1918, and 1919 these leases brought in around $1 million per annum. Nonetheless, for $43,750,000 cash, the railroad parted with 259,000 acres of actual and possible oil-bearing lands in 1920, selling them to the Pacific Oil Company. This land became the basis of Standard Oil Company's extensive California land holdings in 1926 when Pacific and Standard Oil Company (California) merged.[116]

These holdings are of particular importance here, not because of their agricultural value during this period, but because of the fact that later in the twentieth century irrigation reached them. Agricultural value was conferred on land whose prior attraction was the oil it might cover. Conversely, the discovery of oil later in the century on some of the large cattle holdings in the southern San Joaquin Valley and southern California hinterlands gave such holdings a new permanence.

Summary of Landownership, 1870-1918

This period is marked at each end with state reports summarizing the situation in land concentration. These reports will be compared here as far as is possible. The 1872-73 report of the State Board of Equalization has already been discussed in Chapter 1. Ownership lists published for some

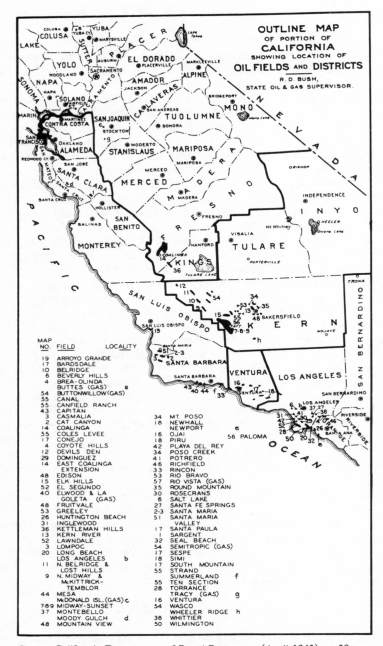

Source: California Department of Rural Resources (April 1943), p. 38.

Map 2.2

counties in 1873 by the Sacramento Daily Union have also been used in this section. There are actually two reports covering the other end of the era, using data from 1916 and 1917. In 1917 the State Tax Commission published, in its annual report, a "Table Showing Report of Land Holdings (2,000 acres or more), October 1, 1916." This table stands alone and is barely mentioned in the text of the annual report. In 1919 the California Commission of Immigration and Housing published a lengthy report on large landholdings in southern California, based on county tax records for 1917.[117]

The 1872 information appears accurate, although in the summary table, owners are sometimes counted several times due to misspellings of their names or variations in the use of initials when several different parcels are being listed. The acreage attributed to "unknown owners" is also treated as a single ownership unit in the summary table. The 1919 study is well documented and also appears to be accurate. The 1917 report is definitely inaccurate, erring on the side of understatement. First, only thirty counties were included and some of the exclusions are well known to have possessed large ownerships. Los Angeles and Santa Barbara Counties, for example, are amply documented in the 1919 report but are missing from that of 1917. Second, in all but one county covered by both reports, the earlier one understates the number of large owners and the acreage involved. This is also true for several counties not in the later report (Fresno, Kern and Sutter for example). Finally, both reports attempt to distinguish between tillable and aggregate acreage, but the 1917 report often is incomplete in one or the other category. Comparison, where possible, with the later information shows that the blanks do not reflect a lack of tillable or non-tillable land but a lack of completeness in the accounting.

Table 2.10 combines the information from both the 1917 and 1919 reports (that is, data for the years 1916/17) to give a picture of land concentration over the state. As with the 1872 data, all large landholdings are included—not just agricultural landholdings. (The tillable acreage column does not adequately distinguish agricultural land from nonagricultural land because holdings used for grazing are regarded as agricultural.) According to it, 802 owners of holdings larger than 2,000 acres accounted for 11,449,579 acres in thirty-three counties. In 1872 1,172 owners of parcels greater than 2,000 acres controlled something between 10,667,493 and 11,323,493 acres throughout the entire state.*

Keeping in mind the above caveats about the data for 1916, it is clear that in the state as a whole the actual acreage encompassed by large holdings was greater in 1916/17 than 1872. Unfortunately, it is not possible to compare the size distribution of the ownerships since the table showing the 1916 data lacks such information. It is known though, that the top end of the size scale was greatly expanded from 1872 when 400,000 acres was

---

*Carr gives 8,658,493 for the 516 largest ownerships. The size breakdown in the summary table allows the setting of the upper and lower bounds.

TABLE 2.10
Large Landholdings In California, 1916/17

County owners	Number of acreage	Total acreage	Tillable
Colusa	32	205,320*	205,320
Contra Costa	15	147,780*	147,780
Fresno	11	406,243	216,964
Glenn	35	231,016	na
Humboldt	17	74,118	2,500
Imperial	8	452,627	93,943
Kern	4	1,475,000	na
Lassen	23	140,180	44,255
Los Angeles	62	512,169	266,826
Madera	53	485,111	423,034
Mariposa	4	61,000	9,500
Mendocino	1	8,466	2,000
Merced	70	766,977	118,914
Modoc	18	104,946	70,365
Monterey	48	483,506	na
Napa	11	42,306	19,300
Orange	7	199,272	65,000
Riverside	31	967,145	179,578
Sacramento	16	112,332*	112,332
San Benito	9	108,714	16,400
San Bernardino	13	1,371,705	81,099
San Diego	29	428,824	83,960
San Mateo	14	90,625	na
Santa Barbara	84	736,707	88,404
Santa Clara	26	257,314	17,975
Santa Cruz	9	59,149	na
Shasta	38	917,988	na
Sierra	10	36,129	11,300
Sonoma	24	132,397	na
Stanislaus	21	105,313*	105,313
Sutter	3	32,345	12,230
Ventura	45	225,467	33,400
Yolo	19	71,326*	71,326
TOTAL	802	11,449,579	2,273,808

Note: Acreages marked with an asterisk (*) are those for which only tillable acreage was reported and not aggregate acreage in large holdings.

the maximum. In 1916/17, the state's two largest single ownerships, Miller and Lux and the Southern Pacific, accounted for over 5.75 million acres (1.25 million for Miller and Lux and at least 4.5 million for Southern Pacific). This is certainly the major reason why fewer owners held more land in 1916/17. It is possible that the remaining holdings tended to be larger, but this is not ascertainable. The table also provides some clarification as to why large holdings were typically in extensive use: less than one-fifth of the land so held was even considered as tillable. Moreover, tillable does not imply tilled. Finally, as was shown above, such tilling as did occur was rarely intensive specialty crops; even the tillable land was in extensive use.

Tables 2.11 and 2.12 provide some comparisons for agriculturally significant counties for which comparable information was available in 1872 and 1916/17. Table 2.11 covers the Sacramento and San Joaquin Valleys for which we have the total number of holdings larger than 2,000 acres in size and the area encompassed by these holdings. Also included is the total acreage assessed in each county and the percent of this subsumed by the large holdings. Table 2.12 covers southern California. The area encompassed by holdings larger than 2,000 acres is not available for all counties for 1872. Thus, it was only possible to present the number of holdings falling into the two categories used by the 1919 report of the 1917 data (2,000 to 10,000 acres, 10,000 or more acres). In both tables the counties sometimes have to be aggregated because of changes in county boundaries between 1872 and

TABLE 2.11
Comparison of Concentration of Landownership
in the Central Valley, 1872 and 1916/17

	1872			1916/17		
County	Number owners	Acreage	Percent assessed land	Number owners	Acreage	Percent assessed land
SACRAMENTO VALLEY						
Colusa Glenn	60	563,913	70%	67*	436,820*	35%
Sacramento	29	185,395	31	16*	112,332*	18
Sutter	13	83,252	23	4*	87,345*	23
SAN JOAQUIN VALLEY						
Fresno Madera	86	1,029,034	76	64*	891,354*	29
Kern	15	433,775	66	4	1,475,000	46
Merced	77	683,020	73	70	766,977	65
Stanislaus	46	264,925	39	21*	105,313*	11

Note: Numbers of owners and acreages marked with an asterisk (*) represent tillable acreage only.

TABLE 2.12
Comparison of Concentration of Landownership
in Southern California, 1872 and 1916/17

	Number owners 2,000 to 10,000 acres	Number owners 10,000 or more acres	Total number of owners	Number owners 2,000 to 10,000 acres	Number owners 10,000 or more acres	Total number of owners
Los Angeles Orange	62	18	80	53	13	69
Riverside San Diego Imperial San Bernardino	55	24	79	60	22	82
Santa Barbara	19	28	47	66	18	84
Ventura	14	8	22	41	4	45

1916/17.

The Sacramento Valley exhibits a stability in the amount of land encompassed by large holdings and the number of owners. In Sacramento and Sutter Counties the amount of land in private ownership did not change very much, while in Colusa and Glenn Counties a great deal of new land came into private ownership. It appears that concentration only declined in Colusa and Glenn Counties. This is not totally true. The table only shows two points in time. Concentration increased during the nineteenth century and was slowly broken down in the twentieth century when subdivision became prominent in the Sacramento Valley.[118]

In the San Joaquin Valley only Kern County showed a big increase in large holdings; Stanislaus County showed a decline (but information is incomplete) and the others seemed on a par with 1872. However, in Kern, Fresno, and Madera Counties the amount of land in private ownership increased significantly. What happened was that new land was taken up to form large holdings, while subdivision occurred on some of the land taken up earlier.

Land concentration in southern California shows signs of mitigation. This is more apparent when it is realized that five of the holdings larger than 10,000 acres in size belonged to the Southern Pacific Railroad. Railroad land accounted for 46 percent of the land in large landholdings in southern California. In fact, it accounted for virtually all the land in large holdings in Imperial County where seven other large owners held only 22,291 acres of the 452,627 acres in large landholdings. Furthermore, the declines in the largest size categories bespeak subdivision of the largest ranchos. Such breakups more than compensated for increases in smaller large holdings, as exemplified by Ventura County. In Ventura County the 315,872 acres were encompassed by large landholdings in 1872, while in 1916/17 large holdings comprised 225,467 acres.

Summary and Conclusions

Developments in the landownership situation were extremely complex during the 1870-1918 period. Two basic processes were occurring; the accumulation of large holdings and the subdivision of some of these holdings. Both processes occurred throughout the period and each raises its own questions. Of concern here are the reasons why large holdings were being formed and the reasons why subdivision left so many holdings unscathed.

The formation of large holdings can be attributed to three factors: the system of land disposal, the success of extensive agriculture, and the value of land as an investment. Most of the public land disposal in California occurred between 1870 and 1918; in total close to 30 million acres the majority of which was federal land, passed into private ownership. The laws governing this land disposal were extremely conducive to the creation of large holdings and were often used for this purpose. In addition, Spanish-Mexican ranchos were taken over by new owners, sometimes being aggregated with land from the public domain or each other to produce even larger holdings.

Through the 1890s California agriculture centered around grain and livestock production, both of which were typically conducted on a large scale and on large holdings thanks to progress in mechanizations. Nascent orchard, vineyard and row crop production received a huge impetus in the decline of grain prices which began in the 1880s. Intensive crop output shot upward in the 1890s and eventually surpassed extensive cultivation (in value) around 1910.

While some large owners put in a few hundred acres of orchards or vineyards (and a very few even put in a several thousand acres), typically these newer, intensive crops came to be associated with subdivision and land sales. The basic problem for large owners was that the cost of developing the land was high and marketing problems left prices too low to warrant conversion. This unhappy situation prevailed until the second decade of the twentieth century when successful cooperative marketing associations were able to correct some of the marketing difficulties. At that time large-scale production began to look attractive. Some conversions were initiated and the first steps were taken towards agglomeration of smaller holdings.

Sometimes, particularly in the Sacramento-San Joaquin Delta, subdivision was circumvented by relying on tenants. In such areas intensive cultivation of large holdings by tenants was common. Generally, most of the land holdings that remained intact were those that for some reason were not being put to intensive use. There were several categories of such holdings. The most obvious were those for which intensive agriculture was not physically feasible, either because of the quality of the land or because they were not irrigable. Such holdings were put to the familiar large-scale extensive uses of grazing or dry-farmed grains. Land used for the former was located in many areas around the state but dry-farming was concentrated in the Sacramento Valley where rainfall was relatively high. Subdivision did not occur on a large scale in the Sacramento Valley until the twentieth century. Second, there was irrigable land suitable for subdivision, but not broken up. Instead, particularly in the San Joaquin Valley, the water was minimally developed and used for irrigated wild grass pastures. Dry grazing land was used in conjunction with these pastures to create profitable large holdings. Some grains were also grown under irrigation. For example, Tulare Lake, where subdivision was not possible because the danger of flooding prevented permanent settlement, was reknown in the twentieth century for grain bonanzas.

Subdivision was therefore not an assured fate for all, or even most, suitable land. Not all owners wished to sell; those who could hold onto it might prefer to do so knowing it would only increase in value. Nor was subdivision a surefire procedure. Failures were hardly unknown since small farmers were afflicted with the same marketing problems that militated against large-scale production. Also, many subdivision were simply poorly planned. Nonetheless, many large holdings were subdivided and small holdings became common in irrigable areas* These small farmers were responsible for the successful development of intensive farming, at the same time laying the foundations for large-scale intensive agriculture. They organized the cooperative marketing associations that lent enough order to and control over marketing for tree crops to become profitable. They also developed a pool of cheap labor. Such labor was responsible for the development of the land and for working in the fields and orchards and vineyards. Because land was often purchased second hand, it was expensive, and because the crops took a long time to come into bearing and prices were not that high, it was desirable to have a labor force very tolerant of low wages. Intensive crops required more labor than a family could provide. Since the early subdivisions and colonies were somewhat scattered and distant from communities of any size, it became necessary to rely on itinerant labor. Also, some of the work was regarded as beneath whites. Hence, there developed a reliance on immigrants, particularly Asians, as suitable laborers.

The Chinese and Japanese were actually essential to the breakdown of large holdings. Without them, the establishment of intensive agriculture

---

*Not all small holdings came from subdivision. But the fact that water rights were often vested in large owners and the need for development of the water supply (the failure of the early irrigation districts left small farmers in a weak position in this regard) did direct interest to already owned land.

would have been significantly retarded and there would have been less incentive to subdivide. To some degree they also abetted large holdings. In the 1870s and 1880s they provided some labor on the bonanza grain farms and were a ready source of tenants through most of the period. this is not, however, the activity that laid the basis for the association we recognize today between cheap labor and large holdings. This association became apparent after the cheap labor force was well developed by the rise of intensive cultivation. For example, land owners found themselves able to turn to rice in the second decade of the twentieth century because there was already an adequate labor supply (both as laborers and tenants). In the next chapters, more examples of this intensification of use of large holdings will be seen, an intensification only made possible by the presence of cheap foreign labor.

It should be emphasized that the successful development of an irrigated agriculture in California assured owners of suitable land big increases in land value. Hence large holdings acquired for other purposes were often retained. The railroad, which supposedly acquired land for resale and did indeed sell much land, held on to several million acres in California. The land owned by numerous oil companies also remained in their ownership despite their ability to sell off surface rights and only keep mineral rights. Most of these lands were of little agricultural worth in 1918 but turned out to be good investments later.

The upshot of events in this period can be summarized statistically. In 1872 approximately eleven million acres were in large holdings. At the end of World War I eleven million was a lower bound on the amount of land in large holdings. Very different land was involved in 1918 than in 1872, particularly in the southern San Joaquin Valley, the northern Sacramento Valley, and the interior of southern California. In 1872 virtually all of the land in large holdings was in extensive uses. By 1918 this association was showing some signs of weakening.

Notes

1. California State Surveyor General, *Biennial Report* for the years 1869-1871 through 1877-1879, 1880-1882 through 1902-1904.
2. United States General Land Office, *Report* for each of the years 1870-1918.
3. Dana and Krueger (1958), p. 45.
4. Robbins (1942), pp. 240-41.
5. Puter (1972), p. 16-17.
6. Robbins (1942), p. 234, 285.
7. Dana and Krueger (1958), pp. 40-41.
8. Key (1938), p. 291.
9. Dana and Krueger (1958), p. 246
10. Quoted in Taylor (1968), p. 24.
11. Nash (1964), p. 209.
12. Gates (1968), p. 642 for General Revision Act; Gates (1975), p. 173 for Haggin.
13. Puter (1972), p. 17.
14. Brown and Shaw (1944), p. 212.
15. Puter (1972), pp. 420, 426.

16. Robbins (1942), pp. 156-57.

17. Gates (1968), p. 439.

18. Gates (1961), pp. 114, 115 for history of scrips; Gates (1975), pp. 174, 175 for Tevis and Chapman.

19. Robbins (1942), p. 334 for terms of the act; Puter (1972), chapter 22, passim for Kern County usage.

20. Gates (1968), pp. 722, 723 for 1872 act; Puter (1972), p. 431 for Yard.

21. Puter (1972), p. 416.

22. United States General Land Office, *Report* for each of the years 1870-1920.

23. Baker (1970), p. 337.

24. Burcham (1957), pp. 147, 256-61.

25. Burcham (1957), p. 155.

26. Santa Margarita in Brown and Shaw (1944), pp. 518-21; Newhall from Newhall (1958), p. 34; Irvine from Cleland (1952), p. 95; other information from California Commission of Immigration and Housing (1919), passim.

27. Beck and Haase (1974), p. 72; Older (1966), p. 172.

28. Lawrence (1933), p. 63.

29. Spanish grants from Treadwell (1950), pp. 55, 58; Kern County in Street (1955), p. 3; dummy entries in Lawrence (1933), p. 54; Visalia in Wilson and Clawson (1945), p. 14.

30. Treadwell (1950), p. 62

31. Land sales in Lawrence (1933), p. 170; irrigation from Cone (1911), passim.

32. Tejon acquisition in Beck and Haase (1974), p. 70; use of Tejon from Crowe (1957), pp. 86, 130.

33. Navigability in Brown and Shaw (1944), p. 14; Modesto in Smith (1939), p. 243.

34. Nordhoff (1973), p. 182.

35. Rogin (1931), p. 120.

36. Rogin (1931), p. 119.

37. Bancroft (1970), Vol. 24, p. 26.

38. Allen (1933), p. 158.

39. McGowan (1961), Vol. 1, pp. 259-63 for all these holdings.

40. Nordhoff (1973), p. 182.

41. Vander (1919), p. 168.

42. Smith (1932), p. 140 for Mitchell; Vander (1919), p. 168 for Cole.

43. Rogin (1931), p. 151.

44. California State Board of Agriculture (1912), pp. 105, 119; California State Board of Agriculture (1919), pp. 114, 128.

45. California State Board of Agriculture (1919), pp. 115-17 for all information but price which is from McGowan (1961) Vol. 2, p. 202; Crow (1917), p. 21 describes all the large rice holdings.

46. California State Board of Agriculture (1919), pp. 111-12 for early refineries; Spreckels from United States Senate, Committee on Education and Labor (1940), p. 22799; other sugar companies from *Walker's Manual of Pacific Coast Securities* for the years 1910, 1918.

47. Acreage from California State Board of Agriculture (1922), p. 182; Irvine from Cleland (1952), pp. 107, 120.

48. Thompson (1958), p. 238.

49. Cox (1918), p. 444.

50. Value of barley and potatoes from California State Board of Agriculture (1919), p. 129; value of beans from Cox (1918), p. 446.

51. Johnston and Dean (1969), pp. 6-53 passim.

52. California Crop and Livestock Reporting Service (July 1947), p. 9.

53. Fuller (1934), p. 98.

54. Paige and Morton from Thompson (1892), p. 19; McGowan (1961), Vol. 1, p. 273 for Hatch and Pock and Stanford, p. 275 for Natomas; Nadeau and Sylmar from McGroaty (1923), p. 481; Fancher from Street (1955), p. 12; Limoneira, Sunny Hills

and Irvine from Williamson (1940), pp. 15, 20, 21; Italian Vineyard Company and Wakhole from California State Board of Agriculture (1919), p. 230.

55. Newhall (1958), p. 70; Cleland (1952), p. 123.

56. First colony in Thickens (1946), p. 26; Thompson (1891), passim for 1891 subdivisions; *Official Map of Fresno County, 1907* for 1907 information; Thompson (1891), p. 12 for deeds; soil survey by Strahorn *et al.* (1914), p. 4; tree and vineyard statistics from California State Board of Agriculture (1912), pp. 162-69.

57. Dumke (1963), pp. 22-23.

58. Ibid., pp. 99-100, 120, 122, 126.

59. Requa and Cory (1919), pp. 71-72.

60. Requa and Cory (1919), pp. 144, 148.

61. *Orchard and Farm* (January 1904), p. 16; California State Bureau of Labor Statistics (1887), p. 207; Forkner from Walker (1941), p. 374; Delhi from Smith (1938), p. 84.

62. Mead (1916), pp. 400-01.

63. United States Senate, Committee on Education and Labor (1940), pp. 17714, 22781.

64. Kraemer and Erdman (1933), p. 4 for first shipments; Webber *et al.* (1967), p. 29 for rest of information.

65. Kramer and Erdman (1933), p. 17.

66. Webber *et al.* (1967), p. 29.

67. Northern California from Kramer and Erdman (1933); southern California from McKay (1924), p. 9.

68. McCurdy (1925), p. 9.

69. Webber (1967), p. 23

70. McKay (1924), passim for description of the Exchange.

71. McKay (1927), p. 8.

72. McCurdy (1925), pp. 59, 62.

73. Kraemer and Erdman (1933), passim for discussion of deciduous growers.

74. Erdman (1958), p. 181; number of organizations from Morrison (1939), p. 16.

75. Vatter (1952), p. 13.

76. Mead (1901), p. 24.

77. Adams (1929), pp. 13-15.

78. Mead (1901), p. 274.

79. Adams (1929), p. 32.

80. Adams (1929), p. 33.

81. Tait (1912), p. 7 for small farmers; Roeding (1911), p. 53 for Miller and Lux; Harding (1960), p. 41 for Herminghaus.

82. United States Bureau of the Census (1922), p. 87.

83. Nordhoff (1974), pp. 89, 130 for Chinese and the Central Pacific; San Bernardino from Chiu (1963), p. 80; Anaheim from Nordhoff (1974), p. 155; California State Bureau of Labor Statistics (1887), pp. 53-54 for information about use of the Chinese in the 1880s.

84. United States Senate, Joint Special Committee to Investigate Chinese Immigration (1877), p. 6.

85. California State Bureau of Labor Statistics (1887), pp. 645-746 are the results of surveys which include wage information for Chinese and non-Chinese agricultural laborers.

86. Nordhoff (1974), pp. 143-44.

87. Chiu (1963), p. 89.

88. Fisher (1953), p. 10.

89. United States Senate, Joint Special Committee to Investigate Chinese Immigration (1877), pp. 257, 571, 931.

90. United States Senate, Joint Special Committee to Investigate Chinese Immigration (1877), p. 571; McGowan (1961), Vol. 1, p. 328.

91. United States Senate, Joint Special Committee to Investigate Chinese

84   COMPLEX TRENDS IN LANDOWNERSHIP

Immigration (1877), p. 931 for Hollister; Coolidge (1909), p. 97 for Sargent.

92. United States Immigration Commission (1911a), Part 25, Vol. 1, p. 657; see Coolidge (1909), pp. 100-106 for lengthy discussion of the causes of anti-Chinese feeling; Fuller (1934), p. 135 about 1890s.

93. United States Immigration Commission (1911b), p. 53 for first appearance of Japanese, p. 15 for quote.

94. Ibid., pp. 53-54.

95. Ibid., p. 55 for wages.

96. California State Board of Control (1920), p. 48.

97. Ibid., pp. 64, 122 for East Indians; United States Immigration Commission (1911b), p. 67 for Mexican immigration and p. 55 for wages;

98. Jamieson (1943), p. 65 for Durst.

99. California State Mexican Fact Finding Committee (1930), p. 18.

100. Ibid.

101. Southern Pacific Annual Reports are summarized on pp. 454-56, 483-84 of McAllister (1939).

102. McAllister (1939), p. 260 for quote and entire discussion.

103. Fellmeth (1973), p. 515.

104. Winchell (1933), p. 89.

105. "The Great San Joaquin and Sacramento Valleys of California—an Irrigation Scheme" (1872), p. 24.

106. Walker (1941), p. 98.

107. Cooper (1954), pp. 82-87 for acquisitions; United States Senate, Committee on Education and Labor (1940), p. 22797 reported 413,000 acres owned in 1939 and Berg (1971), p. 24 reported some 125,000 acres sold since 1900.

108. Cooper (1954), pp. 67-68.

109. Whole discussion follows Berg (1971), pp. 20-22, 24.

110. McGowan (1961), Vol. 2, p. 182.

111. White (1962), p. 12.

112. Hutchinson (1965), pp. 52-53, 71, 151.

113. Latta (1949), p. 34.

114. Dana and Krueger (1958), p. 49.

115. *Walker's Manual of Pacific Coast Securities* for the year 1918, passim.

116. McAllister (1939), p. 488 gives income from leases; Southern Pacific land sale from *Moody's Guide to Railroads* for the year 1946, p. 309.

117. *Sacramento Daily Union* Feb. 1, 1873 p. 3; Feb. 8, 1873 p. 3; Feb. 15, 1873 p. 3; Feb. 22, 1873 p. 2; Thompson and West (1961), p. 361 was used for Ventura County; California State Tax Commission (1917), p. 278 is the table; California Commission on Immigration and Housing (1919) for southern California.

118. Lists of Large Holdings present in Sacramento Valley counties in 1880, 1885, and 1890 were published in the *Sacramento Daily Union* Oct. 5, 1891 p. 2; Oct 19, 1891 p. 2; Nov. 5, 1891 p. 2; Dec. 5, 1891 p. 2; Dec. 19, 1891 p. 2; Dec. 26, 1891 p. 2.

3

Intensive Agriculture and the Consolidation of Landholdings (1918-1945)

Introduction

In the period from World War I through World War II, California agriculture experienced a number of changes in structure. Most of these can be linked to the depressed conditions prevailing in agriculture during the 1920s and 1930s. Prices were a basic problem for farmers. Prices were very high at the close of World War I and slumped dramatically in 1920-1921. They then rose slightly and remained stable until the collapse in the early 1930s. The 1918 price levels were not achieved again until 1945. This very general pattern was followed by all California products but individual deviations became the basis for changes in cropping patterns. California agriculture became more specialized, more oriented towards irrigated crops (in particular, fruits, nuts, vegetables, and cotton) and dairying, products that seemed most promising during these unpromising times.

The Depression and World War II led to greater governmental involvement in regulating the economy. For California agriculture this meant that all of the factors so necessary to its intensification *viz.*, irrigation, labor, marketing, and credit, fell increasingly under the sway of federal and state action. The growth of governmental intervention was accompanied by the rise of special-interest groups in agriculture. The most influential of these had the interests of the large producers at heart. A major theme of this chapter will be the success large landowners had in affecting policies in the areas of irrigation, labor, and marketing (in the course of which activities they also initiated battles still being fought today). The trend in this period was towards further concentration of landownership.

The next section examines changes in land use (cropping patterns) and their relationship to landownership. This is followed by a section describing the effects on landownership of foreclosures, mortgages and credit in general. After a brief overview covering the rise of farm organizations which exerted influence in the areas of marketing, water, and labor, come sections dealing with each of these areas individually. The landownership situation in 1945 is then summarized and the last section provides a general chapter summary and conclusions.

It should be pointed out that most of the large holdings explicitly mentioned in this chapter will be corporations. In part this reflects the general rise of the corporation in the twentieth century. Many large owners were incorporated as the corporate form of ownership had a number of advantages, including continuity of the holding through death and tax breaks. There is also a pragmatic reason for this emphasis on corporations: most of the available information refers to them. Furthermore, the information that does exist about noncorporate large owners does not indicate that these owners were being influenced by a separate set of considerations.

Changes in Production

Overview

Toward the end of the nineteenth century, California agriculture began to switch emphasis from production of grains and livestock to production of irrigated crops, particularly fruits. During the interwar period the priority of irrigated products was even more firmly established. These included fruits and vegetables and a new crop, cotton. Dairying was responsible for most of the growth in the animal industries and this resulted in more irrigated pastures and alfalfa. Federal price supports and state and federal marketing programs aided producers of these crops and dairy products. Irrigated acreage increased by approximately 1.2 million acres between 1919 and 1945, and construction of major projects was initiated during the 1930s. These projects did not begin deliveries until the last years of this period, but anticipation of their water influenced choices of crops.

A marked intensification of production took place in this period. Most branches of agriculture (dry-farmed grains were an exception) showed a greater productivity per unit of input. Multifarious causes, usually lumped under the rubric "better practices" were responsible for higher productivity. These include use of better-yielding varieties of plants, better control of pests and diseases, more use of fertilizers, expanding the use of irrigation or practicing it more effectively, and use of new techniques in plant and animal care.

Many of these changes in practice also required more labor. This was not just at harvest, although demand concentrated then. This period was one of low wages and, except during World War II, labor surplus. During the war, federal intervention helped alleviate labor shortages and maintain earlier wage levels. Work was also initiated to mechanize production, little of which came to fruition during this era, but anticipation of success encouraged production of labor-intensive crops.

Also relevant to changes in production were the foreclosures and bankruptcies induced by the Depression. Immediately after World War I, a number of subdivision and land development schemes, comparable to those of previous era, were initiated. These subsequently failed, bringing to a close the era of subdivision of large holdings. Other victims of foreclosure and bankruptcy could be found in all sizes of holdings, yet the net effect was to encourage consolidation. The rest of this section will describe in detail the situation in landownership associated with different land uses. The availability of adequate labor will be assumed while ramifications and particular aspects of developments in marketing, prices, irrigation, and bankruptcy will be discussed.

Livestock

Animal trends are sometimes unclear because of certain cycles that occur independently of economic factors. Basically, the number of beef cattle remained constant. The number of sheep peaked in the 1930s. Only dairy animals showed a steady increase in numbers. This is no surprise because milk prices were much stronger than meat prices, except for a few years in the early 1930s. Also, per capita consumption of dairy products was increasing. Since California's population more than doubled between 1918 and 1945, the lack of comparable growth in livestock numbers, except for dairy animals, meant that California became an importer of animals and meat. The range livestock industry became a much less significant part of California's agricultural economy. Animal finishing and dairying established themselves as preeminent.[1]

In general, livestock production continued to be associated with large holdings. However, many large grazing holdings had a rough time. In the troublesome 1920s, the Miller and Lux Company was unable to hold its property intact and conduct the business profitably. Some of the land was mortgaged, bonds were issued and land sales were initiated. By 1930 the company held only 330,000 acres in California in the San Joaquin Valley. In 1933 it defaulted on the bonds but continued liquidating so that in 1940 it held 89,000 acres. By 1945 only a few thousand acres, on which the sales contracts were not yet fully satisfied, were nominally owned by the Miller and Lux Company.[2] The breakup of this holding does not appear to have been a boon to the creation of small farms: J. J. Deuel testified in hearings before the Senate Subcommittee on Public Lands in 1947 that "Miller and Lux have sold all their land. It is not in the hands of the average farmer. . . . Unfortunately, a lot of . . .young men have bought 640 acres or a couple of thousand acres or something of the kind."[3] Also, for example, the 13,400-acre Merced Ranch of the Newhall Land and Farming Company was originally owned by the Miller and Lux Company, and Adohr Farms owned 2,479 acres in 1940 in Kern County, which had been purchased from the company between 1930 and 1933. Adohr was an extremely successful dairy enterprise formed in 1916.[4] This purchase is a nice illustration of the new preeminence of dairying over grazing.

Other well-known land and cattle companies, leaders in the world of large landholdings, were kept intact only because of nonagricultural income. In the late 1930s, the triumvirate of well-known land and cattle companies, the Kern County Land Company, Newhall Land and Cattle Company, and the Tejon Ranch all benefitted from significant oil discoveries on their lands. This occurred in 1936 for the first two and in 1937 for the latter. By the 1940s all three were drawing over two-thirds of their income from this source. The Kern County Land Company even initiated a new program of agricultural development in 1941. The Newhall Land and Cattle Company had done this in 1935 and it was certainly facilitated by the oil discoveries.[5]

Field Crops

Most field crops fared poorly. The major ones, grains and forage, suffered from low prices until World War II. Acreage declined in both categories during the 1920s and only barley showed much recovery before World War II. Minor crops, sugar beets, dry beans, and cotton had stronger prices. Cotton was the only one of these to show major changes in production. Acreage expanded greatly through the late 1930s but suffered some setbacks during the war. Cotton was the only field crop to experience a significant change in geographic distribution, shifting from southern California to the San Joaquin Valley.

Much of the acreage in field crops was irrigated. This had been true during the last era. Alfalfa, sugar beets, and rice continued to be almost entirely produced under irrigation. Cotton is completely dependent on irrigation in California. Between 1919 and 1939 the irrigated acreage devoted to major field crops increased by some 566,000 acres. Most of this increase (450,000) was in cotton and barley acreage, and the rest mainly in alfalfa. Because barley was grown as an alternate to cotton when acreage limitations were imposed on cotton by the federal government, most of the increase in irrigated acreage was, in fact, due to cotton. Dry-farmed grains and forage accounted for over 2 million acres in 1939.[6]

Field crop production also continued to be associated with large holdings. Some examples can be found in the Sacramento Valley. There, three companies, River Farms, Sutter Basin Company, and Sutter Buttes Company provide examples of large holdings producing grains, alfalfa and other field crops. In 1945 these companies held approximately 36,000 acres. Sugar beets continued to be associated with large landholdings. The four largest sugar beet processors, the Holly Sugar Company, Spreckels Sugar Company, American Crystal Company, and Union Sugar Company, owned

45,000 acres in 1939.[7]

Grains and alfalfa remained important for large areas in the San Joaquin Valley, but interest turned towards cotton. Commercial production was first established in the Imperial Valley around 1910 and some 85,000 acres were planted to it there in 1919. In that same year about 2,000 acres of cotton were planted in the San Joaquin Valley. However, by the 1930s almost all of California's cotton was grown in the San Joaquin Valley, which remained virtually the only producing area until the 1950s. Insect impairment of production in the Imperial Valley, along with the development of the alcala variety, which was especially well adapted to the San Joaquin area, explains this shift in location. Accompanying this shift was an increase in cultivated acreage from 85,000 acres in 1919 to 300,000 acres by 1929. The acreage fluctuated during the 1930s, reaching a high of over 600,000 acres in 1937. Acreage allotments were then imposed and for the duration of this period acreage hovered between 300,000 and 400,000 acres.[8]

Cotton was exceedingly popular in the 1920s because prices were high, particularly in comparison with other crops. This favorable situation was in part due to the alcala variety, which produced long-staple high-quality lint that was extremely marketable. After 1925 it was against the law to cultivate any other variety in the San Joaquin Valley. In the 1930s, although prices fell, yields per acre increased by about 167 percent. Good yields, price supports, and acreage allotments helped keep cotton a glamour crop. Also, cotton cultivation, except for the harvest, was highly mechanized and harvest labor was plentiful. Thus, in 1944, it was pointed out that "cotton is reputed to be the one California crop that has made some money for growers each year since 1930."[9]

Cotton has been produced on holdings of all sizes. However, in the Tulare Lake and on the west side of the San Joaquin Valley, large-scale production has been dominant. The Tulare Lake area was already well-known for large holdings used to produce irrigated grains and forage. As cotton was able to outcompete these crops, the large holdings switched much of their acreage into the new crop (when the 1937 acreage allotments limited cotton planting, the acreage devoted to other field crops rebounded). New producers bought up large grain holdings and put them into cotton. A similar phenomena could be observed on the west side of the valley, especially in Fresno County. This area was held in large parcels that were languishing as desert. A whole new style of land use came in with cotton and irrigation. That it was based on large holdings was a function, not of original holding size, but of irrigation practices. The only source of water on the west side was ground water located at some depth. Wells that could tap this water were quite expensive to put in, but large holdings in cotton could afford the investment because:

> . . . on the West Side of the Valley with large holdings, who drill very large wells that cost $20,000 or $25,000 per well, with a very large flow [with] Operating on a 100 percent load factor, that is all the time, they [i.e. the large owners] get a very low power rate . . . and their

cost per acre-foot is perhaps only a third of what it is in the small places on the other side of the valley.

So, they are over there raising crops with a very heavy pumping lift which ordinarily you would not find feasible.[10]

Table 3.1 lists a few of the large holdings present in both these areas that were used for cotton in 1946. It should be pointed out that leasing land for cotton production was a common practice. Some large holdings probably were maintained by profits accrued from this. The Southern Pacific and Standard Oil Companies leased their west side land for cotton.

TABLE 3.1
Some Large Cotton Holdings, 1946
Tulare Lake Basin and Upper West Side
of the San Joaquin Valley

Owner	Acreage
Anderson Clayton	19,144
J. G. Boswell	22,676
Camp-Lowe West Ginning Co	9,106
Hotchkiss Estate Co	7,209
South Lake Farms	19,317
Tulare Lake Land Co	12,052
Van Glahn Land Co	21,580
West Lake Farms	7,550
TOTAL	118,688

Source: Wills (1953), pp. 175-98.

Included among the large cotton owners were a number of processors and factors. Anderson Clayton was the largest; others were Calflax (South Lake Farms), Camp-Lowe West Ginning Company, and J. G. Boswell. The attraction of land ownership to processors was the ability to secure a supply of cotton for their gins. This was not the only technique used to achieve this end. Crop contracts were common, and the extensive involvement of the gins or their affiliates in farm finance was basic to the growth of California's cotton industry. An anonymous farmer expresses a common point of view:

It was cotton financing that developed the San Joaquin Valley. When the banks wouldn't loan a red cent the gins let us have the money we needed at 5 or 6 percent. We only paid interest for the time we used it too. A lot of this land that never had anything on it was brought under cultivation by cotton finance money.[11]

The importance of this structure in the cotton industry will become apparent later when the issues of securing the labor, water and government aid that cotton production depends upon are discussed.

Specialty Crops (Fruits, Nuts and Vegetables)

Deciduous fruits and grapes were subject to unwarranted optimism in the early 1920s. This led to plantings that turned out to be excessive when the trees and vines came into production at the end of the decade. Bearing acreage of these crops peaked in the late 1920s and early 1930s, and then declined through 1945. Some orchards and vineyards were pulled up in the 1930s. Citrus and nuts enjoyed a period of optimism along with better prices in the early 1930s. Their bearing acreage peaked in the early 1940s. None of these crops evinced marked changes in geographic distribution with the exception of almonds moving into the central coast area. Acreage expanded fairly uniformly in existing producing regions.[12]

Vegetables had the most favorable prices of all crops. Acreage devoted to all varieties increased; particular leaders were lettuce, tomatoes, and asparagus. Most agricultural regions showed greater acreage being devoted to vegetables during the interwar period. Some particularly significant changes were: the rise of Monterey County and Imperial Valley as lettuce producers; the growth of midsummer cantaloupe production in the San Joaquin Valley (to the point where about half the melon acreage was in the valley and the rest in southern California); the rise of the Sacramento Valley as a major orchard and tomato-producing region; and the reorientation of the delta area from barley, beans, and potatoes to asparagus, processing tomatoes, and other truck crops.[13]

The popularity of "specialty" crops was enhanced by changing consumption practices. Per capita consumption of fruits and vegetables increased. An important feature of fruit and vegetable consumption was the growth of freezing. The frozen vegetable industry originated in the late 1930s and was firmly established in the early 1940s. In 1945 frozen orange juice concentrate was perfected.[14] Longer lasting processed goods opened up much larger markets to California producers. The growth of California's population also meant a much larger home market.

By the end of the era there was a fair amount of land concentration among specialty-crop producers, although small holdings remained the rule. The delta was already in large holdings, and remained so as conversion to truck crops occurred. Some large holdings in the Imperial Valley were owned by vegetable producers. Large orchards and vineyards were still uncommon. Many new holdings belonged to shippers and processors, however. The importance of out-of-state markets and canning increased their involvement in production. To maintain control over their supply, they became large landowners. They also entered into crop contracts covering extensive acreages and were involved in farm production credit, behavior noted above for cotton processors. By the late 1930s specialty-crop production was largely under the control of processors and shippers and, as will be discussed later, they (like cotton processors) had important effects on policies concerning marketing, labor, and water issues. A few of these landholders are listed in Table 3.2.

TABLE 3.2
Large Landholdings of Processors and Shippers

Owner	Acreage
American Fruit Growers	2,472
Balfour Guthrie	8,535
Calpak*	20,094
DiGiorgio*	16,869
S. A. Garrard	3,405
Libby, McNeill & Libby	5,130
Perelli, Minetti & Son*	2,110
Schenley*	3,873
TOTAL	58,614

Source: *Walker's Manual of Pacific Coast Securities* for the year 1945 for Calpak and Di Giorgio; Wills (1953), pp. 183, 189 for Perelli, Minetti & Son and Schenley (*Moody's Manual of Investments: Industrial Securities* for the year 1946, p. 512 reveals Schenley as the owner of California Vineyards Association); United States Senate, Committee on Education and Labor (1940), pp. 22836, 200290 for the rest.
Note: Asterisked (*) holdings are for 1945/46; others are for 1939.

There were other large holdings. The Irvine Ranch, which had begun citrus planting in 1906, had approximately 3,000 acres in citrus in 1940. The 4,540-acre El Solyo Ranch was formed in 1918 when five dry land grain farms were consolidated. The land was irrigated and a wide variety of crops, including fruits were planted. This holding existed at the end of the era, albeit with different owners. In 1943 the Gallo Brothers acquired the Valley Agricultural Company — 3,648 acres, mostly orchards, in six counties.[15]

There were two basic changes in farming strategy that facilitated creation of large holdings in orchards and vineyards. The first was that specialty crops were almost always only one use of the holding. The second was that a number of holdings were consolidations of smaller holdings. In these years of failure those who were financially able, such as processors and shippers, were in the happy position of being able to purchase already developed land, probably at distress prices. All but 280 acres of the Di Giorgio holding were acquired between 1919 and 1945 in a series of more than twenty-five purchases. Calpak acquired approximately 17,000 acres in nine purchases after 1918.[16] Sometimes, as with Calpak and Di Giorgio, the holdings were not contiguous. In part this reflects the buyers' varied interests that were being conducted in different localities, and in part the vagaries of land availability.

Vegetable producers frequently preferred to rent land. This was especially true for lettuce, of which it was said (in 1941) that "estimates by packers, realtors, and banking officials have indicated that from one half to two thirds of the lettuce grown in the Salinas and Imperial valleys is produced on leased land."[17] As with cotton, leasing probably made it possible for some existing large holdings to be maintained with a minimum of effort by the owner. A major factor behind the preference for leasing among leasors is that truck crops are soil depleters and it is more profitable to lease and leave when the soil is exhausted. Also, the highly speculative nature of fresh vegetable production provided an additional motive to lease rather than own land.

Oil

Oil development played a dual role. It provided a number of large holdings with an income that sustained them and even allowed for agricultural development. It also continued to account for the amassing of large holdings by oil companies. The oil industry underwent significant changes between 1918 and 1945. In the 1920s Los Angeles became the chief field, but there was no opportunity to accumulate large, oil-bearing holdings there. Then, in the 1930s, new discoveries were made at already existing fields, such as Kettleman, in the southern San Joaquin Valley. At the same time, significant quantities of natural gas were being produced in the Sacramento Valley.

It was mentioned above that several of the largest land and cattle companies benefitted significantly from oil discoveries on their land. Many dimmer lights in the large holding firmament were also involved with oil and gas. Six examples are the Holly Sugar Company, the Valley Agricultural Company, Productive Products, Weyl-Zuckerman Company, Sunny Hills Ranch and Limoneira Ranch. The first two formed oil companies to develop their lands. The Holly Oil Company was incorporated in 1921, with 50 percent of its stock owned by the Holly Sugar Company, to develop oil lands the sugar company owned in the Huntington Beach field. The first years were its most profitable; from 1931 through 1945 its net income never exceed $70,000 while earlier it had ranged in the hundreds of thousands of dollars. The Valley Agricultural Company, taken over by the Gallo Brothers in 1943, formed its own oil company, the Valley Oil Company in that same year, to develop whatever could be found on the agricultural company's lands. As of 1945 it had not met with any success. The last four companies were also recipients of income from leases to gas and oil companies. This amounted to minor sums, several thousand dollars, for all but the Limoneira Ranch, as discoveries were not made. The Limoneira Ranch, which is adjacent to the Newhall Land and Cattle Company land, shared its luck and received substantial income from oil leases.[18]

It is difficult to judge exactly how much the landholdings owned by oil companies increased between 1918 and 1945. A major obstacle is the complexity of the mergers that occurred. Much of the land in large holdings probably derived from smaller properties owned by absorbed companies and does not reflect new additions to the pool of land held by oil companies. Another obstacle is the lack of information about company holdings. Typically, what is reported is the amount of land and mineral rights owned in fee. Mineral rights owned in fee are, of course, valuable to the companies but are not relevant to surface land tenure. Table 3.3 makes use of information from a Bureau of Reclamation report on landownership in 1946 of 2.3 million acres in three areas to be serviced by the Central Valley Project. Clearly the size of these holdings are minima only. Also included is the Standard Oil holding, as reported in *Moody's Manual*. The Bureau of Reclamation found 214,624 acres to be owned by oil companies. The relationship between these holdings and the Central Valley Project is one reason for their interest here. Just as large landholdings acquired for agriculture became valuable for oil, large landholdings acquired for oil became valuable for agriculture.

TABLE 3.3
Oil Company Landholdings, 1946

Company	Acreage
Belridge Oil Co	30,120
Fullerton Oil Co	2,480
Honolulu Oil Co	4,250
CC Midway	9,932
Richfield Oil Co	10,718
Shell Oil Co	17,860
Standard Oil Co	293,192
Tidewater Associated Oil Co	25,554
TOTAL	363,986

Source: The Bureau of Reclamation survey as reported in Wills (1955), pp. 173-98; *Moody's Manual of Investments: Industrial Securities* for the year 1946, p. 650 for Standard Oil.

Farm Real Estate Credit

Agricultural credit can be divided into two categories: short-term production credit and long-term real estate credit. This section is largely concerned with the latter, which had a definite impact on landownership. Short-term credit can affect holding size if its availability varies significantly for different size farms. I was unable to locate any information on this point and cannot say whether or not size discrimination occurred. Long-term credit was necessary to cover capital improvements, land purchases, and also to refinance farmers carrying too much short-term debt. Because these debts were secured by mortgages, defaults led to transfers of ownership. This section will be concerned with the effects such transfers had on the concentration of landownership.

California's Farm Mortgage Debt originally leaped from $107 million in 1910 to $338 million in 1918 to finance the expansion of agriculture during World War I. It continued to grow through 1931, when it reached $615 million and then began to decline. It was down to $337 million in 1945.[19] Table 3.4 shows the farm mortgage debt and rate of forced sales for the years 1926 to 1939.

TABLE 3.4
Farm Mortgage Debt and Forced Sales, 1926-1939

Year	Farm Mortgage Debt (in thousands)	Forced Sales and Related Defaults (per thousand farms)
1927	550,858	15.0
1928	546,493	16.5
1929	557,214	17.7
1930	614,810	13.3
1931	615,322	24.9
1932	594,850	40.6
1933	559,560	45.0
1934	504,398	40.0
1935	460,735	21.0
1936	445,307	22.3
1937	439,736	17.5
1938	432,802	15.6
1939	422,938	15.7

Source: United States Senate, Committee on Education and Labor (1940), p. 18892.

The liquidation of farm mortgage debt in the 1930s was largely due to distress-transfers of land. The actual incidence of involuntary losses is probably understated in the above table. Many sales listed as voluntary were actually forced transfers from mortgagors to mortgagees that occurred without going through the process of foreclosure.[20]

The foreclosure wave had no lasting impact on land concentration for three reasons. First, all sizes of landholdings were involved in the disaster. Second, although major institutional lenders, like commercial banks and after 1933, the federal government, held a large number of mortgages and hence became owners of large acreages, such holdings were temporary because these creditors were interested in selling off the properties. (They were not exactly ephemeral, however, as it was usually necessary to operate the property for some time before sale became feasible.) Third, defaults on large properties were normally unaccompanied by subdivision of the property.

Federal involvement in farm mortgages began in 1916 when the Federal Land Bank system was created.[21] This system was divided into twelve districts, each served by a Federal Land Bank. The banks pooled their mortgages and then issued tax-free bonds with the mortgages as security. The controversial tax-free feature was upheld by the U.S. Supreme Court in 1921, when it ruled for the constitutionality of the Land Bank system. Although the banks were very active in the 1920s, they were limited to first-mortgage loans representing a maximum of 50 percent of the land value and 20 percent of the value of improvements. This prevented them from rendering much assistance to farmers needing refinancing or more extensive loans. Between 1929 and 1932 their loans were simply not very attractive, despite low interest rates.*

After 1933, Farm Land Bank loans became more popular and the federal government came to carry an ever-increasing share of farm mortgage debt. This was possible thanks to a 1932 congressional appropriation of $125 million to the banks, a 1933 executive reorganization that put the bank system under the aegis of the newly created Farm Credit Administration, and most importantly, the 1933 Emergency Farm Mortgage Act. The latter first of all changed the appraisal formula to "normal value" of the farm, which was that "which would be likely if the prices of farm products were at the 1909-1914 level," with adjustments for changes in taxes and expenses. Second, it provided for refinancing up to 75 percent of this normal value, where the Farm Land Banks loaned up to 50 percent and the Land Bank Commission loans made up the difference. Third, the Federal Farm Mortgage Corporation was created in 1934 to handle commission loans. A majority of the Land Bank Commission loans were made in 1934. In 1945 Land Banks were allowed to loan up to 65 percent of the normal farm value and the authority to make commission loans was allowed to lapse in 1947.

The Federal Land Banks and Land Bank Commission loans were the major forms of federal real estate credit for agriculture in these years. Of very minor relevance to California was the Bankhead-Jones Act (1937), which provided for tenant-purchase loans. By 1945, only 229 of these loans, covering 13,579 acres were made in California.[23] In the 1930s both the Land Banks and the Farm Mortgage Corporation acquired farms through foreclosure. Most of this land was sold off from 1941 to 1946 when the agricultural recovery made sales relatively easy.

Bank of America experienced tremendous growth in these years; affiliates and branches proliferated and other banks were acquired. Along with the acquisition of banks went the acquisition of the farm mortgages they held. Less than one-fifth of the farms foreclosed in the 1920s by Bank of America

---

*Their average interest rate was over 1 percent less than for other categories of lenders.[22]

were originally mortgaged by it. This one bank held roughly 10 percent of the total number of foreclosures of those years (which is comparable to the amount of farm mortgage debt the bank was carrying).[24]

By 1929 Bank of America owned 1,025 farms in California and California Lands Inc. was established, as a subsidiary of Transamerica Corporation,* to manage and sell the farm land acquired by the companies in the Transamerica group. California Lands' acme as a landowner occurred in 1936 when it owned 2,642 farms consisting of 531,000 acres scattered throughout the state. By 1939 this had dropped to 1,718 farms encompassing 395,000 acres and this decline continued. In 1941 California Lands merged with Capital Company, its twin for urban land owned by Bank of America. In 1945 Capital Company held 103,230 acres, mostly in California. California Lands dissolution was carried out under "a policy to break up its larger properties for sale," and there is no reason to doubt that this policy was followed. It is, however, likely that other large holdings formed in these years included bits and pieces of farms held by California Lands. For example, in accumulating land in the 1920s and 1930s, Calpak acquired 83 acres from California Lands in 1930.[25] This would be the only way in which California Lands could have made a direct and lasting contribution to land concentration in California, and it is impossible to determine the extent to which this occurred.

Another way to handle long-term credit was to issue bonds secured by mortgages. Many corporate owners of large holdings did this. Default on the bonds, followed by foreclosure, trustee sales, and sometimes reorganization by bondholders committees, was a common occurrence during the 1920s and 1930s. Normally, such failures did not result in break-up into small holdings. We saw this to be the case for the Miller and Lux Company (whose holding became smaller, yet still large, holdings), the largest one to default on bonds. The same holds for other prominent defaulters. The Alameda Farms property, 10,130 acres in Sutter County, was purchased by Sutter Buttes Company in 1934 after a bond default. Sutter Buttes sold some of the land but still held 6,048 acres in 1945. The Bastanchury Ranch consisted of 2,650 acres in Orange County, 2,200 of which were in citrus orchards. It defaulted on its bonds in 1933 and was reorganized into the Sunny Hills Ranch which in 1945 was somewhat reduced, owning 1,850 acres of which 1,350 were citrus orchards. California Delta Lands owned 39,337 acres in the delta before it was forced to reorganize in 1929. The reorganization created four new land companies: Empire Company (13,700 acres), McDonald Island Farms (3,423 acres), Productive Properties (13,598 acres), and Weyl-Zuckerman (2,704 acres). California Delta was reduced to 6,400 acres. Empire was taken over by the bank in 1941 but the others remained in 1945. Another delta holding, Rindge Land and Navigation Company (22,000 acres), also defaulted and was taken over by

---

*Transamerica Corporation is a holding company created in 1928, one of whose principal investments is Bank of America.

Pacific States Savings and Loan. The holding remained intact through the 1960s when it was broken into several smaller, but still large holdings. The Valley Agricultural Company, purchased by the Gallo Brothers in 1943, was itself a 1926 bondholders reorganization of the Lucerne Vineyards. One last example is the Northern Counties Land & Cattle Company, 53,000 acres in Tehama County. In 1934 the Diamond Ranch acquired the property from the bondholders protection committee. Diamond sold out in 1941 to S. E. Ayer.[26]

Rise of Farm Organizations

Large landowners* did not have their own organizations separate from small owners. Instead, they and large operators in agriculturally linked industries came to dominate most of the organizations serving California agriculture and were able to promote their interests through these organizations. Of course, their interests were not necessarily opposed to those of small producers, nor can it be fairly claimed that small producers and farm interests in general were not also served at times.† But the large producers were able to achieve much that was only for themselves through these organizations.

Agricultural organizations existed in California prior to 1918. As indicated above (Chapter 2) some of the largest and most powerful cooperative marketing associations were of this type. However, in the post-World War I period agricultural organizations came to dominate California agriculture. Organizations of relatively narrow purview, dealing primarily with marketing or labor issues, numbered in the hundreds.‡ Marketing associations were by far the most prevalent. The number of organizations dealing with particular producing commodities or producing areas increased from 237 in 1915, to 479 in 1930. Some of these collapsed during the Depression and numbers fluctuated during the 1930s, but the bulk of these remained intact so that in 1944 there were 438 of them.[27] These organizations included all sized growers but as the La Follette Committee§ noted:

---

*In this and subsequent sections the terms large growers and large landowners will be used synonymously. This is not quite accurate since many large owners were not large producers and not all large producers fall into the category of large owners (especially specialty-crop producers). However, because these two groups overlapped in membership and coincided in terms of interests, this seems to me to be an acceptable usage.

†However, many actions that appear to help the small operator in the short run, by also aiding large farmers, often disproportionately, contribute to competitive disadvantage for the small growers in the long run.

‡Irrigation was not an issue evocative of specialized organizations. The Irrigation Districts Association was perhaps the only such organization. More general farm organizations handled water issues.

§The La Follette Committee is the Senate Subcommittee of the Committee on Education and Labor whose 1940 hearings are listed in the bibliography. Senator La Follette was chairman of the committee and it is often referred to in this manner.

> Membership in the typical association is held by corporations or their representatives in addition to individual owner-operators. It usually included most of the important units in the industry. The activities of the associations are supported by assessments on a volume or value basis so that the bulk of the funds is supplied by the larger corporations or individual operators in the industry.[28]

Thus, large grower interests were able to dominate such associations.

In the 1930s some marketing associations became involved with labor issues. A number of organizations were also created to deal solely with labor concerns. One of the first of these was formed in 1917. By 1946 there were seventy-four labor bureaus alone, besides a number of other kinds of employer associations.[29] As with the marketing associations, the La Follette Committee noticed that:

> An analysis of the structure and control of these employers associations indicates that they are likely to be dominated by the industrial interests and the large-scale or corporate producers .... Oftentimes, these producers are shippers, handlers, or processors of agricultural products operating in the industry on a vertical basis. The labor policies of these associations naturally reflect the attitudes and interests of the industrial groups that sponsor and support them. Inevitably, the small independent producers, who may be more numerous in a given crop area, fall into line behind the tremendous economic and trade influence of these more highly organized and integrated forces.[30]

Several organizations with broad agricultural concerns whose point of view coincided with that of the large farmer were also formed. The California State Chamber of Commerce was one of these. The State Chamber of Commerce was created in 1920, an amalgam of the already existing California Development Board and California Industrial Association. It dealt with agricultural questions through its agricultural committees at both the state and regional levels. Representatives of the various marketing and labor associations, along with representatives from interested secondary industries served on these committees.[31] The extent of the Chamber's alignment with large growers will become apparent in the discussions of irrigation and labor below.

The Chamber of Commerce worked quite closely with the California Farm Bureau Federation. The Farm Bureau was the most influential of all farm organizations in these years; it was involved in practically every major issue facing California agriculture. Its history is worth reviewing.

County Farm Bureaus came into being in 1914. Tetreau describes the reasons for their creation and their early functions as follows:

> About 1913 an agricultural extension division was created in the College of Agriculture, University of California at Berkeley. The functions of this division were to be and still are of a purely educational nature, to extend to farmers the knowledge which agricultural colleges, experiment stations, and the United States

Department of Agriculture have gained. . . . It was felt that the work of the Agricultural Extension Service among farmers would be facilitated if it operated with and through local farmers organizations in each county. As there were no suitable organizations in existence at the time, it was decided to promote the formation of county farm bureaus as had been done in several other states. It was the definite intention of the sponsors of the farm-bureau movement that the functions of the county organizations would be purely educational—the channels through which county farm advisors and the extension specialist would work in reaching individual farm operators . . . . The appointment of a farm advisor to any county was made contingent upon the formation of a county farm bureau with at least 20 per cent of the farmers in that county as members.[32]

The bureaus soon broadened their scope. In 1919 the thirty-five existing county bureaus combined to form the California Farm Bureau Federation to permit group action in many areas (including an abortive foray into a marketing cooperative). For the next twenty years statewide membership fluctuated around 20,000, in approximately forty counties, with the greatest concentration of members in southern California and the San Joaquin Valley.[33] Its close ties with the Agricultural Extension Service and the Department of Agriculture help explain the Farm Bureau's puissance; it had the status of a quasi-governmental organization. The directions in which it chose to exert itself can be understood from Clarke Chambers' observation that while the members included farmers of all sizes, "probably mostly small and medium sized," the leaders were mostly "large farmers with substantial economic interests. Many of them were also active in the economically powerful marketing associations."[34]

Marketing and Prices

Two important things were occurring in this period that affected marketing and farm prices. The first was the increasing concentration in marketing; a relatively small number of private concerns and cooperative marketing associations handled a large percentage of California production. The second was the development of federal and state programs to ameliorate prices, control production, and expand marketing. The degree of control over production by processors and shippers has been adverted to several times. In 1938 four companies ginned 66 percent of California's cotton production. In 1935 three California packing companies packed 40 percent of the total U.S. production of dried prunes and raisins and three California wineries handled 26 percent of the California wine grapes produced during the year. At the same time, ten cooperative wineries handled an additional 21 percent of California's wine grape production, the California Fruit Exchange marketed 12 percent of the U.S. production of table grapes, and the California Fruit Growers Exchange moved 47 percent of the U.S. production of fresh oranges and 10 percent of the U.S. production of fresh grapefruit. These are only a few examples of the concentration of control in marketing Californian products.[35] This concentration of control meant that when the leaders of these economically powerful cooperatives and/or private companies banded together (as in supporting the Farm Bureau), they had a great deal of political clout.

The first federal support effort was the Federal Farm Board, created in 1929 with the intention of improving agricultural marketing and stabilizing prices by purchasing and storing surpluses.* Its $500 million revolving fund was inadequate, and without powers to control production it was in a hopeless position. It was abolished in 1933 and replaced by the Agricultural Adjustment Administration (AAA). The AAA was the first program to make use of the concept of parity. Parity was an idea that had been bruited about since the 1920s when it was introduced by George Peek and Hugh Johnson in the defeated McNary-Haughen Plan. The parity price for a commodity was defined as the ratio of current prices to prices paid by farmers in the years 1910 to 1914. The exact percentage of parity that was sought varied over the years. In order to achieve the chosen level of prices, the AAA was authorized to:

> . . . enter into voluntary agreements with farmers for the reduction of basic crops, to store crops on the farm and make advances on them, and to enter into marketing agreements with producer and handlers for stabilizing prices. The act also provided for the levying of processing taxes as a means of financing the crop reduction program and for other purposes, authorized the Secretary to license handlers and processors for the purpose of enforcing the provisions of marketing agreements.[36]

Cotton, wheat, corn, rice, tobacco, hogs, and dairy products were defined as basic crops and this list was expanded in 1934 to include rye, flax, barley, sorghum grains, cattle, peanuts, sugar cane, and sugar beets.† Potatoes were added in 1935. In the original form of the act, marketing agreements were to apply only to the basic commodities. California specialty-crop producers, through the efforts of the California Farm Bureau, succeeded in having these provisions apply to nonbasic crops. California citrus and walnuts were under marketing orders from 1933 onwards; deciduous tree crops, grapes, asparagus, hops, olives, raisins, dates, prunes and cantaloups were under agreements for various seasons between 1933 and 1945.

The Commodity Credit Corporation (CCC) was created in 1933 to handle nonrecourse loans to farmers and to store the surpluses that accumulated from these loans. Nonrecourse loans are advances that need not be repaid. If the price of the commodity rises above the loan rate, the farmer can sell on the market and repay the loan. Otherwise the CCC takes the crop and the farmer in essence receives the loan rate for his crop. In this way, minimum prices are fixed. The Federal Surplus Relief Corporation (later renamed as Federal Surplus Commodities Corporation) was also created in

---

*Unless otherwise stated, the discussion of federal policies follows Benedict (1953).
†Sugar was handled by a separate act, the Jones-Costigan Sugar Act (1934).

1933 to dispose of these surpluses.

Cotton production was successfully controlled by taxes on ginning imposed by the Bankhead Act (1934). Each producer was given a certain allotment that would be exempted from the tax. This approach to production control was declared unconstitutional in the Hoosac Mills decision (1936), which invalidated the production control and processing tax features of the AAA. The marketing agreement provisions were not invalidated and were reinvoked separately by the Agricultural Marketing Act (1937). Similarly, the marketing quota features of the Jones-Costigan Act were reenacted by the Sugar Act (1937). Production control fell under the aegis of the Soil Conservation and Domestic Allotment Act (1936), which provided an acceptable method to impose acreage limitations on producers. Crops were considered either soil depleters or soil conserving and farmers were paid to shift from depleting to conserving crops. Since those crops in excess supply were soil depleters, this affected production controls. This was recognized as a stopgap measure and a new Agricultural Adjustment Act (1938) was passed.

The 1938 act incorporated the 1936 act and, additionally, provided for wheat insurance, marketing quotas with grower approval through referendums, wheat insurance and nonrecourse loans to producers of basic commodities under certain conditions at rates ranging between 52 and 75 percent of parity. This act remained in effect until 1948. Beginning in 1941 it underwent major amendment. The Steagall amendment (1941) raised CCC loans to 85 percent of parity. After Pearl Harbor, the issue became one of controlling prices, not raising them. The Emergency Price Control Act (January 1942) set ceilings on agricultural prices at a rather high level (the maximum of 110 percent of parity or the price of the commodity on certain dates) and this was rolled back by the Stabilization Act (September 1942). Under that act, the ceiling was set at 90 percent of parity, or the maximum price between January 1, 1942 and September 15, 1942, with a clause permitting the President to set lower prices if necessary to avoid gross inequities. Additionally, this act raised the loan rate to 90 percent of parity and guaranteed this rate to apply for the first two postwar years. Cotton rose even higher, to 92.5 and then 95 percent of parity in 1944, and ultimately the CCC paid full parity in 1944 and 1945. In 1944 all acreage allotments were revoked except those for tobacco.

These programs had their largest impact on California producers of basic commodities, especially cotton, sugar and rice. It was noted previously that these were crops whose prices made them particularly attractive in these years. They were also commodities dominated by large producers. Table 3.5 lists Agricultural Conservation payments made to some large landholders in 1939. The price supports they received were substantial. Although large producers' payments were only commensurate with their size, the fact that products so oriented towards large-scale production were being aided served to help insure continued large-scale production of these crops.

TABLE 3.5
Agricultural Conservation Payments to
Some Large Landholders, 1939

Landowner	ASCS Payment in 1939
J.G. Boswell	$53,822
Calflax	29,200
Camp West Lowe	43,489
Giffen, Bernal	28,117
Giffen, Russell	43,428
Hambury, Sam	17,161
Hotchkiss Estate *et al.*	72,876
Kern County Land Co.	31,945
O'Neill, J. E.	38,337
River Farms Co.	34,211
Weyl-Zuckerman	14,213

Source: United States Senate, Committee on Education and Labor (1940), pp. 22889-906.

Although federal marketing agreements existed for some specialty crops, the Farm Bureau also agitated at the state level for further aid. Its efforts resulted in the California Prorate Act (1933), which the Bureau wrote, sponsored, and even "indirectly administered."[37] The Prorate Act provided a mechanism for regulating the flow of products into markets. Producers petitioned for proration, and once it was granted each producer was given certificates allowing the marketing of only certain amounts of produce through the primary and secondary trade channels. It was expected that prices would be raised by limiting the amounts growers were allowed to market. The act was most used in the 1930s. Between 1933 and 1948 twenty-five programs were instituted under it for varying lengths of time. Only two of these programs remained in 1948.

Many small farmers were opposed to proration claiming that it was controlled by large producers who were able to manipulate it for their own benefit while the small farmers suffered price decreases. In response to these complaints the act was amended in 1939 and administration of the program was removed from the growers and given to the State Department of Agriculture. It is unclear whether the program actually worked and whether price increases or decreases that occurred under proration resulted from it or from broader economic forces that were outside its scope. The importance of proration here is that it demonstrates the power of the Farm Bureau. However, despite the hysteria proration induced in the small-farmer based Simon J. Lubin Society, it may not be an example of the Farm Bureau pushing something that would best benefit large producers.[38]

Water

In this era the ability of private and local initiative to develop irrigation reached its limit and the state and federal governments took over water development. Some of the reasons for this change are apparent from the information about irrigation provided by the U.S. Census of Agriculture. Unfortunately, the census provides two sets of figures: one based on the irrigated acreage reported by enumerated farms and the other the irrigated acreage reported by irrigation enterprises. The former is always smaller than the latter and is the basis for reports of irrigated acreages devoted to various crops, while the latter is the basis for all information about the characteristics of irrigation enterprises (source of water, type of enterprise and so on). Both sets of figures are available for 1919, 1929, and 1939, but only a subset of the information from the farms is available for 1945.[39]

Between 1919 and 1939 the irrigated acreage increased by about 800,000 acres (from 4.2 million acres to 5.0 million acres). Based on the irrigated acreage reported by farms for 1945 and the relationship that figure bore to the acreage reported by irrigation enterprises in earlier and later years, an estimate of 5.4 million acres seems reasonable for 1945. The 1919 to 1939 increase mostly came about because of greater reliance on pumped wells (1.8 million more acres received water from pumped wells in 1939 than in 1919). Most of this development was carried out by single farms. There was also a significant increase in reservoirs, whose capacity more than doubled in the twenty-year span (increasing from 1.1 million acre feet to 3.6 million acre feet). This sort of development can be attributed to irrigation districts.

The emphasis on wells led to problems with overdraft of ground water in certain areas. Surface water was also overcommitted, resulting in shortages during dry years and also creating navigation problems on the Sacramento River and excess salinity in the delta area. In addition, existing reservoirs were inadequate and flood control was a problem in wet years. These problems were outside the scope of those responsible for most of the water development in these years. This was recognized early; in 1919 Chief Geographer of the U.S. Geological Survey Robert Marshall presented (as a personal and not official report) a plan, for comprehensive water development in California ever-after referred to as the Marshall Plan. This plan

> ... provided a series of dams on the tributaries of the Sacramento and San Joaquin Rivers, including a major structure at the Iron Canyon site on the Sacramento River. Grand canals were to lead down the east and west sides of the Sacramento and San Joaquin Valleys in order to transfer water from the Sacramento to the San Joaquin Valley.... The main canal down the west side of the valleys was to cross the Carquinez Strait by means of an inverted syphon across the Benicia harbor. Some water was to be diverted from the canal for use in the San Francisco Bay area.[40]

The Marshall Plan was a starting point for the Central Valley Project. In 1921 the California legislature authorized the first of a series of investigations of state water resources with the goal of producing a comprehensive plan for development and management. These investigations continued over a period of ten years, culminating in 1931 in a report to the legislature on the state water plan. In these same years, the federal government was also involved in a series of California water studies, but these were of a more specific nature than the state's. A joint Federal-State Water Resources Commission was also appointed in 1929. This commission reported favorably in 1930 on two proposals, one of which was essentially the Central Valley Project. [41]

In 1933 the state legislature passed the Central Valley Project Act (AB 259). The project was designed to deal with all the problems mentioned above: the need for irrigation water in the San Joaquin Valley, flood control, salinity control in the delta, and improvement of navigation. A concomitant to construction of the project was the generation of hydroelectric power. Some of the power was necessary to pump project water south, but the rest would be available for sale to help finance the project. The act also provided for financing by up to $170 million in revenue bonds. A state Water Project Authority to construct and operate the project and cooperation with the federal government were additional features of the act. [42]

The power feature quickly became contentious and the Central Valley Project Act was opposed by a referendum movement led by Fred Athearn, a San Francisco attorney for Pacific Gas & Electric Company (PG&E). In 1933 California voters had the opportunity to approve or disapprove their legislature's act by referendum. PG&E was the most active opponent, being disconcerted at the possibility that the power to be generated by the hydroelectric units of the project would be distributed by the state, breaking the PG&E monopoly in northern California. Southern California, which stood to gain very little from the project, was also opposed. Proponents included California Governor Rolph, State Engineer Hyatt, the California Grange, the State League of Women Voters, most of the State Chambers of Commerce and the California State Federation of Labor. The Farm Bureau Federation failed to take a stand. Member Farm Bureaus were divided along regional lines and took their own stands. The referendum, which was worded so as to be against the act, was defeated 459,712 to 426,209. [43]

The Depression and general economic hardships of the 1930s left the state in a weak position financially so it sought federal aid for the project. The first federal allocation of funds was made in September 1935 from the Emergency Relief Act, and field surveys were begun by the U.S. Bureau of Reclamation. The project was declared feasible and recommended as a Federal Reclamation project and approved as such in December 1935. The first allocation of funds, as well as the next made by the First Deficiency Act (1936), declared that the project was "reimbursable in accordance with reclamation law." The project was reauthorized for construction by the Secretary of the Interior under the Rivers and Harbors Act (1937), and section 2 of this act made the project subject to reclamation law. By 1945, $193,113,000 had been appropriated by the federal government.[44]

Construction began in 1937 but suffered slowdowns during World War II. By 1945, most of the water storage, flood control, and power generation facilities were in operation while very little had been achieved in the way of irrigation. In that same year it was estimated by the Bureau of Reclamation that the cost to complete the initial features would be $208 million, bringing the total cost of these features to $322.3 million.[45]

The state had turned to the federal government because it was recognized in several of the studies prepared on the Central Valley Project that the project costs could not be met if the interest rate was greater than 3 percent or 3.5 percent and only the federal government could obtain money at such rates.[46] These studies were based on cost estimates of around $160 million. Similarly, when the Bureau of Reclamation studied the project's feasibility in 1935 it used the state's $170 million estimate when reaching its favorable decision. Yet project costs almost doubled and it was no longer clear that the costs could ever be reimbursed. This is particularly important because the price of water for the farmer was determined by the distribution of the repayment burden. The way costs are allocated and the extent to and manner in which they are met is responsible for what is now referred to as "the water subsidy," which simply means that water users are not charged anything close to the actual cost of supplying the water.

Cheap water is a boon to all sized farmers, but large owners are especially favored by it as it enhances their ability to use the land for extensive cultivation of lower-value crops. It was necessary if much land were to continue to be used for irrigated grains, other field crops, and hay and forage crops. These uses accounted for over half of the irrigated acreage reported by farms in 1929 and 1939.[47]

Repayment procedures were established by the Reclamation Project Act (1939). The Central Valley Project was brought under the terms of this act by the Appropriation Act (1940). Under that act, any costs allocated to flood control, navigation and recreation are classified as nonreimbursable and are borne by the federal government. Other costs, such as irrigation and power, are reimbursable. These include annual maintenance and operation as well as construction costs. Construction costs allocated to irrigation and power are subject to repayment over a period of forty years; power costs include interest of not less than 3 percent but irrigator repayments are interest free. Furthermore, irrigators actually have a fifty-year period because a ten-year development period was granted with no payments required. The act did not establish how the reimbursable costs were to be allocated.[48] But regardless of how this was done, a fifty-year, interest-free repayment period constitutes a significant subsidy for irrigators. This issue, along with the allocation of yearly costs and the fixing of water prices, will be discussed in detail in the next chapter, which covers the time period when the Central Valley Project was finally serving irrigators and when cost-benefit analyses indicating bright prospects for repayment were being used to justify expansion of the project.

More notorious than repayment and more directly relevant to landownership is the 160-acre limitation. Federal reclamation law has a complex history with respect to the limitation. The Newlands Act (1902) that established the reclamation program was concerned with preventing monopolization of lands to be served by federal projects. Most of its provisions along this line governed the amount of public land within the service area, that could be entered by a single individual. This was never a crucial issue for the Central Valley Project because it served lands already in private ownership. But the 1902 act had this to say about privately held land:

> No right to the use of water for land in private ownership shall be sold for a tract exceeding 160 acres to any one landowner, and no such sale shall be made to any landowner unless he be an actual bonafide resident on such land, or occupant thereof residing in the neighborhood of said land, and no such right shall permanently attach until all payments therefor are made. [49]

Notice that the limitation is not on the amount of land an individual could own within the service area but only on the amount of land owned by an individual that could receive water from a federal reclamation project.

Supplemental acts were passed reaffirming the 160-acre limitation and expanding it to cover private lands receiving supplemental water from projects. Anti-speculation features were also initiated in a 1914 act. In 1924, a document referred to as the Fact Finders Report made recommendations to remedy weaknesses in the then-existing reclamation law. The Omnibus Adjustment Act (1926) incorporated many of these recommendations. This act provided that repayment contracts had to be executed with irrigation districts before water could be delivered, that only 160 acres of land in a single ownership were eligible to receive water, and that land in excess of this amount would be furnished water only if the owner executed, with the Secretary of the Interior, recordable contracts to sell the excess land at prices fixed by the Secretary (which were to be based on pre-irrigated values, thus controlling land speculation in the service area). [50]

This was the last act of general applicability containing acreage limitation provisions. Later acts referred to specific projects and, after 1938, the trend was towards exempting specific projects from the limitation. The issue of the acreage limitation did not surface in California until 1943. Montgomery and Clawson describe the previous years:

> The period after the Central Valley Project was adopted as a Federal undertaking in late 1935 until 1943 was one of drift as far as the acreage limitation provisions were concerned. Throughout that period there was widespread support by numerous divergent groups for the appropriation of Federal funds for the Project and funds were expended in construction. The Project gradually passed from a proposal into an active reality. The issue of acreage limitation was either not raised at all or was not raised in decisive fashion during this period. [51]

It was inevitable that the acreage limitation would become an important issue since the project area included a significant amount of excess ownerships. In 1946 the Bureau of Reclamation reported that out of 9,366 ownerships totalling 619,688 acres in the regions encompassed by eighteen water users organizations, 284 ownerships held 142,622 acres (23 percent) in excess. A separate landownership survey covering 2,362,430 acres in the Upper San Joaquin Valley that could be eligible for Central Valley Project Water found 841,968 acres (35.6 percent) of the land to be excess.[52]

A September 1943 publication of the California State Chamber of Commerce describing the status of the Central Valley Project relegates the issue of the acreage limitation to a footnote that ends tellingly with the statement that:

> This provision has been waived in certain instances by Congressional action, and the subject is being studied by one of the Central Valley Project study committees of the Bureau.[53]

The battle for exemption began two months later when the California Farm Bureau Federation and the Irrigation Districts Association of California passed resolutions protesting the application of the limitation to the Central Valley Project. Several months later, in March 1944, the Omnibus Rivers and Harbors Bill (HR 3691) was passed by the House of Representatives with a rider granting the Central Valley Project the desired exemption. A storm ensued in the Senate and this rider (known as the Elliott Amendment) was defeated in December 1944 after lengthy hearings. California Senator Downey made his appearance as a champion of exemption in this battle. The immediate result of failure to achieve exemption was that in 1945 the Southern San Joaquin Valley Irrigation District signed a repayment contract with the United States that prescribed compliance with the acreage limitation.[54]

Several arguments that were to appear again were first voiced at this time. These were: (1) other projects had received exemptions; (2) most of those affected had not been aware of the limitation when the Bureau was asked to take over the project; and (3) the limit was unenforceable. The latter was based on the fact that many landowners relied on ground water for irrigation. Rather than receive surface water from the project, they would be able to reap the benefits of ground water replenishment without incurring any responsibility to the project. The question was whether ground water seepage constituted a delivery of water. This remained an open question for many years.[55]

The law was also falling under more liberal interpretations in these years. The theory that it would be acceptable to receive water for the first 160 acres even without a recordable contract for the excess was accepted by Leland Graham, regional consul for the Department of the Interior in 1945. The theory that because California is a community property state, the limit should actually be 320 acres for an owner who was married met with favor in the opinion of Fowler Harper, Solicitor of the Department of the Interior in 1945. Harper also indicated agreement with Graham in this opinion.[56]

The Central Valley Project was not the only source of Bureau of Reclamation water in California. The Orland Project in the Sacramento Valley was begun in 1909. However, it had no problem with excess ownerships because of a 40-acre limitation accepted by landowners when the project was begun.[57] The Imperial Valley had begun receiving water from the Colorado River Project in 1940 and by the end of this era plans were made to bring water from the same source to the Coachella Valley. The 1946 Bureau of Reclamation Survey of Landownership, mentioned above, indicated 402 ownerships larger than 160 acres in the Imperial Valley. These encompassed 257,949 acres which meant a maximum of 193,629 acres (44 percent) in excess.* In the Coachella Valley, 14 percent of the surveyed area, or 9,612 acres were in excess. It is not known how much of this land was in large landholdings as that term is used here. As noted above, in 1917 the Imperial Valley contained only seven large holdings besides that of the Southern Pacific Railroad. The railroad sold 236,000 acres in Imperial County between 1917 and 1939. Perhaps some of this land became individual large holdings.[58]

The situation in the Imperial Valley came about in the following way. In 1922 the seven states (Utah, Wyoming, Colorado, Nevada, Arizona, New Mexico, and California) that used the Colorado River signed the Colorado River Compact. This compact established how the water in the river basin was to be divided. Unfortunately, it was based on an overestimate of the flow of the river and this led to difficulties in later years. The determination of the exact share to which California was entitled was only recently settled in the courts. The Boulder Canyon Project Dam (Hoover Dam) was authorized in 1928 as the first multipurpose project of the Bureau of Reclamation. The act provided for the Hoover Dam and the construction of the All-American Canal in southern California (the act also divided water in the lower basin between California, Nevada, and Arizona). The receipts from the sale of power was to cover the reimbursable costs of the Hoover Dam. Funds were authorized under the National Recovery Act in 1933 and reclamation law was to apply. In 1933, Secretary of the Interior Wilbur signed a letter opposing application of the acreage limitation to the Imperial Valley. This was done without a formal solicitors legal opinion but seemed to become binding. In 1945 when the same issue arose with respect to the Coachella Valley, which was to be served by an extension of the All-American Canal, Secretary of the Interior Ickes recognized the applicability of the acreage limitation to the Coachella Valley, but he did not follow the logic of his solicitors opinion and repudiate Wilbur's letter.[59] This is another question only recently settled in the courts and will be discussed again in the next chapter.

---

*The report does not indicate how much of the land was actually in excess because at that time the project was considered to be exempt. See below for information on this point.

In summary, water development in this era became more comprehensive and also came under the control of the federal government through the Bureau of Reclamation. Questions were raised towards the end of the era when these projects were becoming functional as to how the relevant laws on repayment and acreage limitations were to be applied. Both issues vitally concerned large landowners, the former determining the cost of water and hence what was economically feasible to do with it and the latter the size of the holding that could be irrigated. Also, the basis for problems with the Colorado River was laid by the division of water in the Colorado River Compact. This issue affected the availability of water for the Imperial and Coachella Valleys and hence interested all landowners in these areas. The next chapter will pursue these issues in the post-World War II years.

Labor

It was pointed out in earlier chapters that California agriculture had become dependent on the existence of a mobile pool of laborers prepared to work in the fields for only part of the year and for low wages. This dependence grew after World War I as production of labor-intensive crops (fruits, nuts, vegetables, cotton, sugar beets) increased. The number of seasonal laborers required by California agriculture was continually increasing; between 1935 and 1945 the number of workers needed at peak harvest time rose from 145,000 to 225,000.[60] Insuring the existence of such a labor force was not an affair of small moment and labor developments in this era were complex.

According to USDA estimates of supply and demand, the labor supply was more than adequate from 1921 until the United States entered World War II. This is suggested by a decline in the ratio of wages to gross farm income from 24.5 percent in 1924 to 14.2 percent in 1939.[61] In light of labor surpluses of the 1920s and 1930s, it is not surprising that it was possible to keep wages low. The composition of the seasonal labor force also underwent significant changes. From 1918 through about 1934 Mexicans went through a cycle of rising and declining prominence. In the next seven years reliance shifted to the dustbowl migrants (''Okies''). After Pearl Harbor, the defense industries provided more lucrative employment for the migrants, and Mexicans again became the dominant labor force under the Bracero program.

Beginning in the late 1920s and continuing until World War II, strife between workers and employers was frequent. It peaked in the mid-1930s when strike activity and unionization were effectively squelched by grower organizations. After that, wage increases resulting from the World War II labor shortage were kept in line with the help of the federal government, both through wage controls and the use of the Bracero program to relieve labor shortages.

The claim that wages were kept low needs some amplification because the USDA's Crop Reporting Service publishes a series of farm wage rates according to which, in this era, California was a national leader in wages.

Only a few western states ever exceeded California levels. This does not jibe well with the claim that wages were low, or at least too low. This seeming contradiction was investigated by the La Follette Committee. They discovered a number of serious inadequacies in the USDA series. Not only was the sampling procedure condemned as inadequate, both in terms of geographic distribution and number of respondents, but, more tellingly, the categories used were found to be irrelevant. The USDA considers both monthly and daily wages, with and without board. Yet

> . . . probably not more than one-quarter of all agricultural wage laborers employed in California are paid on a monthly or daily wage basis. The series of wages by the day without board purportedly reflects the equivalents of the average daily earnings of hour and piece rate workers, but the preponderant weight of the evidence examined by the Committee indicates that this is not the case. Many of the crop reporters who fill in the schedules upon which the Cooperative Crop Reporting Service bases its estimates, report only the prevailing wage rates of which they have knowledge. There is a tendency among others to think of maximum daily earnings of piece and hour workers as the standard or average earnings when filling in the schedules.[62]

The committee examined the available evidence on piece work rates and found that California made a less sterling showing. In some instances California wage rates were highest but most often this was not the case and in more instances they were lowest. The committee concluded that "California farm operators cannot, without considerable qualification, claim that they are paying the highest wage rates in the country."[63]

Labor Supply—1920s and 1930s

It was mentioned above, in Chapter 2, that when immigration restrictions were tightened in 1917, exemptions were made for Mexican agricultural laborers. These exemptions were not widely utilized in California, but they established a precedent for the next decade. Mexico and other Western hemisphere countries were exempted from the immigration quotas imposed by Congress in 1921 and 1924. When the 1921 legislation was in process, agricultural employers from the Southwest lobbied for Mexican exemption on the basis of dependence upon their labor, and this effort was repeated in 1924. Interestingly, California agricultural employers were not among them. Apparently, in 1924, Californians did not yet feel themselves dependent on Mexicans. Yet Mexicans were becoming an important element in the agricultural labor force, particularly after 1923. They were becoming extremely important for truck crops, especially in the Imperial and Salinas Valleys; in citrus, where, as early as 1919 the California Fruit Growers Exchange estimated that they represented 30 percent of the total number employed in the orchards and packing houses; in grape picking, where they replaced the Japanese; and in cotton, whose production was developed primarily with Mexican labor.[64]

By 1926 California agricultural employers perceived the Mexicans as a necessary source of labor. When it was proposed in that year and again in 1928 and 1930 to place Mexico under quota restrictions because of the heavy post-1923 immigration, they joined the forces lobbying for unrestricted immigration. Representatives from the California Farm Bureau Federation, Chamber of Commerce, Grange, Agricultural Legislative Committee of California (representing approximately forty growers organizations), the Vegetable Growers of the Imperial Valley, and other groups presented their case in Washington. None of the bills passed. It is noteworthy that California employers were seriously involved in the issue. However, in March 1929 Mexican immigration was reduced by administrative restriction and in the next few years a combination of lack of opportunity in the United States and a repatriation program led to an outflux of Mexicans. Nonetheless, many Mexicans had made California their permanent home, staying on to work in agriculture.[65]

A similar immigration pattern was followed by Filipinos. Their numbers increased in California by about 28,000 in the 1920s. Like the Mexicans, they were unaffected by immigration quotas—until 1934 when the Philippines was granted provisional independence and placed under a quota. Filipinos became prominent in the asparagus fields in the delta, in the lettuce fields of the Salinas Valley, and in certain grape areas, but they generally were not favored by California farm employers. Apparently they evoked great racial prejudice. The administrative restriction on Mexicans in 1929 might have advanced the Filipinos position had it not been followed so quickly by the Depression, when many Filipinos also returned to their own country, sometimes being repatriated at U.S. government expense.[66]

The attraction of the Mexican is well described in a 1928 study published in the State report *Mexicans in California.* Questionnaires returned from 1,395 farmers, 145 Farm Bureau farm centers, 55 Chambers of Commerce, 27 Horticultual Commissions, along with field study led to the conclusion that

> He [the Mexican] is today a principal source of farm labor in California. He does tasks that white workers will not or can not do. He works under climatic and working conditions, such as excessive heat, dust, isolation, and temporary employment; conditions that are often too trying for white workers. He will work in gangs. He will work under direction, taking orders and suggestions.[67]

These are virtually the same advantages that Nordhoff attributed to the Chinese in 1872 (see pages 63-64). Like the Chinese, Mexicans were hired through intermediary contractors who relieved employers of the burden of having to deal separately with individuals. They also accepted low wages. In the state study they were found to earn $.23 per day and $.016 per hour less than whites; no other group in the labor force had wages that much lower than whites.[68]

One other point brought out about the Mexicans in other sections of the report was that they were becoming a major burden on urban relief agencies. Growers claimed that the agricultural workers were "homers" and returned to Mexico in the off-season, but this was clearly untrue.[69] Growers were in a sense subsidized by the government, which picked up the tab for the poverty resulting from insufficient employment and inadequate wages. This was the first official mention of the relationship between relief agencies and agricultural wages; other facets of this relationship were to become important in the next decade.

Fuller claims that while the presence of the Mexicans helped assure an abundance of labor, their presence was not crucial and there would have been an adequate supply without them.[70] Suitable information to decide this point is not available. What does seem clear is that both by accepting low wages and by contributing to, if not causing, oversupply, Mexicans (and Filipinos to a much lesser degree) helped maintain low wage levels. It is also likely that at such wages, there was a shortage of other workers.

Unfortunately for growers, the famed docility of the Mexicans began to dissipate in the late 1920s and early 1930s when they became involved in union and strike activity. Soon a less restive element came to dominate the labor supply: the white migrants who began to drift into California after 1929. It is estimated that during the 1929-1939 period some 1.1 million persons migrated to California. The bulk of this influx (60.5 percent) occurred between 1935 and 1938. Over 60 percent of these people settled in urban areas, only 19.3 percent of them were located in the Central Valley. Of those in the Central Valley, around 58,000 were agricultural laborers in 1939.[71] Not all of these were harvest workers, but with a seasonal peak somewhere between 145,000 and 225,000, it is apparent that the migrants were an important part of the labor force and that they contributed to the oversupply of labor prevailing throughout the decade.

Worker Activity—1920s and 1930s

The 1920s, until 1928, had been devoid of labor turmoil. What Jamieson refers to as "the modern period of labor unionism in agriculture" began in 1927 when Mexicans first began to organize into unions.[72] These combined in the next year to form the Confederación de Uniones Obreras Mexicanas (CUOM), which propagated further locals. Grievances covered a wide range of issues, such as wages, working conditions, and the multifarious inequities related to the contract labor system. The union's existence was first felt in the 1928 Imperial Valley strike. The strike ended with some concessions to the workers, although these did not include union recognition. The growers were unenthused about unions. However, they soon had more to contend with: in 1930 several spontaneous strikes occurred in the Imperial Valley and the Communist Party's recently established Trade Union Unity League (TUUL) stepped in to organize, creating the Agricultural Workers Industrial League (AWIL). The strikes were lost and a number of organizers were placed on trial charged with violation of the Criminal Syndicalism Act. This was the first use of the act against farm organizers.[73]

From 1930 through 1932, eleven strikes occurred and AWIL was involved in five of these. When leading the Santa Clara strike, it was transformed into the Cannery and Agricultural Workers Industrial Union (CAWIU), a somewhat misleading name as this was the only cannery activity in which it participated. CAWIU was a prime mover in the 1933 labor explosion. Thirty-one strikes occurred in that year and CAWIU led twenty-five of them. Of these, twenty-one resulted in partial wage increases while four were lost; of the others, half were won and half lost. The CAWIU-led cotton strike was the largest of the year, involving 20,000 workers. It was notorious because it was the first time that American workers received public relief from a United States agency while on strike.[74] The State Emergency Relief Agency (SERA) refused to throw workers off the relief roles as the growers demanded. Although relief agencies were expected by growers to support workers during the off-season, they apparently were not to serve workers during the on-season. The conflict between growers and relief agencies went on through the decade until growers prevailed. How this happened will be discussed below.

CAWIU was officially terminated in 1935 when TUUL, its parent body, and all TUUL affiliates were dissolved by the Communist Party with the intention of merging with or joining the AFL. CAWIU had actually died in 1934 when the newly formed Associated Farmers (AF) rose to the growers' defense. By vigilante activity "in the field" a number of strikes were broken. But most effective was the prosecution of CAWIU leaders under the Criminal Syndicalism Law; eight were convicted in 1935 and these convictions were not reversed until 1937. The Associated Farmers were deeply involved in the case, spending $13,780 to help secure conviction.[75] Despite its ignominious end, CAWIU

> ... was not without lasting effect on agricultural labor in California. Wages were raised in all the major growing areas of the state as a result of the upsurge in 1933, and they never again fell to the low levels of late 1932.[76]

CAWIU was not replaced by any comparable organization. The Congress of Industrial Organizations (CIO) created United Cannery, Agricultural, Packing, and Allied Workers of America (UCAPAWA) in 1937, but this was not particularly successful and in the intervening years neither the AFL nor any other group attempted major organizing in the fields.

Two major problems faced labor organizers in these post-CAWIU years: Okie apathy and grower organizations. UCAPAWA was unable to enroll the Okies for

> These dispossessed, worn-out victims of the agricultural revolution were not soldiers in the army of social equality. Because of their background and their misery, they were pliable, exploitable, too desperate even to attempt what the Mexicans had accomplished in

1933 and 1934. And, rural Americans that they were, their ideologies conformed, not conflicted, with the ideologies of their exploiters.[77]

A sign of UCAPAWA weakness is that while there were major strikes after 1937, many were wildcat strikes completely unrelated to union activities. Although the union tried to capitalize on these strikes, it could not get anywhere. In 1940 UCAPAWA gave up on field workers and moved into the packing sheds and processing plants. The only union that was able to succeed in the post-CAWIU years was FALA (originally, Filipino Agricultural Labor Association, later renamed Federated Agricultural Labor Association). Composed almost entirely of Filipino workers (who, it should be remembered completely dominated certain crops), it not only won strikes but also gained union recognition. FALA became inactive after many of its members went into the armed services following Pearl Harbor.[78] In general, there was little labor agitation during World War II and no union activity.

Grower Activity — 1920s and 1930s

Following upon World War I labor shortages and the first signs of labor militancy before and after the war, employers began to band together to set uniform wages, recruit and distribute labor. One of the first such groups was the Valley Fruit Growers of San Joaquin, formed in 1917. By 1921 this association was able to have their wage scale adopted locally. A similar organization was the Agricultural Labor Bureau of the San Joaquin Valley, formed in 1926 under the auspices of six Farm Bureau centers, six local chambers of commerce and the raisin, fruit, and cotton industries. In subsequent years, the combined activity of marketing associations, farm bureaus, chambers of commerce, and the new labor-oriented organizations meant that most crops and areas in the state were covered by some sort of employer group.[79]

By and large, these organizations did not deal directly with labor unrest. This task was handled by an organization created for that express purpose, namely, the Associated Farmers (AF).* The Associated Farmers was formed in the fall of 1933 by the Agricultural Labor Subcommittee of the State Chamber of Commerce. This committee included the president of the State Chamber of Commerce, the president of the Farm Bureau Federation and representatives from PG&E, Southern Pacific Railroad, Calpak, and Bank of America. The committee arranged for the financing of the AF and it is apparent from the sources of its support whose interests it served. The major contributors included large growers, packers, processors, railroads, banks, marketing cooperatives, utilities, and oil companies. One processor-producer, Calpak, solicited approximately 42 percent of the total funds raised by the AF from 1934 through 1939. Some of the diversity of sources can be explained by the desire to maintain the goodwill of Calpak, an

---

*Several smaller organizations acted in concert with the AF, but the AF was the real leader in this regard.

important customer. The La Follette Committee suggested other possible motives, pointing out that processors might have had an interest in using the AF to handle their own labor disputes. Railroads, utilities, and banks had an indirect interest in keeping wages low. If they went up, farmers might agitate for lower transportation, utility, and interest rates, and business might drop off.[80] Overall, the backing of the AF indicates how much large farm employers were tied up with nonfarm interests.

The Associated Farmers first task was to break CAWIU. As indicated above, they were successful. With this accomplished, the AF became quiescent until increasing labor unrest in 1936. The AF became notorious for extralegal, violent methods of breaking strikes. The AF also became interested in California's relief policy. From 1933 to 1935 the Federal Emergency Relief Administration (FERA) controlled relief and its monies were handled in California by the State Emergency Relief Administration (SERA). In late 1935 control was returned to the state, the State Relief Administration (SRA) was created, and Harold Pomeroy was made director, which he remained as until 1938 when Olson became governor.*

Since FERA money was contingent upon the state following FERA policies, from 1933 to 1935 SERA was forced to give relief solely on the basis of need. If clients were needy because they were on strike, this was regarded as irrelevant and they were still entitled to relief. It was under this policy that strikers were aided in the 1933 cotton strike. Things changed under the SRA. During the Pomeroy years recipients were thrown off relief if agricultural work was being offered at the "prevailing wage," whether or not a strike was occurring. Since the prevailing wage was usually that fixed by the growers labor organizations, this policy meant that relief clients were forced to become strikebreakers.[82]

Because relief frequently paid more than the growers were prepared to pay, the policy of the Pomeroy years was essential if growers were to be able to fix wages at the level they desired. Stanley Faustman concludes, unsurprisingly, that the AF, with some support from the State Chamber of Commerce and the Farm Bureau, was largely responsible for the SRA having this happy policy. After 1939 Olson appointees changed the policy to eviction from the relief roles only for work offered at a "fair wage," as determined by the SRA. This usually was close to what strikers were demanding. The Olson policy lasted only until 1941. In that year the AF campaign to return relief to the counties succeeded. Relief would then be handled by the county boards of supervisors who were "often under the complete domination of farm employer groups."[83] However, by 1941 California was in the midst of the war boom and the migrant relief problem was rapidly fading.

One last grower activity of the 1930s was the lobbying of the Agricultural Producers Labor Committee. This association was composed of leaders in the citrus and vegetable industries and was supported by the AF, the

*Pomeroy went on to become Executive Secretary of the AF in 1939.[81]

agricultural committee of the Los Angeles Chamber of Commerce, and other such organizations. Its purpose was to prevent any extension of the such legislation as the National Labor Relations Act, Social Security Act, and Federal Labor Standards Act to agricultural employees.[84] California employers were not the only ones working towards that end and the programs were not extended.

World War II

After Pearl Harbor, the labor situation changed dramatically. Okies and other laborers went off into the armed services or into higher paying defense jobs. Growers faced labor shortages and high wages. In many cases, they contributed to their own undoing by bidding up wages in attempts to secure labor. The federal government initiated two programs to relieve this situation, a farm wage stabilization program and the Bracero program. In the fall of 1942, the federal government established wartime wage and price controls, which covered most areas of the economy. Agricultural workers were not included because their wage rates were recognized as substandard. Nevertheless, in 1943 the California Asparagus Growers Association requested that maximum wages be established in their industry. This request was granted in March 1943 by the War Food Administration. Ceiling rates were established for various jobs, and provisions were made to handle violators. This program was so successful that other growers throughout the nation asked for ceilings on their wages.[85]

In California, the number of ceilings in effect rose from 4 in 1943, to 20 in 1944, and 28 in 1945 and 1946; these programs created 25 ceiling rates in 1943, 102 ceilings in 1944, 146 in 1945, and 149 in 1946. On November 9, 1946 all wartime controls on agricultural wages and salaries were lifted. The program did inspire some initial grower opposition as they feared no longer being able to bid scarce labor away from other growers. This concern faded as, by and large, the program served them well. A question is how well it served the workers. The procedure for establishing a ceiling called for worker participation during initial hearings to investigate the situation and on committees in charge of individual adjustments. Actual worker involvement was rare. Usually growers or representatives of county agricultural agencies, who were used to acting with the growers, dominated the scene and workers made only token appearances.[86] Furthermore, the body that administered the program, the State Wage Board, did not include any worker representatives on the grounds that:

> . . . it would be a practical impossibility to find representative farm workers who could attend all meetings of the Board. And, that although labor union officials might be willing to take over the job of representation, they lack the technical background necessary to be very helpful in determining what the ceiling rates for specific agricultural operations should be.[87]

Instead its members were "public officials whose experience and background have been that of rendering efficient service to growers. They had little or no background in promoting the interests of agricultural workers."[88]

Wage stabilization was not a complete answer to problems of labor scarcity, so growers pressured for importation of Mexicans. In response to exertions of California sugar beet growers, a committee was formed in 1942 by the Immigration Service to study the agricultural labor situation. The committee was composed of representatives from many branches of the government and they consulted with both employers and representatives of organized labor while drawing up their plan to recruit Mexican labor.[89] In June 1942 negotiations were begun with Mexico and these resulted in July with the Mexican Farm Labor Agreement. The agreement was amended several times between 1942 and 1947, but the basic plan remained the same. This agreement, although financed by Congressional appropriations, was never enacted by Congress. It was intended that the program, like wage stabilization, would end when the war was over. This did not happen (post-World War II history will be discussed in the next chapter). The agreement provided that:

> Mexican workers were not to be used to displace domestic workers but only fill proved shortages. Recruits were to be exempted from military service and discrimination against them was not to be permitted. The round trip transportation expenses of the worker were guaranteed, as well as living expenses en route. Hiring was to be done on the basis of a written contract between the worker and his employer and the work was to be exclusively in agriculture. Braceros were to be free to buy merchandise in places of their own choice. Housing and sanitary conditions were to be adequate. Deductions amounting to 10 per cent of earnings were authorized for deposit in a savings fund payable to the worker on his return to Mexico. Work was guaranteed for three-quarters of the duration of the contract. Wages were to be equal to those prevailing in the area of employment, but in any case not less than 30 cents per hour.[90]

The employer referred to in the agreement was not the grower but the United States government; the grower subcontracted from the government. The program was to be administered by both nations; in the United States the Department of Agriculture was the agency with primary responsibility and within the Department, the FSA actually administered the program.

Several features of the program were changed in directions favorable to growers over the next few years. Originally, the United States government was to be reimbursed for transportation costs by the growers; in 1943 they were freed from this obligation. More important was wresting administration of the program away from the FSA; in 1943 the War Manpower Commission took over. The FSA was never popular with growers. Its labor camp policies in the 1930s reflected a concern for improving the lot of farm workers that was to be its undoing. It was destroyed by 1946. Loss of the Bracero program was but one step along the way. In 1943 the task of determining the prevailing wage was given to the Agricultural Extension Service. The Extension Service was likely to accept growers decisions about wages. Throughout the war, braceros provided roughly 15 to 20 percent of California's seasonal labor needs.[91] Their importance is not reflected by their numbers. Not only were serious shortages avoided but the availability of this labor force at the prevailing wage kept wages in line.

Between 1942 and 1945 the federal government spent approximately $55 million on the Bracero program. California growers (as well as those in other states) got the labor they needed at the wages they wanted to pay. Between 1943 and 1947 braceros were estimated to have earned $205 million.[92] Perhaps agriculture could have successfully competed for labor, had the government money been used to subsidize wages directly instead of preserving the existing pattern of farm employment.

Mechanization

Another approach to the "labor problem" is to banish it altogether by replacing people with machines. For most of California's intensive crops this was not yet possible. But advances were made with some field crops. Rice, hay, dry beans, and sugar beet harvests were all mechanized by the end of World War II. Mechanization of the rice harvest was accomplished in the late 1920s and 1930s; a good mower was available for alfalfa harvesting by 1930; a good combine for bean harvests was developed in 1937 and 1938; and work on sugar beet mechanization, begun in 1931, made such progress that by the end of World War II the harvest was totally mechanized.[93]

A significant feature of these developments was the involvement of the Agricultural Experiment Station. While not alone responsible for these advances, it played an important role. This orientation would become increasingly important after World War II, when mechanization was finally extended to intensive crops. The Agricultural Experiment Station became a research institute in the service of large producers and related interests. In a 1947 publication describing the role of the station, there was no mention of any research geared towards the problems of the workers.[94]

Summary of Landownership, 1918-1945

There is no adequate source of information about the large holdings existing at the end of this period. I have compiled a list (Table 3.6) of 78 owners of holdings larger than 2,000 acres by combining information from the La Follette hearings, the standard financial manuals (Moody's and Walker's), and a study made by the Bureau of Reclamation of the Central Valley Project service areas. The nature of the data does not permit a county breakdown. The entries marked with an asterisk (*) are for 1939; the information comes from the La Follette hearings and is included because updated numbers are not available elsewhere and it is known that the holdings still existed in 1945. Two specific entries should be mentioned: the

TABLE 3.6
Large Landowners, 1945/46

Owner	Acreage
Adohr Milk	3,100*
American Crystal Sugar	11,485
American Fruit Growers	2,472*
Anderson Clayton	19,144
Arakelian, K.	2,430
Bacan, J. L.	3,840
Balfour Guthrie Inc.	8,535
Belridge Oil Co.	30,120
Boston Investment Co.	5,916
Bragg, T. & V.	6,079
California Delta Farms	3,260
Calpak	20,094
Camp West Lowe Ginning Co.	5,199
Capital Co.	103,232
Carmel Cattle Co.	3,347
Chatom Co.	2,832
Di Giorgio	16,869
Diamond Ranch	53,000
Flannagan, Ray	5,665
Fullerton Oil Co.	2,480
Gibson, J. F.	12,517
Hamburg, Sam	6,000
Hammonds Ranch Co.	5,102
Hampel, C. *et al.*	2,560
Holly Sugar	6,500*
Honolulu Oil Co.	4,250
Hotchkiss Estate Co.	7,550
Houchin Co.	5,435
Irvine	90,000
J. G. Boswell	16,776
Karpe, A. M.	5,950
Kerman Cattle Co.	7,981
Kern County Land Co.	409,766
Kings County Development Co.	11,371
Klipstein & Rudnick	3,960
La Hacienda Co.	3,190
Libby, McNeill, Libby	5,130*
Marblehead Land Co.	12,000
McAuley & Montgomery	2,207
Melga Co.	6,626
Midway Oil Co.	9,932
Natomas Co.	73,919
Newhall Land and Farming Co.	84,000
Occidental Land & Development	5,650
Ohio Oil Co.	2,321
Pacific States Savings & Loan Assn.	25,600
Perelli Minetti & Sons	2,111
Richfield Oil Co.	12,648
River Farms	14,000
Rowan, R. A.	2,033
S. A. Garrard	3,405*

TABLE 3.6 (continued)
Large Landowners, 1945/46

Owner	Acreage
Sacramento Valley Colony Co.	2,800
Salyer, E. C.	7,238
Sam Emidio Rancho	15,660
Sawyer, William Jr.	10,240
Schenley	3,873
Shell Oil Co.	17,860
Shoreland Properties.	13,000
Simon Newman	9,813
Smith, Bryan	3,680
South Lake Farms	19,317
Southern Pacific	4,005,840*
Spreckels Sugar Co.	14,800*
Standard Oil Co.	293,192
Sutter Basin Co.	16,587
Sutter Buttes Co.	6,044
Tejon Ranch	300,000
Tidewater Associated Oil Co.	25,554
Tulare Lake Land Co.	12,052
Union Oil Co.	2,700
Union Sugar Co.	12,712
Valley Agricultural Co.	3,658
Van Glahn Land Co.	21,580
West Lake Farms	7,209
Weyl-Zuckerman Co.	2,704
Wishon-Watson Co.	2,016
Yuba Consolidated Gold Fields	19,591
TOTAL	6,019,309

Note: Entries marked with an asterisk (*)
are for 1939.

Newhall Land and Farming and the Irvine holdings. I have estimated the size of these holdings. The Newhall estimate is based on the information in its 1970 annual report about the year of acquisition of its holdings. The Irvine holding has decreased in size some 8,000 acres between 1918 and the present; I have split the difference to arrive at the 1945 estimate.

These 78 owners held 6 million acres. In 1916/17, 802 owners held 11.5 million acres. These figures are not easily compared for four reasons: (1) it is impossible to estimate what proportion of the actual number and extent of large holdings they represent; (2) the number of owners is inflated in the 1916/17 figures because holdings scattered through several counties are counted once for each county; (3) almost all landholdings listed here are known to have been at least partly in agricultural use, while the 1916/17 information referred to all large landholdings; and (4) the counties covered by the 1916/17 figures do not include three counties in which that state's largest landowner, the railroad, owned 1.1 million acres in 1939. It is not possible to compensate for the first three problems so as to arrive at comparable numbers. The last problem can be avoided by dropping the railroad from consideration. This should be done anyway because the size of its holding obscures any sense of what was happening with other large landowners.

A conservative estimate of the size of the railroad holding in 1917 is 4.5 million acres. This is the 1939 total plus the sale to Standard Oil plus a meager allowance for other sales (sales were being made throughout this period). Allowing that the railroad was counted at least twelve times in the 1916/17 figures, this means that 77 owners accounted for 2 million acres in 1945 and 790 owners held 7 million acres in 1916/17. The fact that large holdings covering 2 million acres could be discovered from financial manuals and a survey of only 2.3 million acres, while a rather thorough survey of thirty-three counties in 1916/17 turned up 7 million acres in large holdings is a strong indicator that concentration of ownership was increasing. This supports information about new holdings presented earlier in this chapter. Thus, I conclude that concentration of landownership rose between 1918 and 1945.

Summary and Conclusions

During the 1918-1945 period California agriculture completed its transition from an agriculture dominated by extensive products to one dominated by intensive products. Previously, intensive crops were associated with subdivision into small holdings, while extensive uses were associated with large holdings. The extensive uses—livestock, grains, sugar beets, and so on—continued to be associated with large holdings. That is, large operators had a decisive competitive advantage over small farmers in these relatively low-valued crops. This was the case even though some operators fell upon troubled times. Livestock holdings were particularly problematic. The largest one was broken up and several of the biggest were kept intact only because of mineral discoveries. Nonetheless, land concentration increased in the period between the wars. The big change in this period was that large holdings were converted to intensive, irrigated crops, cotton (a new field crop), as well fruits, nuts and vegetables. Large holdings devoted to cotton, typically in the west and south of the San Joaquin Valley, were converted from other field crops or grazing, and were now irrigated from deep wells. The cost of the latter militated against small landowners becoming cotton producers.

In the previous period large orchards and vineyards were rare because prices did not warrant the costs of development; large owners were better off selling or using the land extensively. Although low prices were a problem during much of this period, large specialty-crop holdings were formed. During the early 1920s, the marketing of specialty crops had become more orderly, new markets were being developed and in general optimism was high. Many orchards and vineyards were planted. Later, when the Depression hit agriculture, the accumulation of debt led to transfers of already developed land, thus opening up another avenue to the formation of large holdings. The problem of costs of development was thereby alleviated. Also relevant was diversification of land use, sometimes accompanied by creation of holdings comprised of discontiguous, scattered parcels.

Another important development in this period was the general economic movement towards concentration of control among shippers, processors, and distributors of California products. A small number of them became dominant and they exerted control over production by financing farmers and/or going into production.

Farmers had to face the problem of low prices in the 1920s and especially in the 1930s. The problem of marketing was therefore keenly felt. One response was to increase the number of marketing cooperatives. Some became quite powerful; the California Fruit Growers Exchange, for example, dominated the distribution of citrus. A number of other organizations concerned with agriculture came into being. The concentration of control in the agriculturally linked industries, along with the increase in large landowners and large producers was reflected in these organizations. Large-scale interests were dominant in the highly influential California Farm Bureau Federation and the California Chamber of Commerce.

Neither the marketing cooperatives nor these new organizations could ameliorate prices sufficiently, however, so in 1933 the federal government initiated a number of programs with this goal. Thanks to their organization, California producers were able to have some effect on federal policies. Most federal programs concerned the basic commodities (grains, cotton, tobacco, and dairy products). The California Farm Bureau was able to secure the creation of the marketing order program to serve specialty crops. Federal programs did not specifically favor large-scale producers, but such producers were able to obtain the greatest benefits simply by virtue of their size. This was most apparent in cotton. Another Farm Bureau achievement was the California Prorate Act, also aimed at specialty crops. Claims that this program served large growers best have not been substantiated.

The dominance of irrigated crops required further water development, principally by local districts and private pumping but the apparatus was being developed for overcoming the limits of strictly local efforts i.e. the Boulder Canyon Project was built for the Imperial Valley and the Central Valley Project for the San Joaquin Valley. Among the greatest beneficiaries were the large cotton producers relying on wells. The project would recharge the ground water as well as providing surface supplies of water. Small farmers of course were also prospective beneficiaries. Although the projects only began to deliver water at the end of this period, two issues surfaced as contentious. The first was the amount of project costs which would be irrigators responsibility to repay. This determined the cost of water and was important for large farmers as it also determined what was economically feasible to produce; in particular, if the extensive uses so easily conducted on a large scale would still be possible, cheap water was necessary.

The second issue was the Bureau of Reclamation's limitation on the maximum amount of land in a single ownership that could receive project water. Large owners initiated a number of unsuccessful campaigns to get rid of this restriction. Large owners in the Imperial Valley were able to secure exemption from the acreage limitation.

Intensive agriculture required sufficient low cost labor. Labor issues evoked the most grower activity of the period. Until World War II there was an excess of labor, wages were kept low, working conditions were poor, and there was worker unrest and attempts at unionization. The growers' major concern was to achieve a large supply of docile workers. Wages could then be kept low. A large number of readily available workers insured rapid, thorough harvests that gave the growers maximum control over marketing their product by allowing them to wait until marketing conditions were most favorable and harvesting crops quickly to exploit their advantage. All growers could benefit from this situation but large growers had the most to gain. Marketing considerations are much more important when a large crop is to be marketed, especially with respect to fresh produce. Thus, much of the grower action involved organizations dominated by large growers.

Grower activity occurred in three areas: wage setting, lobbying for Mexican nationals, and strike breaking. A number of grower organizations whose primary purpose was to fix wages were formed in the 1920s. These organizations were fairly successful at setting wages. They and the Farm Bureau, Chamber of Commerce, and other organizations were also involved in lobbying for immigration laws permitting Mexicans to work in California fields. Throughout the 1920s and early 1930s Mexicans were allowed to work in California agriculture and their presence contributed to the labor oversupply existing in those years. In the 1930s, displaced farmers from other parts of the U.S. flocked to California, helping to assure continued oversupply of labor. Mexicans were no longer needed or allowed in. In the late 1920s, the Mexicans first attempted to organize into unions. This activity continued through the 1930s. Strikes and labor unrest were rampant. The large grower interests formed the Associated Farmers to break all attempts at unionization; in the second half of the 1930s the AF was quite successful. Other organizations worked toward preventing agricultural workers from obtaining the same protections other workers were granted by new legislation.

World War II brought an end to the oversupply of labor. Growers were able to prevent workers from deriving any gains from this situation by using two federal programs created at grower behest. These were the Wage Stabilization Program, which placed ceilings on agricultural wages, and the Bracero program, which provided for importing Mexican nationals to work in the fields again. Growers also came to recognize that the ideal way to achieve the desired labor was to mechanize their harvests. Despite much work in this direction, however, little was accomplished in this period.

In sum, the important thing in the growing domination of California agriculture by large-scale producers was not so much overt discrimination against small farmers and for large ones, but merely that conditions were secured for intensive development, and hence higher profitability, on large holdings. Water supply, labor supply, markets, price stabilization and so on were all expanded and/or improved. This was achieved through collective action, involving both private associations and government intervention. Large growers took the lead in this political action, in alliance with large agriculturally linked interests and small farmers, as necessary. While the latter's interests were frequently served in the short run, it should be pointed out that the entrance of large operators into intensive crop production boded ill for for the long-run survival of the small producers, for the competitive advantage of large-scale operators over small in extensive field crops and livestock was being extended to intensive crops.

At the end of this period California agriculture was becoming dominated by large-scale producers and large interests in the agriculturally linked industries. The next chapter examines the continued movement towards concentration of landholdings in the post World War II period and the developments in production, marketing, prices, water, and labor that made this movement possible.

Notes

1. California Department of Agriculture (March 1943), passim.
2. Lawrence (1933), p. 170 for mortgage; *Walker's Manual of Pacific Coast Securities* for the years 1930 and 1940, for land in those years; United States Senate, Committee on Public Lands (1947), p. 172 for 1945.
3. United States Senate, Committee on Public Lands (1947), p. 172.
4. Newhall (1958), p. 101 for Newhall Land Co.; United States Senate, Committee on Education and Labor (1940), p. 22775 for Adohr Farms.
5. Crowe (1957), p. 137 for Tejon Ranch; Newhall (1958), p. 91 for Newhall Land Company; *Walker's Manual of Pacific Coast Securities* for the year 1945, for Kern County Land Company.
6. United States Bureau of the Census (1922), p. 107; United States Bureau of the Census (1942), pp. 81, 86.
7. United States Senate, Committee on Education and Labor (1940) p. 22836 for sugar beets; *Walker's Manual of Pacific Coast Securities* for the year 1945, for Sacramento Valley companies; United States Bureau of Reclamation (1946), p. 20 for Imperial Valley.
8. California Board of Agriculture (1921), pp. 119-21; Johnston and Dean (1969), p. 110.
9. Metzler (1944), p. 8.
10. United States Senate, Committee on Public Lands (1947), p. 14.
11. Metzler (1944), p. 11.
12. Johnston and Dean (1969), pp. 6-51 passim.
13. Prices from California Crop and Livestock Reporting Service (1951); delta from Thompson (1957), pp. 313-16; other information Johnston and Dean (1969), pp. 54-96 passim.
14. Frozen foods from Williams (1970), pp. 8, 10, 29; Consumption from USDA (1958), vol. 5, pp. 32-36.
15. Irvine from Williamson (1940), p. 21; El Solyo from Street (1955), p. 10; Gallo from *Walker's Manual of Pacific Coast Securities* for the year 1945.
16. United States Senate, Committee on Education and Labor (1940) pp. 17714-15,

22789.
17. Adams and Smith (1941), p. 75.
18. Limoneira from Williamson (1940), p. 15. *Walker's Manual of Pacific Coast Securities* for the years 1930, 1935, 1940, for all others.
19. Farm Mortgage Debt from *Agricultural Finance Review*, Vol. 1-9 (1938-1946) passim.
20. Benedict (1955), p. 49.
21. Discussion of the Federal Land Bank and Land Bank Commission follows Murray (1953), pp. 258-86.
22. United States Department of Agriculture, Bureau of Agricultural Economics (1939a), p. 6.
23. United States Department of Agriculture, Bureau of Agricultural Economics, *Agricultural Finance Review*, Vol. 8, July 1, 1945, p. 81.
24. James (1954), pp. 263, 264, 394.
25. James (1954), p. 395 for 1929, 1936; *Walker's Manual of Pacific Coast Securities* for the year 1946, for 1945; United States Senate, Committee on Education and Labor (1940) p. 22777 for 1939, pp. 22778-79 for sales policy, p. 22781 for Calpak.
26. All information from *Walker's Manual of Pacific Coast Securities* for the years 1930, 1935, 1940, 1945, under the named corporations or in the section of discontinued listings.
27. American Institute of Cooperatives (1945) for 1944; Morrison (1939) for other years.
28. United States Senate, Committee on Education and Labor (1941), p. 417.
29. Galarza (1964), p. 38.
30. United States Senate, Committee on Education and Labor (1941), p. 410.
31. Ibid., pp. 414, 650.
32. Tetreau (1933), p. 8.
33. Ibid., p. 3; Chambers (1952), pp. 207, 208.
34. Ibid., p. 29.
35. Cotton from United States Senate, Committee on Education and Labor (1941), p. 279. United States Federal Trade Commission (1938), pp. 91-92, 95, 129-30, 138-39 includes other information and further examples not mentioned in the text.
36. Tweeten (1970), p. 300.
37. Chambers (1952), p. 133.
38. Crouch and McHenry (1949), pp. 285, 287 for history of act; Chambers (1952), p. 139 for conclusions about act; "Look Into Prorate" (February 1939), for hysteria.
39. United States Bureau of the Census (1920), p. 3-3 is a summary table for 1919-1950.
40. Montgomery and Clawson (1946), p. 21.
41. Ibid., pp. 21-37 passim.
42. Ibid., p. 51.
43. Ibid., pp. 54, 61.
44. United States House of Representatives, Committee on Interior and Insular Affairs (1956), p. 569; Montgomery and Clawson (1946), p. 87.
45. United States Bureau of Reclamation (1945), p. 165.
46. Montgomery and Clawson (1946), pp. 34, 44.
47. United States Bureau of the Census (1942), pp. 81, 86.
48. Goltże (1961), pp. 106-7.
49. Montgomery and Clawson (1946), p. 132.
50. Ibid., p. 143.
51. Montgomery and Clawson (1946), p. 155.
52. United States Senate, Committee on Public Lands (1947), pp. 35-41 describe these surveys and tabulate the results.
53. California State Chamber of Commerce (1943), p. 4.
54. Montgomery and Clawson (1946), pp. 157, 164-71.
55. Ibid.

56. Unites States House of Representatives, Committee on Interior and Insular Affairs (1957), pp. 688, 689.

57. Taylor (1964), p. 1008.

58. United States Bureau of Reclamation (1946), pp. 22, 26; Southern Pacific land for 1917 from California Commission of Immigration and Housing (1919), p. 12; Southern Pacific for 1939 from United States Senate, Committee on Education and Public Welfare (1940), p. 22798.

59. Hundley (1975), p. 5 for the compact; Goltze (1961), p. 106 about the project; Taylor (1975), p. 8 for Wilbur and Ickes.

60. Adams (1938) p. 25 for 1935; California State Reconstruction and Reemployment Commission (1947), p. 9 for 1945.

61. For USDA estimates see USDA *Cooperative Crops and Marketing Services* (July 1942), pp. 148-55 which tabulate the series from 1866 through 1942; 1943, 1944, 1945 are from the quarterly issues of those years; for wages see United States Senate, Committee on Education and Labor (1940), p. 22516.

62. United States Senate, Committee on Education and Labor (1941), pp. 337-38.

63. United States Senate, Committee on Education and Labor (1940), p. 22329.

64. Fuller (1934), pp. 224, 249, 250.

65. Ibid., pp. 229, 238.

66. Schwartz (1945), p. 60.

67. California State Mexican Fact-Finding Commission (1930), p. 171.

68. Ibid., p. 170.

69. McWilliams (1971), p. 127.

70. Fuller (1934), p. 284.

71. United States Department of Agriculture, Bureau of Agricultural Economics (1941a), no pagination.

72. Jamieson (1943), p. 41.

73. California State Mexican Fact-Finding Commission (1930), p. 123; Jamieson (1943), pp. 199-201.

74. Jamieson (1943), pp. 220, 221, 228, 270.

75. Ibid., p. 298 for CAWIU demise; Chambers (1952), p. 108 for criminal syndicalism and AF.

76. Jamieson (1943), p. 298.

77. Stein (1973), p. 251.

78. Jamieson (1943), pp. 472-73 for UCAPAWA; Schwartz (1945), p. 100 for FALA.

79. Galarza (1964), p. 57.

80. Chambers (1952), p. 40; United States Senate, Committee on Education and Labor (1943), pp. 1175-77, 1179; United States Senate, Committee on Education and Labor (1941), p. 19; United States Senate, Committee on Education and Public Welfare (1941), p. 19; United States Senate, Committeee on Education and Public Welfare (1943), pp. 1175-1177.

81. Chambers (1952), p. 49.

82. Stein (1975), pp. 246-47.

83. Faustman (1942), pp. 207, 215, 246; quote from Chambers (1952), p. 92.

84. United States Senate, Committee on Education and Public Welfare (1941), p. 412.

85. Metzler (1946), pp. 1-8.

86. Holmaas (1950), pp. 56, 64 for number of ceilings; Metzler (1946), pp. 34-35 about worker participation.

87. Metzler (1946), p. 27.

88. Ibid., p. 35.

89. Rasmussen (1951), p. 201.

90. Galarza (1964), pp. 47-48.

91. Craig (1971), p. 47 about transportation; FSA from Wilcox (1947), pp. 89-90; immigration figures from Rasmussen (1951), p. 231.

92. Galarza (1964), p. 84 for federal expenses; Craig (1971), p. 46 for earnings.
93. Bainer (1975), pp. 58-63.
94. California State Reconstruction and Reemployment Commission (1947).

4

The Dominance of Agriculture by Large Owners (post-World War II)

Introduction

In the years since World War II, California agriculture has converted from partial to almost total reliance on irrigation. Production centers on specialty crops, livestock and feed crops, and certain crops that have been highly subsidized by the federal government. In the last chapter all of these uses were noted as either being or becoming associated with large holdings. These associations have been strengthened and landownership has become more concentrated in the post-World War II period. Many factors have contributed to this increase in large holdings. The most crucial of these has been the ability of large-scale producers to affect state and federal policies with respect to water, labor, and agricultural research. This influence, a carry-over from the last period, has been increasing.

The next section describes changes in crop patterns. This is followed by a section describing how large-scale producers have developed stronger ties to other economic interests. Then come two sections giving detailed accounts of water and labor developments, respectively. The present situation in large landholdings, based on a recent study undertaken by the author, is then described. A final section provides a chapter summary and conclusions. It should be assumed, unless stated otherwise, that all references in this chapter to existing large holdings are derived from the study presented at the end of this chapter. All references to the uses to which these holdings are put are derived from Villarejo (1980). Unless otherwise indicated, information about crop and livestock production presented in this chapter is derived from the various California Crop and Livestock Reporting Service reports listed in the bibliography.

Changes in Cropping Patterns

There have been four general trends in production since World War II: an increase in irrigated acreage, a decrease in the need for labor, a general increase in output and output per acre for almost all products, and a decrease in the number of farms. The situation with respect to water and labor can be summarized with a few statistics; detailed consideration will be left until later sections.

Between 1945 and 1974 the irrigated acreage increased 54 percent from 5 to 7.7 million acres. In 1974, 90 percent of the harvested cropland was irrigated, while in 1950 (information is not available for 1945) only 66 percent of the harvested cropland was irrigated. The increase in water supply derives mostly from the State Water Project and Central Valley Project. The number of seasonal workers used by California agriculture remained relatively constant until 1964 when the Bracero program ended. Since then the number of laborers required at peak harvest has fluctuated, but overall has declined by about one-quarter. It was estimated that 172,000 workers were needed in 1980. This decline reflects the successful mechanization of a number of harvests. Greater use of chemicals and development of nonharvest machinery have also contributed to lower labor requirements.[1]

Livestock, field crop, and specialty-crop productivity have all increased, thanks to greater use of irrigation, fertilizers, and development of higher-yielding varieties. Better feeds have also become available allowing stock yields to rise. California producers have been able, in the past thirty-five years, to increase production of vegetables some 350 percent and double field crop, fruit, nut, and cattle production.

Strong markets have also been a necessary factor in this expansion. State population has grown from 8 million to 23 million between 1945 and 1980, and per capita consumption of many products has increased. Even at present levels of production California needs to import livestock to meet local needs. But this is not the entire story, for national marketing efforts have allowed California producers to penetrate all corners of the country. Furthermore, crops such as cotton, rice, and sugar beets have been influenced, until the mid-1970s, by their ability to receive good prices, irrespective of demand, because of federal price supports. In the past few years, the world demand for cotton and rice has grown so much that producers no longer need federal aid. Specialty-crop producers have found new markets. The expansion of processing, frozen items in particular, has opened up markets for fruits and vegetables. Also, there has been a tendency for processors, distributors, and retailers to expand geographically; many are now international firms. Thus, producers are able to reach more consumers.

The acreage of harvested cropland has remained relatively constant since 1945. Yet the number of farms in California has almost halved and the average farm size has almost doubled.[2] This increase in farm size has been accompanied by an increase in the number of large holdings. One factor contributing to this increase has been urbanization and agricultural relocation. There are particular causes for the increase in the number of large holdings that are associated with different land uses. All of these will be discussed below. In this discussion the availability of cheap water and adequate labor will only be adverted to in passing.

Urbanization And Agricultural Relocation

Significant changes have occurred in the location of agricultural production. These will be discussed before embarking upon consideration of individual land uses so as to establish the context of other changes. Table 4.1 shows the acreage harvested in 1945 and 1974 in five major producing regions.

TABLE 4.1
Harvested Acreage in Five Major Producing
Regions, 1945 and 1974 (per thousand acres)

Region	1945	1974
Sacramento Valley	1,380	1,516
San Joaquin Valley	2,800	4,307
Central Coast	1,083	772
Southern California	798	384
Desert	764	741

Source: United States Bureau of the Census (1977), p. 1-1; United States Bureau of the Census (1961), pp. 3, 4.

Clearly, crop production was moving inland to the Central Valley. A similar pattern can be observed in livestock location. Table 4.2 shows the number of beef cattle and dairy cows in the same five regions for the years 1947 and 1980.

TABLE 4.2
Dairy and Beef Cattle Numbers,
1947 and 1980 (per thousand)

Region	1947	1980
Sacramento Valley	293	431
San Joaquin Valley	1,054	1,810
Central Coast	536	648
Southern California	349	204
Desert	175	901

Production has been moving into both the Central Valley and the desert area. These movements have encompassed a number of specific relocations. For example, the San Joaquin Valley now leads southern California in citrus orchards and the Sacramento Valley has replaced the Bay Area as the California's prune center. Southern California, where in 1945 there were some 60,000 acres in walnuts, now is almost completely devoid of walnut groves and has also sustained significant losses in vineyards. The milkshed for Los Angeles has moved from that county to San Bernardino and Riverside Counties.

These changes reflect two developments: that most of the expansion of irrigation occurred in the Central Valley and that much agricultural land was lost to urbanization, especially in the southern coastal region and the Bay Area. California's population increased by 15 million between 1945 and 1980. This growth was basically urban. Complaints about urban encroachment on agricultural land began to appear in the 1950s and have continued to appear ever since, the most recent being a 1980 report on the nine Bay Area counties.[3] Although it is possible for production to relocate, it is recognized that this does not compensate for loss of some of the best agricultural soils to subdividers. Farmers are helpless in this situation. Although they receive high prices for their land, they do not necessarily want to sell out (though many do). Because farmland at the urban fringe comes to be assessed at the value of the land for subdivision purposes, the property taxes rise to a level unsupportable by agriculture and force the farmers to sell.

In 1965 and 1966 California took two steps to provide farmers with relief from high property taxes. The Williamson Act, or Land Conservation Act (1965), provided that "owners of prime agricultural land could voluntarily enter into contracts with local governments and the state to keep their land in agricultural use for 10 years."[4] Under the terms of the contracts, the owners are protected from increased assessed values by compensatory payments from the state. Contracts are renewed annually for ten-year terms. Non-renewal means that the farmer cannot sell his land for nine years, during which time his assessment gradually rises to the true market value. The act also permits agreements, not subject to a legislatively determined time limit, to be made between counties and farmers who do not necessarily own prime agricultural land.[5] In 1968 Article 28 was added to the California Constitution. Article 28 is broader in its intent than the Williamson Act. It attempts to protect all open space lands by enabling the legislature to:

(1) define "open space lands," (2) specify enforceable use restrictions for recreation, enjoyment of scenic beauty, use of natural resources, or production of food or fibre, (3) provide criteria to determine when land is subject to such specified use restrictions, and (4) define the measure of value consistent with such use restrictions.[6]

Neither the act nor the amendment appear to have succeeded in saving cropland or farms. Furthermore, the major beneficiaries of agricultural conservation have not even been the farmers at the urban fringe. Instead, the biggest gains have gone to large landowners often located in remote areas. Table 4.3 shows the drop in assessed values (which is ultimately reflected in taxes) enjoyed in 1976 by six owners of large agricultural holdings (timberland owners have benefitted comparably but have been excluded here).

TABLE 4.3
Decrease in Assessed Land Value
for Six Large Landowners, 1976

Owner	Acreage in program	Decrease in assessment
J. G. Boswell	85,134	$2,163,800
Irvine Ranch Co.	48,722	18,607,080
Newhall Land and Farming Co.	44,231	2,002,080
Salyer Land Co.	36,442	1,902,805
Southern Pacific	111,239	8,785,712
Standard Oil Co.	66,663	1,965,575

Source: United States Senate, Committee on Energy and Natural Resources (1978), pp. 832-33.

Also, Tenneco and the Tejon Land Company each had 185,000 and 231,000 acres in the program in 1976. Information is not available about their assessment changes. Little of this land is in danger of catching a developer's eye. Newhall, for example, sold 14,000 acres of its land in the program in 1978 and this land remained in agricultural use. Typically, larger farmers were the ones able to relocate while smaller farmers gave up farming completely. Additionally, much of the land that came into production was already in large holdings and, as will be discussed below, it was often feasible to convert such holdings into large orchards and vineyards. Had the agricultural land conservation acts been more successful, this process could at least have been slowed up.

Livestock

California's population growth has resulted in a larger demand for dairy and meat products. It has been possible to meet the demand for dairy products without increasing the number of cows because milk production per cow has doubled since World War II. The demand for meat has mostly been met with beef and not lamb. Per capita beef consumption has been rising, while consumption of lamb and mutton has been falling. Hence, sheep have not been able to compete with cattle for range land or feedlots. Dairying, unlike meat production, has a limited direct impact on landownership. But dairy animals consume most of the alfalfa and hay produced in the state, besides consuming significant amounts of feed grains and feed concentrates.[7]

The beef cattle industry has undergone a revolution in production since the 1950s; it is now dominated by large-scale feedlot finishing. In 1962 the sixteen largest feedlots (those whose capacity was greater than 16,000 head of cattle) accounted for 34 percent of the cattle marketed. Ten years later there were thirty-three feedlots whose capacity was more than 16,000 head and they accounted for 60 percent of all cattle marketed. Of these feedlots, ten alone marketed 29 percent of the cattle.[8]

This reorientation of the cattle industry has had important repercussions. Many cattle companies have become involved in feed production and/or feedlot ownership. Crops used for animal feed include grain, hay and irrigated pasture, all easily grown and traditionally produced on a large scale. In 1975 it was estimated that 42 percent of the total water applied for agriculture was used to produce animal feed.[9] Thus, with the arrival of cheap water, cattle companies were able to become integrated beef producers, grazing cattle, growing their own cattle, and finishing the cattle. Previous chapters have stressed the importance of mineral production for large cattle holdings. The new ability to use the land for crops has increased agricultural profits and lessened reliance on oil income. Some large owners, as will be discussed below, were also growing other field and specialty crops, not just livestock feeds.

Table 4.4 lists some large holdings being used for livestock production. Those marked with a ''(g)'' also produce feed grains (because information is not complete, lack of such an indication should not be taken to mean that a large holding does not produce feed grains). Obviously, animal production is still associated with large holdings and, in fact, a number of these are familiar names: Newhall Land and Cattle Company, Hearst Corporation, Irvine Company, Tejon Ranch, and Tenneco (previously, Kern County Land Company). The integration of feed grain production is also obvious. Some, like Harris Farms, Tejon Ranch and Wolfsen Brothers both produce grains and own feedlots. Newhall has four feed processing plants.[10]

One name not in the table is that of Oppenheimer Industries. The Oppenheimer foray into land ownership was apparently the only impact, albeit a fleeting one, on land tenure from recent extensive tax-loss investments in the cattle industries. Administrative decisions made by the Treasury Department in 1915 and 1919 permitted farmers to deduct costs associated with growing animals. In 1951 capital gains treatment was conferred on income from livestock sales. Sometime in the mid 1960s investors began to avail themselves of the tax shelters to be found in feeding and breeding cattle, writing off the costs of developing them and then paying capital gains rates on any profits from subsequent sales.[11]

The attraction of these tax shelters reflected both the health of the beef industry and the nonagricultural factors responsible for the presence of the necessary investors. The Tax Reform Act of 1969 reduced benefits in breeding cattle but feeding was largely unaffected. In fact, in 1972 it was estimated that 60 percent of all cattle on feed in California were investor

TABLE 4.4
Large Holdings Used for Cattle

Owner	Acreage Owned
John Anderson (g)	35,211
Bidart Brothers	45,387
Buttonwillow Land & Cattle Co. (g)	13,832
California Land & Cattle Co.	34,363
Coit Ranch	17,977
Bert Crane	5,585
Richard Emigh (g)	3,300
Favier Brothers	16,852
Gallo	28,249
Harris Farms (g)	30,458
Hearst Corp.	115,075
Irvine Co. (g)	92,207
Mouren Farming Co.	10,186
Newhall Land & Farming Co. (g)	124,600
Noble Land & Cattle Co.	24,581
O'Neill Livestock	6,201
Parrott Ranch (g)	38,296
Roduner Cattle & Farming Co.	10,440
Roy Owens Estate	17,106
E. C. Rutherford	16,262
James Stevinson (g)	9,510
Tejon Ranch (g)	270,000
Tenneco (g)	260,710
Triangle T Ranch	14,361
William Urrutia	7,445
Vaquero Farms Inc	6,122
Douglas White	31,724
Wolfsen Brothers (g)	102,470

Note: Entries marked with (g) also produce feed grains.

owned. This bubble burst in 1974 when feed grain prices soared. Landownership did not usually go along with these investments, but Oppenheimer Industries Inc., probably the largest cattle breeding management company in the nation, accumulated some 66,000 acres, of which 53,167 were in San Luis Obispo County and the remainder in Siskiyou County. Most of this was actually in the name of Armendaris Land Development, a corporation in which Oppenheimer had a 16.43 percent interest. At present, all of Armendaris' San Luis Obispo holdings have been liquidated, and Oppenheimer reports that it owns or has partnership interests in approximately 1,900 acres in California.[12]

Field Crops

Field crops can be divided into two categories: (1) those used for cattle feed, and (2) nonfeed crops such as cotton, rice and sugar beets. There is some overlap because cotton and sugar beet byproducts (cottonseed meal and beet pulp) are also used for feed. Feed grains are significantly less valuable than nonfeed crops. Typically, when cotton acreage expands, feed grain acreage contracts. Producers will not necessarily always grow the more valuable crop, however. Production of feed grains may be an integral part of an entire profitable beef enterprise.

All of these crops are commonly produced on a large scale, usually on large holdings and frequently supplemented by land leased from other large holdings. Historically, this has been the case and events since World War II have only encouraged this style of production. Most important in this regard has been the role of the federal commodity programs. Feed grains, sugar beets, cotton, and rice have been covered by these programs, but because of the profits to be had in the last three, it has been the benefits from their support that has most affected land ownership. The rest of this section will deal with these three crops.

Federal involvement began during the Depression when the basic pattern of the commodity programs was established, *viz.* income maintenance through a combination of production controls and price supports. The former involve voluntary acreage allotments and mandatory marketing quotas (when approved in a referendum by a majority of the producers). Price support is contingent upon participation in the production aspects of the program. Farmers are allowed to produce on more acres than their allotment, but only the production from the alloted acres is eligible for price supports. Until 1973 price supports were achieved from nonrecourse loans made by the Commodity Credit Corporation. These loans are fixed at some percentage of parity (whose definition has changed over the years although the basic idea has remained the same). In 1973 the concept of a target price, based on the average world price, was introduced. Deficiency payments were to be made if the price fell below this level. Non-recourse loans at a lower rate remained available. Additional programs include the Soil Bank program created in 1956 to allow the Commodity Credit Corporation to pay rental fees for land withdrawn from production, and the initiation of disaster payments in 1975. Except during the Korean War and the past few years, the government support level has been the best price growers could achieve, hence compliance with the programs. [13]

These programs have been controversial for many reasons. Large producers benefit unduly from them. It is obvious that large producers receive more benefits than small producers simply because their allotments will be larger. But their advantage has extended beyond this simple linear relationship. Cotton, the most important subsidized crop in California, is the best example of this. We have seen how in the pre-1946 era, cotton was being produced by large owners. From 1951 to 1953 there were no acreage allotments. Since allotments are determined by planting history, during these years large landowners went on planting sprees. They took land out of barley and other feed grains and purchased or leased more land. Better access to credit made these expansions and switches more feasible for large rather than small producers. Some rather poor land was used for cotton in these years, but when allotments were reimposed in 1954 these growers could return this unproductive land to other uses.

Another advantage for large growers has been their ability to produce more per acre. The so-called "skip row" planting technique provides for planting one row and then skipping one or more rows. In this way, two-thirds as many plants can yield over 80 percent of the yield of a normal field.[14] At first an acre so planted was considered by the ASCS as 80 percent of a normal acre in computing allotments but

> according to an official in the Fresno office of the ASCS, the big operators complained in Washington. Shortly thereafter, the ASCS began to count an acre of plant-two-skip-one acreage as equivalent to 67 percent of a regular acre.[15]

To achieve great gains from this a grower needs lots of land, machinery, and fertilizer. The former is particularly important, otherwise the possible increase in allotment would be trivial.

Large owners producing cotton could receive enormous ASCS payments. Two notorious examples are South Lake Farms and J. G. Boswell, whose payments averaged $1.5 million and $3.8 million respectively from 1966 to 1970.[16] Because of such guaranteed incomes, holdings associated with cotton remained extremely large and in some areas even became more concentrated. Table 4.5 lists some of the large owners producing cotton.

Many of these have land in the Tulare Lake area and cotton production has contributed to increases in concentration of landownership that have occurred in that area since 1946. For example, the Van Glahn and Tulare Lake Land Company (a total of 33,000 acres in 1946) have become part of the J. G. Boswell empire. In 1948 Van Glahn's lands were acquired by Crockett & Gambody Inc., a company presently controlled by Boswell, in whose name the lands are listed. Tulare Lake Land Company is also now controlled by Boswell and the land is in his name. Boswell has also expanded into Kern County where he acquired some 22,000 acres from Henry Bowles in 1973. In 1978 Boswell and a number of other large cotton producers (Gilkey Farms, Harp and Hansen, Newton Brothers, Salyer, South Lake Farms, and Westlake Farms) combined to form the Tulare Lake Representatives, which purchased 19,000 acres from George Nickel.[17]

Westlands (western Fresno County) is another area where cotton production has maintained large holdings. A tabulation of ownerships made in 1955 revealed 66 holdings larger than 1,000 acres encompassing 323,400 acres. A recent tabulation based on 1978 and 1979 ownership maps found 87 holdings larger than 1,000 acres comprising 343,489 acres. The continued concentration of ownership has occurred despite the forced (by the Bureau

TABLE 4.5
Some Large Landholdings Used for
Cotton Production

Owner	Acreage
J. G. Boswell	188,223
George Bowles	10,044
Buttonwillow Land & Cattle Co.	13,832
Davis Drier	3,190
Price Giffen	8,032
Harp & Hansen	5,063
Harris Farms	30,458
McCarthy Brothers	40,812
W. J. Mouren	7,286
Newhall Land and Farming Co.	124,600
Roberts Farms	33,868
Salyer Land Co.	50,048
South Lake Farms	53,848
J. G. Stone	2,033
Westlake Farms	27,324

of Reclamation) sales of two large cotton holdings comprising 77,000 acres (those of Anderson-Clayton and Giffin Inc.). Much of the land used for cotton in Westlands is leased. This has been profitable for the largest landowner in the area, Southern Pacific (108,000 acres), and has probably sustained other large holdings. [18]

The benefits that attracted large owners to cotton also led to federal action to curtail their windfalls. In 1970 producers were limited to $55,000 in payments for a single commodity. This was probably ineffective. In 1971 a combine of fifty-three investors paid Boswell $1.3 million for a year lease of his cotton allotments and also paid him to farm the leased land. Each of these investors was eligible to receive the $55,000 maximum. The entire situation changed with the Agriculture Act of 1973. Payments were ostensibly tightened by limiting them to $20,000 per person in total direct payments for all feed grains, wheat, or cotton. That the law is now couched in terms of individuals and not producers suggests room for abuse, but it has yet to be really tested. Since 1973 the price for cotton has been above the target price, hence no deficiency payments have been made. Small amounts have been used for nonrecourse loans and disaster payments (since 1977 limited to $100,000 per person). [19] The 1977 Agriculture Act suspended the historic acreage allotments for all crops except rice. The concept of allotments was meaningless anyway since growers were able to sell everything they produced on the world market. Thus, acreage has increased some 700,000 acres since 1973. It remains to be seen, if prices fall again, what effect, if any, the limitations on payments will have on production and landownership.

Rice production is predominantly located in the Sacramento Valley, with some 10 to 15 percent of the acreage in the San Joaquin Valley. Like cotton, rice has a history of being produced by large owners. The situation in rice is analogous to that in cotton in other ways. Rice has been protected by acreage allotments in 1950 and from 1955 on. During the nonallotment years, when acreage soared, the large owners were best able to establish good histories. Their credit advantages over smaller producers were probably especially important since increasing acreage meant reclaiming land.

In 1973 rice also came under the shadow of a payment limitation, which was set at $55,000. The situation in rice has not been as favorable as that in cotton and deficiency payments have been made for some years since 1973. In 1976, for example, 135 producers received deficiency payments larger than $20,000.[20] One hundred of these producers were located in the Sacramento Valley. Unlike cotton producers, rice growers have availed themselves extensively of nonrecourse loans.

Table 4.6 lists some large owners who produce rice. Holdings located in

TABLE 4.6
Some Large Landholdings Used for
Rice Production

Owner	Acreage
Andreotti (s)	5,607
Balsdon & Balsdon (s)	5,863
Britton Co.	9,096
Britz Co.	10,873
Davis Drier	3,190
Davis Ranches (s)	9,820
O. Durst (s)	3,616
Cecil Johnson (s)	3,535
Koda Farms	3,280
M & T Inc. (s)	18,547
Nevada Rice Ranches Inc. (s)	4,572
Nevis Industries (s)	10,100
Pappas Land Co.	3,753
Parrott Ranch (s)	38,296
Redfern Ranch	3,223
River Garden Farms (s)	14,715
Roberts Farms	33,868
Elna Schnohr (s)	8,192
Siller Brothers (s)	19,444
Terhel Farms (s)	13,958
E. L. Wallace (s)	11,481
Woodland Farms (s)	18,462
Zumwalt Farms Inc. (s)	21,512

Note: Entries marked with (s) are located in the Sacramento Valley.

the Sacramento Valley are indicated by an "(s)". The importance of rice as a factor in large holdings in the Sacramento Valley is obvious. Interestingly, a number of these owners are Sacramento River diverters, who, like the large cotton owners in the Tulare Lake and Westlands areas, have been involved in controversies with the Bureau of Reclamation.

Sugar beet programs are separate from the other commodities but involve the same techniques. Additionally, producers are protected from foreign competition by import fees and quotas. Prior to 1977 producers received government support payments directly, but this was changed so that the processors receive payments, paying out a portion to the grower and retaining the balance. Post-1973 prices are significantly higher than for earlier years, but the peak occurred in 1974, resulting in overplanting in the next two years. In the past several years acreage has declined in the San Joaquin Valley due to competition with cotton. Sugar beets have traditionally been associated with large holdings, particularly with those owned by processors. Table 4.7 lists some large owners producing sugar beets.

TABLE 4.7
Some Large Sugar Beet Producers

Owner	Acreage
Amstar Corp.*	2,845
Buttonwillow Land & Cattle Co.	13,832
Heringer Ranch	3,604
M & T Inc.	18,547
Paloma Farms	5,953
River Garden Farms	14,715
Tejon Ranch	270,000
E. L. Wallace	11,481

*Note: Amstar is the product of a merger between Spreckels and American Sugar.

The tables above show considerable overlap. Not only are livestock producers diversifying into crop production, but field crop producers typically grow a variety of field crops. Frequently there is some production of minor crops like dry beans, corn, hops, oats, safflower, or sorghums. Thus, production of these minor crops is also associated with large holdings.

Specialty Crops

Specialty crops can be very attractive since the average value they produce per acre far surpasses anything possible with field crops. For example, in 1979 this was $2,378 per acre for all vegetables and $1,634 per acre for all fruits and nuts; the most valuable field crop, cotton, was worth $800 per acre. Specialty-crop producers have achieved significant market stabilization through the use of federal and state marketing orders and by relying on crops with better markets. These include those intended for processing and those that are California monopolies. Also, there is better timing of crops and year-round production has become common.

Federal marketing orders were initiated under the Agricultural Marketing Act (1937), state orders under the California Marketing Act (1937). Both acts authorize the following kinds of programs: quality regulation, inspection, container or pack regulations, volume control, rate-of-flow regulation, research, advertising and promotion, and unfair trade practices. Both are implemented by a producer referendum. A special feature of the federal program is that when federal orders regulating quality, size, or grade are in effect for a commodity, these same standards are applied to all imports of that commodity. Between 1949 and 1975 various combinations of these programs were in effect at some time for forty-six commodities, most of which were fruits and vegetables.[21] The use of the programs has increased in popularity during these years.

In 1949 only 16 percent of the vegetable acreage, accounting for 9 percent of the total value produced, was under a federal or state marketing order, while in 1975 this had increased to 67 percent of the acreage and 69 percent of the value produced. For fruits, the corresponding percentages are 55 percent of the acreage in 1949 and 88 percent in 1975, accounting for 61 percent of the value in 1949 and 86 percent of the value in 1975. The programs regulating marketing (quality control, volume control, rate-of-flow, and inspection) have been used fairly consistently over the years, while there has been tremendous growth in use of research programs since the late 1960s. A 1975 study of the effect of the regulation of marketing on prices found significant enhancements under the flow-to-market and volume control regulations.[22] Oranges, lemons, almonds, raisins, prunes, and walnuts have been covered by such programs.

While it is apparent that producers benefit, it has not been clear that consumers gain anything from price stabilization. As one author of the study pointed out, "it is only when the basic sources of instability are in demand (which is not the usual case for milk, fruits, or vegetables) that consumers benefit from price stabilization."[23] Much research on mechanization has been, at least in part, financed through these programs. As will be indicated, mechanization has played a big role in forming large holdings.

Acreage harvested to vegetables increased from 677,000 acres in 1946 to 928,000 in 1979. Most of this increase has occurred since the mid-1960s; in earlier years the acreage simply fluctuated around 650,000 acres. Approximately three-fourths of this increase can be attributed to expansion of acreage devoted to lettuce and processing vegetables, especially tomatoes. Between 1954 and 1979 the bearing acreage of all fruits and nuts increased by 470,000 acres to 1.8 million acres and 63 percent of this came about in almonds and walnuts. Another 34 percent is accounted for by wine grapes (an increase that has occurred since 1970). Almonds are a California monopoly and walnuts a Pacific coast monopoly. Both sets of producers are highly organized and as noted above are reaping the gains from being under marketing orders. Pistachios are an up-and-coming crop that is also a California monopoly. Producers are presently benefitting from disturbed relations with the major foreign producer (Iran). The wine grape boom is a function of a corresponding boom in consumer demand for wine.

A significant number of large holdings producing specialty crops have appeared. These include both large holdings devoted primarily to specialty crops and large holdings primarily in extensive use that have put some land into specialty crops. The most profitable vegetables are items like lettuce and melons, which are marketed fresh. The marketing of fresh produce is very risky. Gluts can occur all too easily. There is less risk with processing vegetables, but it is necessary to obtain contracts with processors and this can be an obstacle. Thus, vegetable production is often only one aspect of a producer's operations. Of the thirty-one large owners I know to be involved in vegetable production, none solely produces vegetables. The need to rotate crops and rest the soil may be inflating this assessment. Nonetheless, it is difficult to attribute many large holdings directly to vegetable production. An exception is John Anderson. Anderson owns 35,000 acres in the Sacramento Valley. Although some of the land is used for field crops, it was amassed (since the mid-1960s) for the purpose of producing processing tomatoes.[24] Processing tomatoes are one of the few vegetables whose harvest is mechanized. Anderson is a prime example of the effect of mechanization on holding size.

Actually, large vegetable producers, especially of fresh produce, often prefer to operate on leased land. Sun Harvest, the nation's largest lettuce grower, owned only 70 acres of the 18,358 it operated in 1978. Other leaders, like the D'Arrigo Brothers, Bruce Church, Maggio Inc., and the Antle operations in Imperial Valley are also operating mainly on leased land. Most of the land leased by these particular operators is in small holdings but it is likely that some large owners are benefitting from being able to lease their land out for such use.[25]

The formation of large fruit and nut orchards has become quite common. Some holdings including large orchards or vineyards are listed Table 4.8. The existence of large orchards and vineyards is largely due to the same factors noted in Chapter 3: aggregation of smaller holdings and willingness to invest in plantings now that crops are profitable. Two new factors have become relevant in this period: mechanization and tax-loss farming. The technology to harvest nuts mechanically was available in the 1960s and the wine grape harvest is presently undergoing mechanization. Large orchards and vineyards are not necessary to take advantage of the savings in production costs that mechanization can achieve. However, the orchards and vineyards have to pruned and planted in special ways in order to be amenable to mechanization. Because mechanization became possible during planting booms, those who were planting new orchards and vineyards have been able to realize these savings. These were often large owners. Furthermore, knowledge that mechanization would be available encouraged large-scale plantings.

TABLE 4.8
Some Large Landholdings Containing Large
Orchards or Vineyards

Owner	Acreage Owned
Apache Grove Land Co.	6,255
Blackwell Land Co.	21,910
Buttes Gas & Oil Co.	8,060
Calplans Agricultural Fund	10,309
Gallo Brothers	28,249
Guimarra Brothers	9,577
Irvine Co.	92,207
McCarthy Brothers	40,812
National Distillers	5,877
Newhall Land and Farming Co.	124,600
Seagrams & Sons Inc.	5,200
Superior Farming	37,941
Tejon Ranch	270,000
Tenneco	260,710

Orchard and vineyard development has also been affected by tax laws. The same administrative decisions which permitted the development of growing animals to be tax deductible also permit the development of standing crops to be deducted. The Revenue Act of 1942 provided for capital gains treatment of trees and vineyards. The Internal Revenue Code of 1954 included special deductions for soil and water conservation and land clearing costs (these were qualified by conditions on how long the land had to be held to be for exemption to be granted). The Tax Reform Act of 1969 cut back deductions for citrus and almonds but did not affect other trees or vines. Use of the tax laws is typically associated with "tax-loss farmers" — that is, with high-income investors who buy into a syndicate that purchases some land, develops it, and then sells it. During the years of development, investors get a nice tax deduction to offset their nonfarm income, and when the land is sold they only have to pay capital gains rates on their profit.

The big attraction is the deductions, which is why, when these were disallowed after 1969 for citrus and almonds, investors turned to other nuts (pistachios were a big favorite) and grapes. Most of the activity in this area occurred from the late 1960s through 1976. The Tax Reform Act of 1976 curtailed new syndicated offerings and hence tax-loss farming as syndicates accounted for the bulk of the investments.[26] Some syndicates remain. Apache Grove, Buttes Gas and Oil, Calplans Agricultural Fund, and Tejon

Agricultural Partners (which is unique in that the land is not to be sold) are all such syndicates. Their names are in Table 4.8

These same tax deductions are available to those not looking for tax losses and, as intended, make orchard and vineyard development easier. It becomes especially attractive for large owners who have the largest taxable incomes. Clearly, tax considerations are not the crucial factor in tree and vineyard development since post-1969 almond plantings (which are exempt from deductions) have exceeded those of earlier years. However, they have facilitated large-scale orchard development.

Agribusiness

The previous section showed that large owners have significant involvement in all aspects of California production. Frequently a single holding is put to many uses. This concentration of control over production would be reason to expect large landowners to have some effect on policies concerning them. Their effectiveness is heightened because much more than control over production is involved. In the past few decades the word "agribusiness" has entered common parlance, reflecting the fact that farming has become big business. This phenomenon is especially noticeable in California, where farming has been described as a business since the 1930s. This section will consider two aspects to the growth of agribusiness: expansion of firms involved in agriculturally linked industries and the entrance of economically powerful firms and other nonfarming interests into production. The upshot is more ties between large owners and powerful outside economic interests.

The number of cooperative marketing associations has declined from 455 in 1947 to 277 in 1976. This is in keeping with the increase in concentration of control in marketing. It was pointed out in Chapter 3 that large-scale producers dominated the more powerful co-ops. With the number of large producers increasing, this has become even more true. There are also ties to other interests. For example, Sunkist Growers Inc. (previously, California Fruit Growers Exchange) had interconnecting directors with Castle & Cook and the Newhall Land and Farming Company in the early 1970s (Robert Di Giorgio was then and still is on the Newhall board of directors).[27]

A number of companies involved in processing and distribution have become highly diversified corporations of international scope. This is true of Anderson Clayton, R. J. Reynolds (present owner of Del Monte, previously, Calpak), Amstar, Di Giorgio, Consolidated Foods (present owner of Union Sugar), Heinz, and others. That these companies have many interests, including production of a wide variety of processed products, scattered throughout the world has opened up new markets for producers. Such firms handle significant amounts of California production and many producers deal with them. These companies can decide to whom they will award contracts and they prefer to deal with larger producers. Dealing with large producers allows them "to minimize the costs and inconvenience by buying and assembling farm products in the large volume lots that they require and by controlling quality tightly."[28]

Additionally, the low prices paid by processors can often only be borne by large producers.* Similarly, the growth of major retailers like Safeway (which operates internationally) and Lucky has both expanded markets for producers. They prefer to deal with large producers and large co-ops. When the large lettuce and grape producers were having labor troubles, they were able to rely on Safeway and Lucky and other retailers to carry their products.

In the 1960s agriculture looked its brightest and large corporations began to invest in farming. Several oil companies already owning large tracts began to develop and farm the land themselves.† Thus, the Getty Oil Company began to farm its lands acquired in the early 1900s and formed the Minnehoma Land and Farming Company in 1969 to handle part of this. The Belridge Oil Company formed Belridge Farms in 1966 to operate its 33,000 acres of land, 22,000 of which were used for crops in 1978. Belridge also became briefly involved with other agricultural ventures in the late 1960s. In 1979 Shell Oil, already a large owner, acquired Belridge. (This was not, of course, for its agricultural resources.) Several oil companies have bought in. Tenneco purchased the Kern County Land Company in 1967. Tenneco, like Shell, had nonagricultural reasons for this acquisition, but initiated extensive agricultural land development. Tenneco also began a series of land sales that totaled some 100,000 acres in 1979.‡ Included in these sales was one in 1971 of 30,000 acres of agricultural land to Hollis Roberts. Roberts later sold 22,000 acres of this to the Superior Oil Company, which formed the Superior Farming Company to operate this land.[31]

Other sorts of corporations have been involved. Dow Chemical, which had a tie to Bud Antle through producing film for lettuce wrappers, bought part of Antle in 1969. Profits were not as high as anticipated so Dow dropped out and Castle & Cook acquired Bud Antle in 1978. Of late, wineries and vineyards have become popular acquisitions. National Distillers acquired Almaden Vineyards (2,000 acres) in 1977. Seagram acquired Christian Brothers and Paul Masson. These are only a few examples. These corporations appear to be primarily interested in production.[32]

---

*Ironically, as small producers get driven out of business, the remaining producers find themselves in a stronger position to achieve better prices from the processors. Processing tomatoes are an example.[29]

†Standard, the largest land owner among oil companies is an exception. Standard, like the Southern Pacific, the state's largest private land owner, still only leases its agricultural lands. Neither company does any actual farming, but with large-scale farming attractive and profitable, so too is leasing.

‡The Southern Pacific has sold 62,993 acres in Kern County, 8,065 acres in Kings County, and 58,724 acres in Fresno County since 1947. I suspect that this land has gone to other large owners. Oscar Rudnick, for example, owns four townships of railroad land in Kern County.[30]

There is a another reason for investment in farming. It was pointed out in 1979 that "recently farmland in the U.S. has had more value as an investment asset than as a productive asset."[33] Typically, the motives for acquisition are mixed between interest in land investment and production. This can be seen in the many Prudential Insurance investments in agricultural partnerships, including several with the McCarthy Brothers, one with John Anderson and one with the Tejon Ranch Company. Over 50,000 acres are involved in these ventures. The Blackwell Land Company is involved in a similar partnership with another insurance company, John Hancock Mutual Life Insurance Company. Blackwell has also attracted a number of foreign investors, including Midhurst Corporation (a subsidiary of S. Pearson and Son of Great Britain). Foreign investment is not usually regarded as motivated by production considerations, but Midhurst appears to be interested, at least in part, in the potential of pistachio nuts. Bangor Punta's ownership of South Lake Farms is another example of foreign interest in both production and land. As noted above, South Lake Farms has been extremely profitable, yet Bangor Punta recently indicated an intention to sell it to "realize appreciation and redeploy proceeds into working assets."[34]

It was reported in 1979 that foreign interests own 212,000 acres of California farmland. Blackwell and South Lake Farms, along with Shell Oil account for 120,000 acres. Of the remaining 92,000 acres, over 20,000 are in large holdings owned by corporations incorporated in the Netherlands Antilles and 4,000 acres are owned by a Swiss corporation. Many thousands more are held in small holdings owned by Netherlands Antilles corporations. The basis for these holdings is a United States-Netherlands income tax treaty that gives certain tax benefits to Netherland corporations and business entities on income derived from sources within the United States France and Switzerland have similar treaties with the United States It is not known who is behind these corporations, but it is probably United States investors taking advantage of the tax benefits. The fact that William Coblentz, a University of California regent, is managing director of several of these corporations lends credence to this theory. These holdings are a good example of investment in land simply for speculation in its value.[35]

Another example of land investment involves groups of individuals who combine to purchase large holdings so as to circumvent the 160-acre limitation. This has been common in Westlands and is one reason why the Anderson Clayton and Giffin sales did nothing to cut back on land concentration. With this technique, the large holdings are held in separate parcels by each purchaser, but they are always operated as a single unit. Most of the purchasers "own the land not to farm it, but as an income producing investment."[36] Technically, this has not resulted in large holdings, but the difference is subtle, to say the least.

One important aspect to the presence of these new interests in farming is their ability to outcompete small farmers simply because they have better access to credit. Large corporations and small farmers operate in different credit markets; besides, the former, with their larger resources and tax-loss interests, are better able to endure several years of losses. Furthermore, there are close ties between the larger producers and the major creditors, Bank of America, Wells Fargo Bank, and so on. Safeway, Lucky, Tejon Ranch, and Tenneco all share a member of their Board of Directors with Bank of America. The president of Bank of America is also a director of Standard Oil of California and the chairman is on the Getty Oil Board of Directors. Newhall Land and Farming Company shares a director with Wells Fargo Bank.[37]

These new investors in farming have a stake in issues like water, labor, and mechanization. Water is of particular concern as it has such an impact on land value. Thus, the oil companies and others with land in the San Joaquin Valley have been very interested in water development, particularly with respect to the State Water Project. The Westlands investors, of course, are concerned about enforcement of reclamation law. Coblentz has been criticized for his support of University of California research on mechanization because of his investments.

The next two sections describe developments in water and labor. The influence of large landowners' developments will be apparent. This influence is not just the result of agribusiness. Old friends, like the American Farm Bureau Federation, have consistently taken the same positions as large owners on these issues and have been active lobbyists.

Water Development

Most of the acreage brought under irrigation since World War II is either the result of private development of ground water or huge public projects capturing and distributing surface water. In the last era, the former accounted for most of the new irrigated land. Now the balance has tipped towards reliance on large projects, either directly or as a means of recharging ground water sources. Until 1960 all large-scale water development was due to the federal government. The federal government charges very low prices for its water, so low that the Central Valley Project became virtually bankrupt in the 1970s. Low water prices are very important to large landowners. Despite increased involvement with specialty crops, these landowners are often large producers of feed grains, forage, and cotton, lower value crops that can only be produced if water costs are low.

Large landowners are limited in their ability to take advantage of federal water because of the acreage limitation and residency restrictions applicable to Bureau of Reclamation projects. Since 1946 large owners have followed two general strategies to attain unlimited access to cheap water: turning to the state for water and subverting the Bureau of Reclamation regulations. Both strategies have been fairly successful. State water is without restrictions and the price, which is much higher than that of federal water, has been lowered significantly for agricultural users by the use of surplus water. Few large holdings have been dismantled because of the Bureau of

Reclamation's restrictions. This section will describe these strategies in detail.

State Water Project

Excess landowners in the Central Valley have been involved in a complex series of manuevers to circumvent the 160 acre limitation. The 1944 bid for congressional exemption was repeated in 1947, with Senator Downey a prime mover. Lengthy hearings were held, Downey published a book (*They Would Rule the Valley*), but the bill died in committee. At the same time as congressional exemption was being sought, the state was making proposals to purchase the Central Valley Project from the federal government. The 1944 purchase proposal was repeated several times and this remained a live issue until 1954 when Governor Knight accepted the fact that the cost would be too high. The last study of the idea, a State Assembly Report entitled *Central Valley Project: Federal or State*, pointed out that "in large measure, State purchase of the Central Valley Project has been supported since 1944 as a means of rendering excess land provisions no longer applicable to the project."[38]

Under the influence of the large owners, the state then turned towards developing its own water project as a means of eluding the acreage limitation.[39] The first steps in this direction came in 1951 when the state legislature approved Feather River (Oroville Dam) as a state project. Numerous studies were conducted in succeeding years. The first version of the State Water Plan was published in 1956 and this plan was authorized by the legislature in 1957. Studies continued, culminating in 1959 in the State Department of Water Resources' *Bulletin #78*, which presented the final form of the project. Like the Central Valley Project, the State Water Project brings water from the north to the south. Most water is intended for urban use in southern California or agricultural use in the southern San Joaquin Valley. The Map 4.1 shows the units and the service areas.

Neither the plan nor the authorization said anything about an acreage limitation. Such a proposal was made several times in the state legislature between 1957 and 1961, and each time it was defeated. In 1960 voters approved a plan to issue $1.75 billion in general obligation bonds to finance the project, but no acreage limitation proposal ever faced the public at large. Once the bonds were passed, construction began. The San Luis Dam was completed in 1967 and the Oroville Dam in 1968. In 1971 the aqueduct reached over the Tehachapis to southern California. Deliveries began as early as 1962 to Plumas County and the Livermore Valley, but Kern deliveries did not begin until 1968 and the Metropolitan Water District first received water in 1972.[40] Most of the features of the project are completed. Remaining is the controversial peripheral canal that is intended to carry Sacramento River water directly to the California Aqueduct during periods of low runoff. Approved by the legislature in 1980, the canal has been

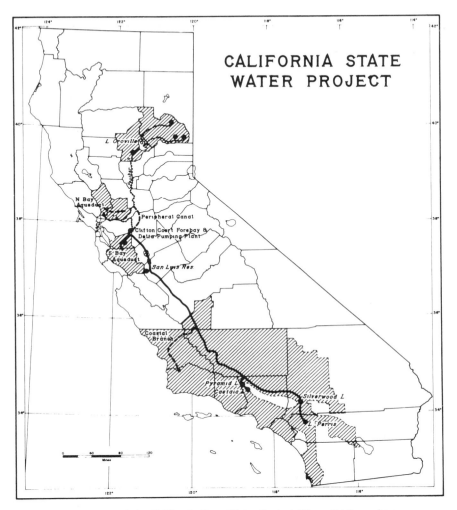

CALIFORNIA STATE WATER PROJECT

Note: Major features of the California State Water Project. The solid lines show the California Aqueduct and adjunct canals in operation in 1976. Dashed lines reveal projected aqueduct extensions. The dotted lines indicate connecting rivers. The large dots indicate major reservoirs. Shading delineates agency areas with contracts for Project water.

Source: Lantis *et al.* (1977), p. 447.

Map 4.1

stalemated by a popular referendum to be voted on in 1981.*

The State Water Project has been highly criticized, particularly with respect to cost issues. Since the Bureau of Reclamation had, in 1945, included development of the Feather River in its long-term plans for the Central Valley, it is quite likely that the Bureau would have undertaken the project. As a federal project it would have been eligible for federal interest-free irrigation funds. Paul Taylor has stated that this involved a savings in construction costs of around $500 million. The state's determination of financial feasibility has also been criticized. Bain *et al.* computed, in 1968, that it would pay for itself by the year 2039 only if the capital invested bore an interest rate of 4 percent or less.[41] The present rate is actually higher. In 1974 the Department of Water Resources reported that

> The State Water Project is a financially viable project, producing revenues which are sufficient to pay all costs of operation and maintenance, repay all capital expenditures with interest and eventually producing surplus revenues for any future additions to the State Water Resources Development System what may be authorized.[42]

This happy conclusion might not be accepted by all observers, especially when it is considered that the project is also paid for by Tidelands Oil income.

State water rates are composed of a delta water charge (representing the construction and operating costs of the facilities necessary to bring the water to the delta pool) plus a transportation charge (representing the cost of the aqueducts and pumping used to move the water to the contractor). In the San Joaquin Valley this averaged around $59 per acre foot in 1979, the greatest cost being for the the Kern County Water Agency ($61.98).[43] These rates are not fixed and usually increase each year. These rates are high compared to federal projects (where the maximum is $16.50 per acre foot with most users paying substantially less) because the state allocates to water users 80 percent of the costs of capital investment. The federal government allocates 47 percent of these costs to irrigators. However, these rates do not tell all. These are the prices paid by contractors for what is called their entitlement water, the water that they have a contract for and whose costs of development they are paying.

Presently, the Metropolitan Water District of southern California (MWD) is the largest contractor of state water. The MWD never uses all its entitlement water, but must cover its assigned share of capital costs anyway. The unused water is sold as surplus to other users; the biggest users of surplus water are agricultural users in the southern San Joaquin Valley: the

---

*The referendum was defeated.

Kern County Water Agency (KCWA), Dudley Ridge Irrigation District, and Tulare Lake Basin. Charges for surplus water are very low, being based on power costs, administration, and replacement. This water has been available for every year since 1968 except 1977. Surplus water is as cheap as federal water. When it is mingled with entitlement water, the average rate drops significantly, although always remaining well above federal prices. However, it often beats the cost of pumping water and there are the extra gains from groundwater recharging. For example, in 1976* the KCWA received 439,000 acre feet of entitlement water costing $45.36 per acre foot. It also received 442,000 acre feet of surplus water costing $2.71 per acre foot. The average cost per acre foot was thus $23.96.[44]

The service entities within the KCWA who contract for State water serve a number of large landowners. By comparing the information I collected about large holdings in Kern County from the AGRI-LAND map with a map of the service areas I was able to compile a list of large holdings in these areas. Some of these are listed in Table 4.9 with an estimate of the amount of land they own that receives state water. My information was organized by sections and the service areas sometimes include only part of a section. Holdings in these sections were simply dropped. Also, Tenneco and J. G. Boswell both own thousands of acres that receive state water, but because I did not use the AGRI-LAND map to determine the size of their holdings, I am unable to deduce the actual extent in the service areas.

Central Valley Development

In 1946 the Central Valley Project consisted of what are referred to as its initial features (those described in the last chapter) and provided water to 138,553 acres. By 1951 these units were completed and fully operational. Since 1946 the project has expanded considerably and in 1978 supplied water to 3.1 million acres. The Rivers and Harbors Act (1944) authorized the Army Corps of Engineers to construct dams for flood control purposes at Folsom on the American River, at Pine Flat on the Kings River, at Isabella on the Kern River, on the Kaweah River, on the Tule River and at several other locations. In 1949 Folsom Dam was taken over by the Bureau of Reclamation and incorporated into the Central Valley Project. This unit was completed in 1956. The Corps of Engineers built the Pine Flat and Isabella Dams in the early 1950s, and in the early 1960s constructed dams at Terminus on the Kaweah River and at Success on the Tule River. The dams are still owned by the Corps but their irrigation features are operated by the Bureau of Reclamation. They are not part of the Central Valley Project.[45]

A Sacramento Canals Division to the Central Valley Project was authorized in 1950 and construction began in 1953. The major feature is the Tehama-Colusa Canal. The Trinity Lake Division was authorized in 1955

---

*1979 cost figures were not available at the time this was written, and 1977 and 1978 were aberrant years due to the drought.

TABLE 4.9
Some Large Landholdings in the Kern
County Water Agency

Owner	Acreage receiving state water
American Dev. Co.	8,020
Corky Anderson & Kenneth Puryear	7,399
Bellumoni Brothers	3,879
Bidart Brothers	3,622
Blackwell Land Co.	14,721
Bonanza Farms	2,874
Buttonwillow Land & Cattle Co.	13,763
California Dev. Co.	6,085
A. J. Cattani	6,020
Chevron Oil Co.	21,507
Christina Inv. Co.	3,133
Costersian Farms	3,153
C. E. Erickson	4,774
Getty Oil Co.	37,666
Jameson Trust	3,530
Kern Property Co.	3,243
Paloma Farms	5,860
Loren Ritter	2,189
Roberts Farms	18,878
Shell Oil Co.	29,433
Southern Pacific	15,998
Superior Oil Co.	10,035
Tolleneare & Hansen	3,940
Union Oil Co.	3,188

and the dam was completed in 1960. The most controversial addition to the Central Valley Project has been the San Luis Unit, authorized in 1960. This has been a unique division because it shares facilities with the State Water Project. Both projects use the State built and operated San Luis Dam reservoir and the California Aqueduct (103 miles long from the dam to Kettleman City). Federal deliveries from this unit began in 1968. Map 4.2 shows the location of all these units.

Judging from the actual extent of enforcement of the acreage limitation on Bureau of Reclamation projects, landowners need not have encouraged the State Water Project. Recently, this issue has once again entered the limelight. In 1976 the District Court ruled in *National Land for People* vs. *Bureau of Reclamation* that approval of any further contracts for excess land sales was enjoined until the public rule-making procedures were initiated. This led Secretary of the Interior Andrus in 1977 to propose regulations calling for rigorous enforcement of the acreage limitation. At that time 2.9 million acres were receiving water from the Central Valley Project and 1.8

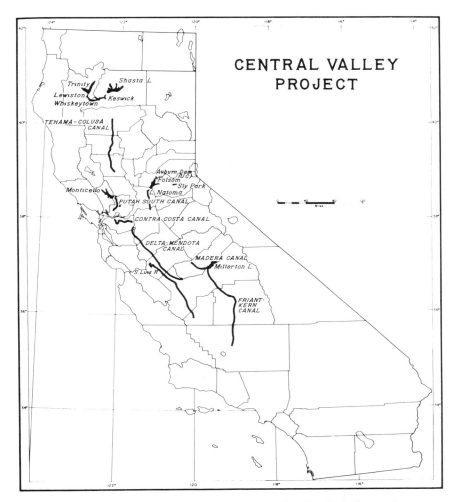

CENTRAL VALLEY
PROJECT

Note: Major features of the Central Valley Project. The San Luis Reservoir complex and connecting aqueduct are operated jointly with the California Water Project.

Source: Lantis *et al.* (1977), p. 270.

Map 4.2

million were estimated to be in excess. Excess landowners were aghast at Andrus's proposal, the more so as he was also proposing to enforce residency requirements and establish limits on leasing. To stay his hand, lawsuits were filed by four California counties, a number of irrigation districts, and some farmer organizations, claiming that the Department of the Interior should provide environmental impact statements to evaluate the impact of its proposed actions. An injunction was granted in December 1977 until the environmental impact statements were prepared.[46] This has so far prevented any action by the Department of the Interior.

In the meantime, landowners have lobbied for preventive legislation.* Their latest attempt is HR6520, which would, in effect, wipe out the acreage limitation. It is not exactly clear where the bill is in Congress. In any event, not only has enforcement been lacking, but when sales have been affected, their substance has often deviated sharply from the intent of the law. The Army Corps of Engineer projects and the Sacramento River diverters are the most egregious examples of outright avoidance of enforcement, while the San Luis service area (Westlands) epitomizes the feebleness of what is enforced.

The River and Harbors Act (1944) extended reclamation law, and hence the acreage limitation, to cover irrigation uses of water from works constructed by the Army Corps of Engineers. The Corps of Engineers denied this for many years and large landowners fought for construction by them for this reason. In 1958 the Attorney General confirmed that reclamation law affected Corps projects. By that time Pine Flat and Isabella were long completed and delivering water to what were extremely large landowners. In 1957 Pine Flat alone was serving 266,302 acres in excess holdings of which 196,466 were held by fifty-two owners in the Tulare Lake Basin.[48]

Landowners made a temporary contract with the Bureau to cover their share of operating costs and repayment obligation. After several years, they offered to pay off, in a lump sum, their share of the repayment obligation in exchange for release from the acreage limitation. A test case went to the courts. This case dragged along for years. The Ninth Circuit Court (in *United States vs Tulare Lake Canal*) decided that the acreage limitation applied, without exception, to dams built by the Corps of Engineers. In 1977 the United States Supreme Court let this decision stand. At that time it was apparent how radically tenure could be affected by enforcement. In 1977 it was estimated that Pine Flat served 322,000 acres of excess land (an increase since 1957) and Isabella 167,820 such acres. Estimates are not available for the other projects encompassed by the 1.5 million acres receiving water from Army Corps of Engineer projects. Landowners in the Pine Flat area (organized as Tulare Lake Farmers) have been lobbying extensively and expensively for congressional action.[49] HR6520 would

---

*Oil companies, who had much to lose if residency and leasing restrictions were enforced, were urged, in an industry magazine, to support some of this legislation.[47]

exempt projects of the Corps of Engineers from the acreage limitation.

Landowners along the Sacramento River have benefitted, since Shasta Dam was completed in 1944, from an assured summer supply of water. Deliveries from the dam become commingled with the flow to which these owners are entitled by virtue of their riparian rights. The Bureau of Reclamation found settlements difficult to arrive at and dropped negotiations for a number of years. Contracts with the Sacramento River diverters (now organized into the Sacramento River Water Contractors Association) were finally executed in 1964. These contracts allow diversion of 1,840,00 acre feet, of which 330,000 are considered project water.

This is a strange decision since it gives more water to diverters as nonproject water (i.e., as that to which they have riparian right) than they were ever diverting before Shasta was built. Furthermore, the contracts do not prevent ineligible lands from receiving water; instead they simply calculate how much project water should be delivered to the contractor on the basis of the amount of eligible land and this amount may be averaged over all landowners in a contracting district. In 1978 there were twenty-seven members of the Sacramento Water Contractors Association, a number of whom are private parties (not irrigation or reclamation districts). These private parties and the acreage they hold are shown in Table 4.10.

Many other large owners are encompassed by the irrigation and reclamation districts. The 1977 threat of enforcement of the acreage limitation led the association to help sponsor S2818 in 1978, which included congressional validation of the contracts. The bill did not pass. Its failure

TABLE 4.10
Private Parties in the Sacramento
Water Contractors Association

Owner	Acreage
Carter Farms	4,237
Davis Ranches	9,820
Hershey Land Company	3,282
Woodland Cooperative Rice Farms	2,869
River Garden Farms	13,165
Terhel Farms Inc.	13,958
Wallace Construction Inc.	5,764
Roger Wilbur	2,053
Woodland Farms	18,790
TOTAL	73,938

Source United States Senate, Committee on Energy and Natural Resources (1978), p. 1291 for names of contractors; Appendix B for acreage.

has been followed by similar clauses in HR6520.

The San Luis unit has a long history. In 1942 the large landowners in the present service area formed the San Joaquin Valley Water Service Landowners Association (later, Westlands Water District) to encourage development of supplemental water. They were anticipating problems of overdraft, for without a source of water to replenish their groundwater the cost of pumping would eventually exceed the value of the water. The association requested the Bureau of Reclamation to investigate the San Luis project and put up $40,000 to finance studies, which were initiated in 1943.[50] Throughout the 1950s these landowners lobbied for the San Luis Project and finally obtained congressional authorization in the 1960 San Luis Act. The San Luis site was one the state proposed to use for its water project. The state had actually planned deliveries to the Westlands area but the landowners pushed for federal development. This may seem anomalous behavior for an area that in 1959 consisted of at least 68 percent excess lands, over half of which was in holdings larger than 5,000 acres. But the water was cheaper (this is some of the most marginal land in the San Joaquin Valley) and they never seriously expected to be affected by the acreage limitation. As Representative Clair Engle pointed out in 1955:

> I call your attention to the fact that in 26 years since the recordable contract provisions have been in the reclamation law, not in one single instance has the Secretary of the Interior ever set a price on land and sold the land under a recordable contract. . . . They find ways to get around it. They set up corporations and partnerships and every adult or child has 160 acres and if there are not enough of those they bring in the uncles and aunts and, as a consequence, they spread it around so that the pro forma title at least is within the limitation.[51]

Landowners did attempt to get an exemption included in the 1960 act but failed. Nonetheless, they have succeeded in eluding the limitation in the manner suggested by Engle.

Since the district began receiving project water in 1968, owners have placed 351,425 acres of the approximately 400,000 excess acres in the district under recordable contracts. In 1976 the situation in Westlands was investigated and it was found that over 100,000 acres had been sold under the terms of recordable contracts.[52] But it was pointed out by Ralph Brody, the district's manager and chief counsel that "most of the buyers are . . . members of a group of people who joined together to purchase land located in the same general area with a view toward their land being farmed together, at least during the initial years of their ownership."[53] These people were usually nonresidents simply interested, as indicated previously, in the land as an investment. Sometimes they were members of the same family. Again, as mentioned earlier, these joint owners never attempted to partition out their own particular 160 acres from the entire unit. Furthermore, it was found that these sorts of group sales prevented family farmers from buying land in Westlands. As of 1979 only 134,000 acres of excess land had been sold. Southern Pacific, the largest landowner in the district placed approximately 84,000 acres under recordable contract between 1971 and 1976, but by 1979 had only managed to sell 2,500 acres. The rest is still being leased.[54]

Westlands illustrates the effects of a particularly invidious administrative decision the Bureau made about the acreage law. The Bureau decided that because the Omnibus Adjustment Act (1926) said nothing about the residency requirement, it must have been repealed. This issue was tested inconclusively in the courts in *Yellen* vs. *Hickel*. The 1968 decision of the case ruled that the notion of repeal by implication was unacceptable. But the last appeal was dismissed on the grounds that the plaintiff lacked standing and the issue was left unresolved.[55] The practice of ignoring the residency requirement has been one important reason why the group sales in Westlands were accepted by the Bureau.

The situations described above regarding Corps of Engineers projects, the Sacramento River diverters and Westlands are not unique. A 1972 General Accounting Office study of the acreage limitation concluded that "the 160 acre reclamation law limitation has not resulted in preventing large landowners and farm operators from benefitting under the subsidized irrigation program or landowners and farm operators from retaining or acquiring large landholdings."[56] The study found that leasing, corporation control, family partnerships, and trusts were common techniques used to avoid the law. It looked at seven California irrigation districts and found that in 1971 the single largest operators in each controlled, in total, 14 percent of the land in all seven districts, owning half and leasing the other half. The report gave a number of examples of dubious transfers and also pointed to another unfortunate Bureau policy, *viz.* permitting an individual to own up to 160 acres of eligible land in any number of irrigation districts.[57]

This particular policy played a part in one of the few known successes of the acreage limitation, the breakup of the Di Giorgio holdings in Kern County. Di Giorgio had signed a recordable contract in 1951 with the Delano-Earlimart Irrigation District. Ten years later Di Giorgio still owned the land and delayed sale for another three years, arguing with the Bureau over reappraisal of the land. The new appraisal setting high prices was followed by permission for owners of land receiving project water in other districts to purchase Di Giorgio land. Di Giorgio was also allowed to finance purchases and operate the land for absentee owners. Sales were completed in 1969 and Di Giorgio then ceased involvement.[58]

One last feature of excess land sales should be mentioned. The law stipulates that the resale price should not incorporate increases in value due to the project. Nonetheless, it was found, both by the General Accounting Office in 1972 and the Senate Select Committee on Small Business in 1976, that the Bureau was not following this policy and sellers were reaping such benefits.[59]

Imperial Valley

The situation has been relatively simple in the Imperial Valley. Imperial landowners have devoted themselves to denying the applicability of the acreage limitation, basing their case on the 1933 letter of Secretary of the Interior Wilbur that denied its applicability to them. Secretary Ickes had affirmed this position in 1945 and Secretary Krug did likewise in 1948, and this, despite several departmental solicitor's opinions to the contrary, remained the department's position until 1964. At that time, Secretary Udall accepted Department of Interior Solicitor Barry's opinion that the acreage limitation applied and entered into negotiations with the Imperial Irrigation District for a contract incorporating the limitation. The failure of these negotiations led to the federal government's filing suit in 1967 to force the Imperial Irrigation District to renegotiate the water contract. In 1971 the District Court ruled against the government. The government did not appeal but the ruling was appealed in 1974 by third-party family farmers trying to enforce the acreage limitation. This case was decided in 1977 by the Ninth Circuit Court of Appeals. The ruling reversed the decision of the district court. The case was appealed to the United States Supreme Court, which in June 1980 ruled unanimously against application of the acreage limitation to the Imperial Valley. This decision in no way carries over to other projects. Although "safe," the Imperial Valley landowners have secured clauses in recent proposed legislation guaranteeing their exemption; thus preventing any sort of congressional change to their situation. Such legislation has not yet been passed. However, the Senate recently adopted a provision barring the Department of the Interior from spending any money on enforcement of the limitation in the Imperial Valley.[60]

This has been an important victory for the Imperial landowners, for enforcement of the limitation could dramatically change the pattern of landownership in the valley. In 1977 it was estimated that 265,000 acres were in excess in the Imperial area. Much of this was in very large holdings. According to the Imperial Irrigation District, in 1978 only 25,210 acres, or 14.1 percent of the land in the district, was in holdings smaller than 160 acres; 28.3 percent, or 154,217 acres was in holdings of 1,280 acres of more. There were sixty-eight of these latter holdings, giving an average size of 2,268 acres. Included in these large holdings were 4,451 acres owned by the Southern Pacific and 5,417 acres owned by the Irvine Company.[61]

Subsidies

The failure of Reclamation Law to prevent concentration of land-ownership in federal service areas has meant that in many instances subsidies from the projects have gone to large landowners. These subsidies have three parts. First, a certain portion of costs are written off as nonreimbursable, i.e., assigned to flood control and recreation. Second, reimbursable costs are largely underwritten by other users. Reimbursable costs are those allocated to irrigators for repayment to the federal government. In 1971 the Bureau estimated that 47 percent of the costs of the authorized and completed main features of the Central Valley Project would be allocated to irrigators. Estimates vary as to how much of this is actually being paid, but some studies indicate that irrigators only pay 17 percent while power users pay 72 percent and municipal and industrial users pay about ten percent.[62] Third, and most important, besides not paying their fair share of the costs allocated as repayable, irrigators are further subsidized by a fifty-year grace period (ten-year deferment and forty-year repayment) that carries no interest. The implicit subsidy depends on what interest rate one thinks should be used, but amounts to at least half the total even at low rates.

Because of low repayable costs, federal water prices are low. Furthermore, the projects deal in forty-year contracts with the rates fixed in advance. Many of these contracts were written in the 1950s when the maximum water rates were $3.50 per acre foot for Class I (assured) water and $1.50 per acre foot for Class II (supplemental) water. Later contracts are at higher levels. The Bureau of Reclamation reported that in 1978 the highest price paid by irrigators in the Central Valley Project was $16.50 per acre foot but this is not the common rate. The Westlands contract, which runs until 2008, sets the price at $10.50 per acre foot. The water is actually valued at $35 or more per acre foot and the cost of delivery alone exceeds $10.50 per acre foot. Imperial and Coachella Valley users pay $7.50 per acre foot.[63]

The combination of low prices and unrestricted water has made it possible for most of the irrigated acreage in California to be in field crops. For example, a 1972 study found that out of 9.1 million irrigated acres in California, 6.3 million were used for alfalfa, pasture and field crops. Only 2.8 million acres were used for truck crops and orchards. More recently, the 1978 annual report for the Bureau of Reclamation indicated that only 682,000 acres of the 2.1 million acres of harvested cropland and pasture, receiving water from the Central Valley Project were used for vegetables, fruits, and nuts. The situation in the Boulder Project service area is obfuscated by extensive multiple cropping. In 1978, 123,000 acres of the 497,000 acres of harvested cropland and pasture that received project water were multiply cropped and, in that same year, a total of 133,000 acres were used for fruits and vegetables.[64]

Water prices have not increased commensurately with the increased costs to develop the water. Thus, it has been possible for large holdings to continue cropping patterns established under the cost structure that existed before the enormous projects were built. Furthermore, previously unirrigated land has been able to move into production of field crops. Some of this land was already in large holdings; some of it was aggregated into new large holdings. For reasons other than cheap water, these holdings have also come to be used to produce specialty crops.

Labor Developments

Growers have relied on two strategies to assure themselves an adequate labor supply: importation of Mexicans and increasing use of advanced technology to decrease labor needs. Thus, grower pressure led to the continued importation of aliens under the aegis of the federal government and further work by federal and state agencies towards mechanization of the harvest. Importation of Mexicans was the major strategy used to create a demoralized labor force, unable to assert itself successfully because of oversupply and grower dominance. Technological advances have been used to circumvent the entire issue of workers by providing a substitute for them. The basic goal of the growers has been to avoid work situations in which certain worker rights are recognized and in which, as a consequence of the existence of these rights, employers accept certain responsibilities to the workers. That is, much more than wages or benefits is at stake. For example, if workers are regarded as having a right to regular employment, the whole character of California agriculture, based as it is on extreme seasonal labor demands, would have to change. Growers might have to diversify or otherwise conduct their operations differently. Thus, the fundamental concern of growers is whether they will maintain complete control of their operations or whether workers will have some say in how things are done.

Labor Supply

Growers have been quite successful in sidestepping worker demands and this has created a climate favorable to large scale operations and large holdings. The kinds of production noted as evocative of large holdings have been predicated on the ability to hire a nonmilitant labor force as needed. Labor developments since World War II have obstructed this somewhat, but worker organization has not reached the point where fundamental changes might have to be made in the structure of the industry. Wages have risen but, as will be seen, their rise can easily be supported.

In 1947 PL45, authorizing the Bracero program, expired. Growers were not prepared to relinquish this valuable source of labor. Importation of Mexicans, continued under the 9th provision to Section 3 of the 1917 immigration law, the basis for the pre-Depression importation of Mexicans. The United States and Mexico made executive agreements in 1947, 1949, and 1950 to control the program. Importation was not a big thing in those years. The 1947 agreement introduced the practice of legalizing illegal Mexicans and most of the contract workers used between 1947 and 1951 were actually "dried out wetbacks" and not new workers brought into the United States.[66] In addition, many "wetbacks" continued to work illegally. The flaws of the system in these years were well described in a 1950 study of migratory labor made by a presidential commission. Their report makes it clear why the Mexicans were so attractive to employers and in so doing adumbrates events of the next decade and a half. The commission recognized the fundamental problems of migratory labor and the failure of national policy in this area:

> We have long waivered and compromised on the issue of migratory labor in agriculture. We have failed to adopt policies designed to insure an adequate supply of such labor at decent standards of employment. Actually, we have done worse than that. We have used the institutions of government to procure alien labor willing to work under obsolete and backward conditions and thus to perpetuate those very conditions. This not only entrenches a bad system, it expands it. [66]

They found with respect to contract labor that:

> The agencies of Government responsible for importing and contracting foreign labor have not been successful in protecting domestic farm labor from detrimental effects of imported contract alien labor. We find alien labor has depressed farm wages and, therefore, has been detrimental to domestic labor. [67]

The major cause of this wage depression was the way prevailing wages, the minimum wages contract laborers received, were determined. They turned out to be the amount farm employers fixed, long in advance of the season, as the wage they wanted to pay. Public employment agencies accepted this rate and if workers were not available at it, they certified a shortage and contracted for aliens as supplemental labor. [68]

Contract workers were not alone in depressing wages. This was also noted as an effect of illegals, whose employment was quite common in California. The presidential commission found that it was because of pressures exerted by the employers of illegal aliens that the Immigration and Naturalization Service (INS) did not properly enforce the law. [69]

The commission put forward a number of recommendations, all based on the desirability of relying on American workers and eliminating dependence on foreign workers. In order that domestic workers might be attracted to farm labor, they recommended improving working conditions by bringing farm laborers under the Labor Management Relations Act (1947), under minimum wage legislation, umemployment compensation programs, general assistance (even when lacking legal residence status), the Social Security Act, and child labor laws. [70]

The commission's report had absolutely no effect on national policy. Instead, grower pressure, abetted by Korean War labor shortages, led in 1951 to the passage of PL78, which established the Bracero program. PL78 constituted a formal agreement between the United States and Mexico to provide Mexican laborers for United States agriculture. It was originally scheduled to expire on December 3, 1953, but a series of extensions conferred upon it a seeming immortality. It did not expire until December 31, 1964. Under PL78 Mexican workers would be imported to fill existing labor shortages, as long as this could be done without having an adverse effect on the wages and working conditions of similarly employed

Americans. A number of ostensible protections were written in: employers had the responsibility of making reasonable attempts to obtain domestic farm labor, Mexicans could not be used to fill jobs left vacant because of strikes or labor disputes, employers using illegals were to be denied braceros, and employers had to "pay the Mexican worker not less than the prevailing wage to domestic workers for similar work at the time the work is performed."[71] How this wage was to be determined was not stated.

On the United States side the program was administered by the Secretary of Labor through the Bureau of Employment Security, whose field agency in California was the State's Farm Placement Service. The program was set up so that the Farm Placement Service certified the existence of a labor shortage and then contracted for the necessary workers. It was then responsible for enforcing the wage, housing and general working conditions of the contracts. Employers were responsible for transportation costs of the workers, fulfilling their portion of the contracts and making attempts to find domestic workers.

This program was not very different from the earlier program and conferred the same benefits to growers, particularly during the 1950s. These were the years when Ed Hayes headed the Farm Placement Service, years when it was "subservient to growers."[72] Thus, growers associations continued to establish prevailing wages, token attempts to locate domestics workers were accepted, braceros were used to break strikes and for uncertified tasks, illegals were employed along with braceros, and, in general, the terms of the work contracts with the Mexicans were flouted resulting in underpayment and violations of their rights.

The biggest opponent of the program was the National Agricultural Workers Union (NAWU) headed by Ernesto Galarza. NAWU was an American Federation of Labor (AFL) affiliate formed in 1947 under the name National Farm Labor Union (NFLU). In that year it became active in California and initiated a three-year strike against Di Giorgio that ultimately failed. In 1955 it became NAWU and in 1960 essentially became defunct. In the attempt to organize farm workers, it became apparent that the Bracero program was presenting insuperable obstacles—hence, the NAWU campaign against the program. The campaign included Galarza's 1956 exposé *Strangers in Our Fields*, which brought public attention to the pernicious influence of the program. Finally, Ed Hayes was forced to resign in 1960 and in the next few years the Farm Placement Service became more supportive of the intent of the program. For example, in 1960, director Irving Perluss refused, despite heavy grower pressure, to allow braceros to be used by growers affected by strikes.[73] Growers began to reform but it was too late. The program was on its way out; its faults had become too glaring.

The early 1960s were a time of endless negative reports on the Bracero program. For example, a 1961 report of the California Senate Fact Finding Committee found that:

The Bracero program had been used by farmers in some areas of the

State to freeze wages at low levels, that domestic labor was being discriminated against in favor of the braceros and that farmers and farm associations who hired braceros actively impeded domestics from applying for work or harassed them to the point of not returning once they were hired.[74]

In that same year, Arthur Goldberg stated:

Evidence accumulated by the Department of Labor proves beyond doubt that the mass importation of Mexican labor has had, and is having, an adverse effect on the wages, working conditions and employment opportunities of United States farm workers.[75]

Nonetheless, the program was extended until 1963, and then a final one-year extension was made to give growers time to adjust to the end of the program.

The growers' already strong organization was fostered by the Bracero program. Rarely did individuals contract for braceros. Instead, grower organizations, many formed expressly for this purpose and others already existing, did the contracting for their members and handled all the mechanics of the program. These were the same organizations that set the prevailing wages and decided how many braceros to recruit. They were well able to send lobbyists to Washington to fight for their cause. This is why growers were able to obtain such a long life for the program.

Growers did not give up on Mexicans and attempted to circumvent the termination of the program by bringing in braceros under PL414, the McCarran-Walter Act. This was effectively squelched by administrative decisions made by Secretary of Labor Willard Wirtz, that set conditions under which Mexicans might be employed. Mostly, these were similar to those of the PL78 program. They were more rigorous with respect to what constituted genuine efforts to recruit domestic help. Most critical was inclusion of a minimum wage for California workers of $1.25 an hour from January 1, 1965 through March 31, 1965, after which it rose to $1.40 an hour. The previous minimum, established in 1962, had been $1.00 an hour. Growers found these new standards prohibitive and importation of contract Mexicans came to an end. In 1964, the last year of the PL78 program, the peak number of foreign contract workers was estimated at 63,900. In 1965 this dropped to 11,400 and then to 7,800 in 1966, after which none were used.[76]

Illegals had been used throughout the PL78 years and they did not leave the fields along with braceros. Enforcement of immigration laws has been feeble. Rochin, after considering the number of illegals returned to Mexico, infers that there has been an increase in the number of illegals since the end of the Bracero program. He also points out that on January 31, 1977 there were 22,671 legal commuters living along the United States-Mexican border plus untold numbers with false identification.[77] Unfortunately, it is impossible to find much precise information about the numbers of illegals working in California agriculture. As the state's Rural Manpower Report for

1974 indicated, "*No one* knows exactly the magnitude of the illegal alien problem."[78] However, the Immigration and Naturalization Service (INS) estimated that during 1974 at least 122,000 illegal aliens worked in California agriculture, displacing domestics and probably lowering wages. Also, in September 1976 the regional chief of the U.S Border in Pleasonton stated his belief that approximately 150,000 California farmworkers were illegal aliens from Mexico. In the 1979 lettuce strike, the use of illegals as strikebreakers and lack of enforcement by the INS was extensively documented by the United Farm Workers Organizing Committee (UFWOC).[79] Unfortunately, the presence of illegals makes it difficult to assess the impact of the braceros. To some degree illegals seem to have replaced braceros and mitigated the effects of the departure of the contract workers. The actual extent to which this occurred is not ascertainable; there is simply not enough information.

Certainly, it is difficult to find an obvious effect of the end of the bracero program on agricultural production. Table 4.11 shows for selected years, from 1960 to 1966 the acreage harvested of a number of crops whose labor force was dominated by braceros. The total labor force required at the employment peak in 1960 and the percentage of Mexican nationals in the peak labor force are also indicated. There is no overall pattern, no exhibition of one set of trends before 1965 and another set after the end of the program. Snap beans and processing tomatoes were the only crops to

TABLE 4.11
1960 Percentage of Mexicans in Labor Force and Acreage
Harvested for Bracero-dominated Crops, 1960-1966

	Labor (1960)					
Crop	Total Number	Percent Mexicans	Acreage (per thousand acres)			
			1960	1964	1965	1966
Asparagus	10,050	55%	73.5	65.5	54.9	51.9
Snap Beans	7,400	35	7.8	8.8	11.2	14.6
Cotton	21,200	15	946.0	743.0	725.0	618.0
Lemons	8,850	80	50.7	42.9	42.1	40.5
Lettuce	7,600	85	124.9	115.1	115.6	120.7
Oranges*	6,250	48	76.3	62.1	63.2	64.9
Sugar Beets	7,700	51	206.6	354.3	309.7	269.7
Strawberries	17,958	56	11.7	9.0	8.3	7.8
Tomatoes*	44,000	85	130.0	143.0	122.8	162.5

Source: Labor information from University of California, Division of Agricultural Sciences (1963), p.17; acreages from reports of the California Crop and Livestock Reporting Service.

Note: Valencia oranges and processing tomatoes only.

show a response to the end of the program. The change in snap beans is not obvious from Table 4.11, which reports total acreage. The composition of the acreage changed; the number of acres in beans marketed fresh was declining throughout the 1960s while the acreage in processing beans increased, most conspicuously after 1964. A mechanical harvester for processing beans was introduced in 1963. The 1965 acreage decline in processing tomato acreage was recouped in 1966 when braceros were successfully replaced by machines. The percent of acreage machine harvested increased from 25 percent to 65 percent from 1965 to 1966. Total lettuce acreage remained constant, masking shifts towards greater production of winter lettuce and less of fall and spring varieties. Fluctuations within each lettuce category seem to follow prices, as shown in Table 4.12.

A year of good prices is followed by overplanting and price collapse. Sugar beet and cotton acreages changed largely in response to allotments. Thus, the 1965 plummet in sugar beet acreage was due to the reimposition of acreage allotments. Strawberries were affected by overproduction in 1957, the resulting poor prices drove many small producers out of business and also led to decreases in plantings. Asparagus began a decline in acreage in 1959 that is still continuing and is mostly due to the loss of the white asparagus market.[80]

This lack of pattern is particularly interesting in light of the fact that wages rose, some rather significantly, after the program ended.[81] It was pointed out in 1964 that ". . . even if farm wages were doubled, and the entire cost was passed on to the consumer, it would have the effect of raising the supermarket price on a pound of tomatoes by 1 cent per can, from 25 cents to 26 cents. The example of tomatoes is very much the rule rather than the exception."[82]

It was found that after the braceros left and lettuce wages rose to $1.40 an hour, the cost per head rose only ¼ cent a head.[83] Growers, although preferring low wages, did not appear to need them for survival. This will be

TABLE 4.12
Price Fluctuations for Winter Lettuce, 1962-1967

Year	Winter lettuce acreage	Average price (per cwt)
1962	37,700	$4.30
1963	41,800	3.95
1964	40,308	5.40
1965	46,700	3.15
1966	42,600	6.80
1967	49,400	3.35

discussed again below in considering the effects of unionization. Yet the growers had claimed great dependence on braceros and dire predictions had preceded the termination of the program. Judging from the aftereffects (even allowing for some compensation by illegals), the intensity of the desire for braceros was not matched by a genuine need. Other factors appear to have had a more noticeable effect on agricultural production. As was seen above, these other factors also led to increases in large holdings.

The question here is whether braceros also contributed to the increase in large holdings. All employers benefitted from the wage depression and assurance of a labor supply that came from the Bracero program. However, it is large-scale producers who rely most on hired labor. These producers tendency to flourish could only be aggrandized by the presence of the braceros, but it is not clear whether or not the bracero role was fundamental. This would depend on the alternatives. Since it appears that higher wages could be borne, the limiting factor would be the availability of sufficient labor. Yet, had wages and working conditions improved, owing to an absence of braceros, it is not likely that workers would have been unavailable. Clearly, the growers were aiming for a special type of labor force, a pliable, poorly paid one, but it is not evident that their success depended on anything more than the presence of an adequate labor force. There is no evidence that large producers fared poorly after the program ended. For example, Calpak, Di Giorgio, D'Arrigo Brothers, and Bud Antle were among the larger users of braceros. Yet they had existed before the program and continued to endure.

The most important aspect of the Bracero program for employers was its prevention of organization among the workers. The only active union between 1947 and 1960 was NAWU. Although it led a number of strikes and met with some success, its energies were ultimately dissipated in the battle against the Bracero program, its largest obstacle to success. In 1960 the AFL-CIO created the Agricultural Workers Organizational Congress (AWOC), and in the next few years this rather ineffectual union led a number of strikes (including the ones Perluss refused to break with barceros) and made minor gains for workers. In 1962 César Chavez organized the Farm Workers Association (FWA, later NFWA, then UFWOC, finally UFW). Its first major activity was the 1965 grape strike and grape boycotts, which resulted in 1967 in contracts with such wine grape growers as Schenley, Di Giorgio, Perelli Minetti, and Gallo. In 1968 they moved into table grapes, began another boycott, and by 1970 had brought Guimarra Brothers and other growers under contract. When contracts began running out, growers tried to switch to the Teamsters and yet another round of boycotts began, with Gallo and Guimarra the most prominent targets.

During all of these boycotts, Safeway and Lucky stores continued to stock produce from the struck growers. Both chains were often picketed. At the same time lettuce became the scene of battles between the Teamsters (brought in by Bud Antle in 1961) and UFWOC. In March 1978 the Teamsters agreed to give up jurisdiction of field workers. Other strikes have occurred during the years. The most recent have been in lettuce and garlic.

Because of UFW activity, farmworkers have made some gains since the bracero years. One important victory was the passage of the state's Agricultural Labor Relations Act (1975). This act is so supportive of unionization that employers now cast longing eyes at the once-spurned Management Labor Relations Act (1947). Also prominent have been wage increases. Again, large growers have not borne this with equanimity, but they have not been leaving agriculture because of it. Schenley is one exception. It sold its Delano vineyard to the tax-loss farmer, Buttes Gas and Oil, creating a new large owner, while still owning several thousand acres further north. Di Giorgio sold out because of the Bureau of Reclamation, but Bud Antle, Guimarra, and Gallo, for example, are still carrying on profitably.

Although there have been other achievements, farmworkers do not appear to have accomplished enough to affect growers seriously and they may never do so with more and more crops coming to be harvested mechanically. In other industries with strong unions, the negative effects of mechanization on workers have been controlled to some degree. California agricultural workers are not in a strong enough position to ward off the deleterious effects of unemployment, income loss, and high accident rates or to force development of programs to retrain displaced workers. Under these circumstances, growers not only lower costs with mechanization but they also maintain control over their operations. Avoidance of unionization has been cited by many as a major reason for mechanization.[84] That is, the UFW has been successful enough to push growers to seek a substitute for labor.

Labor Substitution

Almost all farm labor needs have fallen because of technological advances. Less labor is needed to water the crops because of drip irrigation and automatic sprinkler systems. Pesticides and fertilizers are applied by sprinklers, airplanes and so on to lower labor requirements. Better tractors, plows and discs allow fields to be more quickly prepared for planting. Vineyards and a number of orchard crops are currently susceptible to mechanized pruning. In 1976, 15 percent of all grapes, 33 percent of cling peaches, 10 percent of freestone peaches, 10 percent of lemons, and 10 percent of walnuts were mechanically pruned. Some crops have experienced significant decreases in the labor needed to thin and hoe, owing to chemical control of weeds, chemical weeding, and mechanical thinning. Use of herbicides has increased very rapidly lately. Better weed control and cultural practices have been responsible for decreases in the labor required to hoe potatoes, thin dry beans, and thin and hoe sugar beets. In 1976, 15 percent of apples were chemically thinned and 40 percent of apricots were mechanically thinned.[85]

The largest cutbacks in labor have resulted from harvest mechanization. The first harvests to be mechanized after World War II were sugar beets and cotton. Work on sugar beet mechanization was hastened by the World War II labor shortages. During the war, machinery manufacturers, agricultural experiment stations (University of California operated), sugar companies, and the United States Department of Agriculture all worked together to produce prototype harvesters. After the war, these came into wide use. In 1945 only 28 percent of the acreage was machine harvested; in 1951 it was 75 percent of the acreage planted (which was twice the acrea planted in 1945), and within a few years the entire harvest was mechanized. Much hand labor is still required for weeding and thinning beets, hence the continued use of braceros during the years they were available.[86]

Cotton strippers first came into use at the end of World War II. In 1945, 8 percent of the California crop was machine harvested, in 1951 54 percent, and in 1962 approximately 95 percent of the crop was harvested by strippers.[87] Although the Agricultural Experiment Station does not appear to have been directly involved in the development of the stripper, they did a great deal of work studying its performance and helping farmers in its use.

Work on mechanizing the harvest of deciduous fruits began in 1942. For these crops mechanization also involves cultural practices affecting the way trees are pruned and because trees are long-lived crops, adoption of a viable machine is often slowed up by a lack of suitable orchards. Thus, even though mechanization was possible in the 1950s for nuts and prunes, it was not until the mid 1960s that the entire crops were mechanically harvested. Other fruits have been less prone to mechanization. In 1978 only 9.8 percent of the apricot acreage, 30 percent of the cling peach acreage, 10-15 percent of the olive acreage and 30 percent of the wine grape acreage were mechanically harvested.[88] Citrus fruit harvests have not been mechanized at all.

Mechanization of vegetables has been most successful with processing varieties. The prime example in California is processing tomatoes. Work on varieties of tomatoes suitable for mechanical harvesting began in the 1940s and work on a machine began in 1947. This was a University of California project in its entirety. By 1961 a viable machine was available but it did not catch on until the Bracero program ended. By 1969, 99.5 percent of the crop was mechanically harvested. Presently, further developments in terms of electronic sorters are being introduced. All of processing asparagus, snap beans, and celery are presently mechanically harvested.[89] Of vegetables that are not used for processing, potatoes, carrot and beans were mechanized in the mid 1960s and in the past two years a fresh tomato harvester and a lettuce harvester have been produced by the University of California Agricultural Extension Service. An onion harvester is available but not yet widely used.

Mechanization has come in for a great deal of criticism because so much of the research and development has been performed by a public institution, the University of California (through the Agricultural Extension Service and Agricultural Experiment Station), yet only a few have benefitted. Those few are the large-scale producers. This is not always because of the scale of production necessary to use harvesters profitably. Many crops can be mechanized by small or medium sized growers. Among specialty crops vegetable harvesters have the highest requirements. The new tomato harvester/sorter needs 250 to 300 acres of tomatoes and the onion harvester needs 250 acres for optimal results. Farm size would actually have to be much larger to accommodate the rotations required by field crops and vegetables. Requirements for orchards and vineyards are smaller. Walnut harvesters need 25-30 acres, olive harvesters 75 acres, prune harvesters 50 acres, cling peach harvesters 80 acres and wine grape harvesters 160 acres. Furthermore, extra land for rotations is not necessary. [90]

Cotton and sugar beets were already being produced on a large scale before mechanization. Thus, mechanization could not be directly responsible for large holdings used for these crops. Processing tomatoes have been an exceptional crop in that their mechanization is directly responsible for increases in holding size. The average size of tomato farm rose from 32.3 acres in 1963 (before mechanization) to 363.3 acres in 1973. [91] As John Anderson, the large owner discussed above, has said "without mechanization, we would not be here." [92] For fruits and nuts the high initial cost of mechanization militates against the adoption of new technology by small owners and operators. Either new plantings or restructuring of existing orchards and vineyards are necessary (the latter is not even always possible). The large orchards have been planted since mechanical harvesters have become available.

In general, regardless of the scale of production necessary to mechanize, large owners, because of their overall rosier financial picture will be able to mechanize first. Their production costs will be lower than those of hand-harvest producers and, in time, the smaller operators will either be driven out of business or forced to mechanize. The latter may not be financially possible for them.* Mechanization not only helps make large-scale production feasible; it, combined with their credit advantages, gives large-scale production definite advantages.

Who Owns the Land?

This section summarizes the results of the study described in Appendix A. The complete results of the study are presented in Appendix B. In sum, 757 owners hold 6.7 million acres of agricultural land. Table 4.13 shows their distribution by eleven size categories and indicates the acreage held in each category. It must be emphasized that this only refers to agricultural land; nonagricultural land was excluded from the study so far as was possible. The total Southern Pacific Railroad landholding, for example, is

---

*This is not an obstacle to the extent that they can avail themselves of custom harvesting and leasing of machinery. But there can be dangers in this, in that the small operator would be must susceptible to neglect by the custom harvester in favor of his larger customers. This could be disastrous when there are deadlines to be met at the cannery or the crop needs to be harvested.

not counted — only the portion that was deemed agricultural land.

Almost all (94.4 percent) the holdings are smaller than 20,000 acres but these holdings only account for 57.8 percent of the land in large holdings. The largest holdings dominate the landownership situation. Table 4.14 gives a county breakdown of the acreage. The total acreage is smaller than that in the first table because some information did not include county breakdowns. The biggest holdings left out are Tejon Ranch and Tenneco Inc. (which are mostly in Kern county); I preferred to use sources other than the maps to ascertain their size. That over 100 more holdings are counted in this table than in the first table is indicative of the large number of multi-county holdings. A phenomenon similar to that of multi-county holdings is the lack of contiguity within individual holdings. Most frequently, large holdings are scattered through several townships. Often a number of such holdings are commingled in these townships. Forty counties contain at least some land in large holdings. The Central Valley, unsurprisingly, shows extensive concentration of ownership. The central coast also encompasses many large holdings while southern California shows much less concentration. It is possible that the latter is due to scanty information; the fact that the same sources were used for southern California and the central coast, though, does suggest that southern California is not just under-reported but actually has fewer large holdings. Appendix B lists all 757 holdings, with county

TABLE 4.13
Size Distribution of Large Landholdings

Acres	Number of holdings	Percent of total holdings	Acreage	Percent of acreage
2-4,999	425	56.3	1,319,654.80	19.6
5-9,999	201	26.6	1,385,215.39	20.6
10-19,999	87	11.5	1,181,400.74	17.6
20-29,999	15	2.0	366,093.00	5.4
30-39,999	9	1.2	304,907.61	4.5
40-49,999	2	.3	86,199.46	1.3
50-74,999	4	.5	214,122.10	3.2
75-99,999	4	.5	349,990.40	5.2
100-149,999	3	.4	342,145.09	5.1
150-199,999	2	.3	380,451.99	5.7
200-299,999	3	.4	792,151.60	11.8
TOTAL	757	100.0	6,721,324.18	100.0

breakdowns where applicable.

There is no comparable statistical information from the beginning of this period that can be used to adduce an increase in concentration of landownership. But that such an increase occurred is apparent from the content of the rest of this chapter. It is clear that in the major agricultural counties of California significant amounts of land are in holdings larger than 2,000 acres. Some 4 million acres or 59.8 percent of the total area in large holdings is actually in holdings larger than 10,000 acres. The tendencies described above towards expansion and diversification of production are reflected in the fact that 113 owners own land in several counties. That individual holdings are often noncontiguous and that such holdings are also often commingled provides additional explanation for the trend towards larger operating units noted above. Many large holdings are not owner-operated but are leased. They are nonetheless being used for large-scale production.

Summary and Conclusions

Significant changes have occurred in California agriculture since World War II. The most general of these are an increase in irrigated acreage of 2.7 million acres, an intensification of production, a decrease in labor needs and a rise in average farm size. Urbanization has resulted in relocations, mostly of orchards, to the well-irrigated Central Valley. The livestock industry has undergone a major reorientation toward finishing cattle, often on large-scale feedlots. Producers have become involved in feed grain production and approximately 40 percent of the water used for agriculture is used for crops related to livestock production. Production of other field crops, besides feed grains, has risen. This is most noticeable with cotton, rice, and sugar beets, crops highly supported by the federal government. Vegetable production has shown the most dramatic increase, especially in lettuce and processing vegetables. Among orchard crops, most new acreage has been devoted to nuts and wine grapes.

Overall, output has increased. This growth has been encouraged by the expansion of markets and stable prices. The growth in California's population has created larger local markets for all products. In fact, California is no longer able to supply the local demand for beef, nor is there adequate production of feed grains. Both livestock and feed are imported to the state. The federal government, through its commodity programs, has provided a good market for cotton, rice, and sugar beets. Presently, the first two are enjoying strong world demand. Marketing of specialty crops has been stabilized to some degree by federal and state marketing order programs. The development of new varieties of processed foods (frozen, freeze-dried and so on) has opened up new markets as has the expansion of distributors and processors.

Behind these developments has been a confluence of factors favorable to large producers and large landowners. The most fundamental of these has been the growth of large owners' ability to influence federal and state policies with respect to water, labor, and mechanization. Also relevant are certain marketing and price advantages of large owners and tax laws. In the post-World War II period large owners have also developed strong ties to

TABLE 4.14
County Breakdown of Acreage in Large Landholdings

County	Total acreage	Number of holdings
CENTRAL COAST		
Alameda	9,467.00	3
Contra Costa	24,312.00	9
Marin	4,800.00	1
Monterey	219,362.83	30
San Benito	93,809.22	10
San Luis Obispo	277,819.89	29
Santa Clara	15,713.00	1
Sonoma	17,054.15	6
SACRAMENTO VALLEY		
Butte	144,258.80	35
Colusa	143,276.85	22
Glenn	110,195.00	20
Sacramento	10,088.00	3
Solano	109,066.00	35
Sutter	56,778.00	17
Tehama	109,815.05	17
Yolo	206,131.80	37
Yuba	68,914.00	17
SAN JOAQUIN VALLEY		
Fresno	671,983.44	102
Kern	1,348,256.65	128
Kings	464,303.36	38
Madera	295,097.32	60
Merced	461,287.40	68
San Joaquin	160,662.00	40
Stanislaus	88,245.00	11
Tulare	469,027.22	73
SOUTHERN CALIFORNIA		
Imperial	45,594.00	10
Los Angeles	12,677.00	4
Orange	145,967.00	4
Riverside	105,603.00	4
San Bernardino	16,559.00	4
San Diego	33,614.00	2
Santa Barbara	48,161.00	3
Ventura	19,288.00	3
OTHER		
Amador	33,000.00	1
Lassen	21,640.00	4
Modoc	59,752.00	7
Placer	5,500.00	2
Plumas	7,510.00	2
Shasta	6,400.00	1
Siskiyou	29,983.00	6
TOTAL	6,209,721.98	870

other economic interests—the ever-larger marketing cooperatives, processors, distributors, retailers, and nonfarm interests who have invested in production. From this has come greater political clout.

Large owners have been influential enough to prevent enforcement of the acreage and residency restrictions by the Bureau of Reclamation. They have also developed another, completely unrestricted source of water throughout the State Water Project. The higher costs associated with the latter have been reduced through the magic of surplus water. Their success is obvious from the concentration of large owners in the service areas of these projects. Large owners have also been able to assure themselves of the labor they need. They were able to keep the Bracero program alive until 1964 and they also were able to have much of the research and development necessary for mechanization performed by the University of California and by agencies of the USDA.

Other advantages for large owners have derived from being favored by processors, distributors, and retailers and, in the case of large cotton and rice producers, the ability to achieve significant gains from ASCS programs. The entrance of conglomerates and other nonfarm investors into production has hurt small farmers. These investors are better able to bear bad years. Furthermore, vertically integrated corporations are sometimes able to make up losses at the farm with higher profits from processing (low prices at the farm means lower production costs for the processor). All these larger interests are able to reap various tax benefits not available to lower income entities.

These factors have an unequal weight for different products. Because large owners have been diversifying their land use, these differences are not always apparent. Cheap water is the predominant factor for extensive uses. Much land would not have been brought into production, nor would water be squandered on these crops, if large owners had to bear the full costs of development. Labor and marketing factors have been most relevant for intensive uses. Without the presence of readily available labor, production of specialty crops would have been impossible. It was not, however, that large owners needed cheap labor to survive. Their real advantage over small farmers, however, came with mechanization, which has given them a competitive edge. In the years prior to mechanization, or for crops like lettuce that remain unmechanized, large growers have achieved prominence because of marketing advantages.

Thus, large-scale operators and large owners have come to dominate California agriculture. The concern here is only with the latter. There are 757 of them, owning 6.7 million acres of land in California's major agricultural regions. This is only a lower bound on their number; the tabulation is not complete.

Notes

1. Irrigated acreage from United States Bureau of the Census (1977), p. 1-1; seasonal workers from California Employment Development Department (1980) for 1980, California Employment Development Department (1979) for 1966 to 1979 and California Department of Employment, *Annual Report* for each of 1952 to 1965.
2. United States Bureau of the Census (1977), p. 1-1.
3. *San Francisco Chronicle*, (Nov. 14, 1980), p. 4.
4. Land (1968), p. 432.
5. Land (1968), pp. 433-34.
6. Land (1968), p. 435.
7. King *et al.* (1980), p. 23.
8. Cothern (1973) p. 6.
9. King *et al.* (1980) p. 2 for 42 percent.
10. *Walker's Manual of Pacific Coast Securities* for the year 1978, p. 975.
11. Davenport (1972), p. 1073 for administrative decisions; Carman (1978), p. 1 for capital gains.
12. Carman (1978), p. 12 for 60 percent; Carman (1976), p. 7 for 1974; ASCS records for San Luis Obispo County, 1978 at California Institute of Rural Studies for original Armendaris holding; San Luis Obispos County Assessor's letter, 1978 at California Institute for Rural Studies; Oppenheimer Industries, *10-K Report* for the year 1980 for 1,900.
13. Cochrane and Ryan (1976) passim.
14. Fellmeth (1973), p. 71.
15. Ibid.
16. Krebs (1972) pp. 3058, 3091.
17. Wills (1953), p. 168 for Crockett and Gambody; Krebs (1972), p. 3091 for Tulare Lake Land Co.; AGRI-LAND map for Tulare County for ownership listing; Villarejo (1980), p. 43 for Tulare Lake Representatives and Bowles.
18. United States of America, Congress (1959), p. 7669 for 1959; Personal communication from Jerry White for recent holdings; United States Senate, Committee on Energy and Natural Resources (1979), p. 338 for Southern Pacific.
19. Krebs (1972), p. 3091. United States Department of Agriculture, Agricultural Stabilization and Conservation Service, *Annual Report* for each of 1973 through 1979.
20. United States of America, Congress (1977), pp. 11139-40.
21. French, *et al.* (1978), pp. 2, 23.
22. Ibid., pp. 50-54, 64-65; United States Comptroller General (1976), pp. 52-53 for 1975 study.
23. Ibid., p. 57.
24. Villarejo (1980), pp. 22-29.
25. Villarejo (1980), pp. 61-62 for Sun Harvest; ASCS records at California Institute for Rural Studies for others.
26. Dangerfield (1973), p. S9248.
27. Carman (1978), p. 13.
28. *Cooperative Digest.* . . (1951), p. D-21 for 1947; *American Cooperation, 1979-1980* (July 1980), p. 449 for 1975-1976; Krebs (1972), p. 3119; *Standard and Poor's Register of Corporations, Directors and Executives, 1981*, Vol. 2 and 3 passim. (1981), pp. 238, 1676.
29. Kyle *et al.* (1972), p. 9; also see Fellmeth (1973), p. 70 about Spreckels preferring to deal with large growers.
30. Friedland and Barton (1976), p. 5.
31. United States Senate, Committee on Public Lands (1947), p. 958 for 1947 holdings.
32. Krebs (1972), p. 3123 for Tenneco land in 1970; Tenneco *10-K Report* for the year 1980, for present holdings (the difference is approximately 100,000); Krebs (1972), p. 3124 for sale to Roberts; Villarejo (1978), p. 53 for Roberts' sale.

33. United States Senate, Committee on Agriculture, Nutrition and Forestry (1979), p. III.
34. Villarejo (1978), pp. 47, 48, 51, 63; "Onward and Upward with the Arts," *New Yorker* (Oct. 13, 1980), p. 79 for pistachios; Bangor Punta *10-K Report* for the year 1979.
35. *Dixon Tribune* (Aug. 28, 1980), p. 13 for 221,000; United States Senate, Committee on Agriculture, Nutrition and Forestry (1979), pp. 266, 268 for treaties; *Daily Californian* (Jan. 1, 1980), p. 1 for Coblentz.
36. United States Senate, Select Committee on Small Business (1978), p. 8.
37. *Standard and Poor's Register of Corporations, Directors and Executives, 1981*, Vol. 2 and 3 passim.
38. California State Assembly (1955), p. 209.
39. Kahrl (1978), p. 50; United States Senate, Committee on Labor and Public Welfare (1972), p. 1716.
40. Taylor (1962), p. 25.
41. Taylor (1962), p. 13; Bain *et al.* (1966), p. 570.
42. Kahrl (1978), p. 54.
43. Kahrl (1978), p. 54 for how costs are allocated; California Department of Water Resources (1980), p. 310 for costs.
44. California Department of Water Resources (1980), pp. 227, 312, 314 for entitlement water, surplus water and cost of surplus water; California Department of Water Resources (1977), p. 192 for cost of entitlement water in 1976.
45. Kahrl (1978), p. 50; United States Bureau of Reclamation (1978), *Summary Report,* p. 12.
46. Ogden (1980), pp. 126, 127 for court decision and environmental impact statements; United States Senate, Committee on Energy and Natural Resources (1978), p. 613 for excess land.
47. Upton (1978), pp. 1-3.
48. Ogden (1980), pp. 106, 127; Taylor (1959), pp. 327, 329 for 1957 excess land.
49. Bain (1966), p. 479 for lump sum offer; United States Senate, Committee on Energy and Natural Resources (1978), p. 613 for 1977 excess land; Ballard (1980), p. 49 for lobbying; Taylor (1964), pp. 1008-10; United States Senate, Committee on Energy and Natural Resources (1978), pp. 1289, 1291 for contracts and contractors.
50. Bain *et al.* (1966), p. 404 for 1943; United States of America, Congress (1959), p. 7669 for 1959 owners.
51. Bain *et al.* (1966), p. 405.
52. California Westside Farmers (1977).
53. United States Senate, Select Committee on Small Business (1978), p. 5.
54. Ibid., p. 4 for effect of group sales; United States Senate, Committee on Energy and Natural Resources (1979), pp. 335-37 for extent of sales.
55. United States Senate, Select Committee on Small Business (1978), p. 3.
56. United States General Accounting Office (1972), p. 10.
57. Ibid., p. 11.
58. Reich (1967), n.p.
59. United States Senate, Select Committee on Small Business (1978), pp. 14-15.
60. Taylor (1973), pp. 9-13; *San Francisco Chronicle* (Dec. 12, 1980), p. 16 for Senate.
61. United States Senate, Committee on Energy and Natural Resources (1978), pp. 436, 439, 613.
62. Kahrl (1978), pp. 54, 56.
63. United States Bureau of Reclamation (1978), *Statistical Appendix III,* p. 49; *Daily Californian* (March 30, 1978), p. 8; personal communication from Richard Walker for Imperial costs .
64. United States Bureau of Reclamation (1978), *Statistical Appendix I,* pp. 68, 102.
65. President's Commission on Migratory Labor (1951), pp. 52-54.
66. President's Commission on Migratory Labor (1951), p. 23.
67. President's Commission on Migratory Labor (1951), p. 59.

68. Ibid., pp. 59-61.
69. Ibid., pp. 75-76, 78-80.
70. *Ibid.,* pp. 178-85 passim.
71. Galarza (1964), p. 135.
72. Gunterman (1965), p. 8.
73. Galarza (1964), passim. for flouted rights; London and Anderson (1970), p. 39 for NAWU; California Department of Employment (1960), pp. 50-53 for Perluss.
74. Quoted in Williamson (1965), p. 7.
75. Quoted in "Citizens for Farm Labor Testimony at Department of Labor Hearing" (December 1964), p. 23.
76. California Department of Employment (1964), p. 22; California Department of Employment (1966), p. 10.
77. Rochin (1977), pp. 3, 14.
78. California Employment Development Department (1974), p. 16.
79. Ibid. for 1974 estimate; Rochin (1977), p. 19 for 1976; United States Senate, Committee on Labor and Human Resources (1979), pp. 648-60.
80. Friedland and Barton (1976), p. 1 for tomatoes; Johnston and Dean (1969), pp. 88-89 for strawberries; Barnett *et al.* (1978), p. 177 for asparagus.
81. United States Senate, Committee on Labor and Public Welfare (1966a), pp. 18-19.
82. State of California, Hearings on Farm Labor (1964), p. 8 Appendix A.
83. United States Senate, Committee on Migratory Labor (1966b), p. 158.
84. United States Senate, Committee on Labor and Human Resources (1979), p. 664-68 for 1947 act yearnings; California Employment Development Department (1974), p. 16 for wage increases; California Agrarian Action Project (1979) passim. and "The Latest Threat to Chavez: Mechanization," *Nation* (Jan. 30, 1980), pp. 69-70 for avoidance.
85. Kumar *et al.* (1978), pp. 181, 190-95.
86. Bailey (1952), p. 2-3 for sugar beets.
87. Hedges and Bailey (1954), p. 4 for 1951; University of California Division of Agricultural Sciences (1963), p. B-191 for 1963.
88. Fridley and Adrian (1966), p. 1 and Johnston and Bailey (1969), pp. 47, 51 for history; Barnett *et al.* (1978), pp. 88, 109, 123, 134 for percentages harvested in 1978.
89. Friedland and Barton (1976), p. 1 for tomatoes; Barnett *et al.* (1978), pp. 168, 180 for other vegetables;
90. Tomatoes from United States Senate, Committee on Energy and Natural Resources (1978), p. 730; Barnett *et al.* (1978), pp. 38, 50, 114, 137, 197 for tomatoes again and all others.
91. Villarejo (1980), p. 45.
92. Ibid., p. 29.

5

Conclusions on the Development of Large Landholdings

The most obvious conclusion that can be reached about large agricultural landholdings in California is that there is no single explanation for their existence. The considerable number of such holdings that has been present throughout California's history does not represent the same phenomenon. The use, location, and owners of these holdings have been changing. Although this study has been divided into four time periods, it is most useful here to consider three periods: the pre-American period, the American period through 1918, and the post-World War I period. The latter two are distinguished by the post-World War I cessation of acquisition of new holdings from the public domain and cessation of subdivision of large holdings for more intensive cultivation.

Pre-American Period

The pre-American period consists of the Spanish and Mexican ownerships of California. The Spanish settlement of California began in 1769. It was conducted through a system of missions established along the coast. The missions developed an agriculture that consisted mostly of livestock; each mission also had gardens devoted to fruits and vegetables and produced some grains. The livestock formed the basis of a profitable trade in hides and tallow. The native Indians supplied the necessary labor, being treated rather like slaves.

Spain made a few land grants to private citizens but land grants were basically a Mexican legacy. Mexico did not make significant numbers of grants until after secularizing the missions in 1834. The mission lands were carved up and granted to private citizens who continued to raise livestock on their ranchos and to participate in the hide and tallow trade. The

177

rancheros also availed themselves of Indian labor, managing to keep the Indians in bondage. At the time of the American takeover, more than 800 grants had been made. Ultimately, 588, occupying 8 million acres, were confirmed. These encompassed much of the land along the coast as far north as Sonoma County and some land in the interior valleys.

The most significant aspect of this period is its lack of long-lasting effect. The agriculture established by the missions was largely lost. The rancheros' style of livestock production was superceded by that brought in by the Americans with their new cattle and sheep. The famous Spanish-Mexican land grants, which are often cited as precursors of present land concentration, have had a very limited impact, both because they typically were not located in the present major agricultural regions and because most have been subdivided.

First American Period

In the first American period (1846-1918), large holdings were derived from the grants and, more importantly, from the land owned by the federal and state governments. Until about 1870 interest centered on the state land. The most distinguishing characteristic of public land disposal was the ease with which large holdings were acquired. The railroads were simply given millions of acres. Laws with the ostensible purpose of limiting one person's acquisition were easily circumvented. This was not unique to California. What was unusual was the degree to which these large holdings endured. This can best be understood in the light of their use.

Large holdings were acquired for any of a number of purposes: livestock production, grain production, speculation and mineral production. California agriculture, until the 1890s, was basically livestock and wheat production. The Americans brought their own cattle and sheep and reestablished the livestock industries during the 1850s. At first cattle predominated, but between 1860 and 1877 sheep were more important; wool was an important California product. Drought wiped out the industry and it never returned to its 1877 prominence. Livestock production remained important. The spread of cultivation forced livestock inland, to drier and/or topographically rougher areas where large holdings would be necessary for production. The largest individual holding of this period (outside of the railroad) belonged to Miller and Lux Company, a cattle company. In fact, the largest holdings formed in this period were all devoted to livestock.

Wheat production began in the 1850s. A highly profitable trade was soon established with Great Britain and production expanded rapidly. Mechanization made wheat production feasible on a large scale and wheat bonanzas came to dominate the Central Valley. In the 1880s wheat prices collapsed and fruit production, then in its infancy, became quite popular. What happened during this period was that livestock and mineral holdings endured; there was no reason to subdivide them. Speculative holdings (including that of the railroad), acquired for their resale value, were constantly being subdivided and after the 1890s some large grain farms were also being subdivided.

Large holdings were subdivided for fruit production because the costs of large-scale development were not warranted by the condition of fruit markets. The owners were best off either selling out or putting the land into irrigated extensive crops. Most of the subdivision was handled by speculators and not the actual large farmers. Advertising campaigns and the profits the highly erratic fruit markets could sometimes produce attracted small farmers, many of whom later went bankrupt. However, the surviving small farmers were able to successfully establish fruit cultivation as a profitable enterprise and this created the basis for later large-scale production.

Three factors were important with respect to intensive cultivation: markets, water, and labor. Farmers were able to solve many of their marketing problems through cooperative marketing associations. Initial efforts were made in this direction in the 1880s and by the second decade of the twentieth century several powerful co-ops were in existence. Some large owners even began to convert some of their land into large orchards.

Water development presented many problems. California had adopted two conflicting sets of laws concerning water rights: riparian and appropriative rights. Much litigation resulted, increasing the cost of development. The biggest gains in irrigation development occurred in the years after marketing associations became somewhat effective and by 1918, the end of this period, 4.2 million acres were irrigated. Yet, most of this acreage was used extensively, for pasture, hay, or grains.

The production of highly seasonal crops, of low profitability, led to a need for a cheap labor force incapable of making demands on the growers. Indians were briefly used in the early American years, but the Chinese were really the first source of cheap labor. Chinese had been brought to California to work on the railroad. When the railroad was completed, they went to work on other construction projects, in agriculture, and in other menial forms of employment. They became a major source of agricultural labor. Their immigration was banned in 1886 resulting in their dropping out of agriculture. During the 1890s Americans left unemployed by industrial depression supplied labor to agriculture. Also, the Japanese began to work in agriculture. Soon the Japanese replaced the Chinese. Towards the end of the period, Mexicans began to take the Japanese's place.

Typically, an oversupply of laborers existed and this rendered vain any attempts made by workers to organize. Because intensive production was associated with small holdings during these years, the existence of a cheap labor force was most important to the success of subdivision and not the persistence of large holdings.

It should be mentioned that in the delta area, foreigners played an important role as tenant farmers, whose presence enabled a number of large holdings to endure. The row crops grown in the delta were highly profitable. It does not appear to be feasible to develop orchards and vineyards with tenant farmers. Even today, tenancy is uncommon with orchards and vineyards. Had it been possible to develop orchards with tenant farmers and had prices been stronger, many large holdings would not have had to subdivide.

Second American Period

Shortly after World War I agriculture fell into depression, remaining there until World War II. Since World War II agriculture has been fairly stable because of the federal support programs initiated in the 1930s. During the Depression, bankruptcy and foreclosure were common. In such a climate subdivision languished and it did not return with prosperity. Instead, concentration of operations and aggregation of holdings became the prevailing tendencies. These tendencies achieved their full expression in the post-World War II period, but their basis was laid during the interwar period.

During the interwar period, livestock, field, and row crop production continued, but the general trend was toward more intensive irrigated production. Two new irrigated crops, cotton and rice, rose to prominence. Both are easy to produce on a large scale. Previously unirrigated large holdings were brought into cotton production because the owners were able to bear the costs of sinking deep wells. Other irrigated large holdings switched to these crops. Federal commodity programs kept these crops valuable. Specialty-crop production was attractive because fruit prices became demoralized later than those of field crops, and vegetable prices remained relatively strong throughout the Depression. Federal marketing orders and the proliferation of marketing cooperatives gave some help to producers. Also, changes in consumption patterns and development of new processed products opened up more markets. Large-scale production of specialty crops became more common. Those with adequate financial resources, including some successful corporations in the agriculturally linked industries, became large owners by purchasing land owned by less fortunate farmers. Some of this was already developed land, thus providing another route to large holdings devoted to specialty crops. Large holdings were sometimes composed of a number of smaller, discontiguous parcels; that is, the scale of production on each parcel was not very large, although overall, the owner was a large-scale producer.

In the post-World War II period dependence on irrigation has increased. Irrigated acreage has grown by more than 2.5 million acres. Livestock production is more oriented towards irrigated pastures and feed grains (the latter are often grown in rotation with other more valuable irrigated crops). Much large-scale vegetable production occurs on leased land, but large orchards and vineyards have become quite common, mostly reflecting continuing development from the interwar period and, in part, because of mechanization and tax breaks. Specialty crops are significantly more valuable and expansion of their production has been encouraged by growth in their markets. Developments in food processing and the expansion of marketing cooperatives, distributors, processors, and retailers have opened up new markets. Diversity of production on large holdings has become common. Not only are large holdings being used for livestock and field crops, they are also growing fruits and vegetables.

Since World War I, three sets of actors have become especially important for California agriculture: the state and federal governments, farm organizations, and nonfarm interests who have become involved in some aspect of agriculture. Much of the governmental involvement was initiated during the Depression. The commodity programs, marketing orders, the state prorate act, the Bureau of Reclamation's Central Valley and Boulder Canyon Projects were all begun then. The most important federal involvement with labor issues began during World War II with the Bracero and wage stabilization programs, although immigration policy with respect to Mexico has been an issue since World War I. Since World War II the state has been active in water development (the State Water Project), the commodity and marketing order programs have continued, the Bracero program lived its unexpectedly long life, immigration policy has involved tacit nonenforcement of laws against illegals, and the University of California Extension Service and Agricultural Experiment Station have become highly involved in mechanization research.

Large-scale producers have been able to influence all of the above areas of activity thanks to their increase in numbers, the formation of organizations serving their interests, and their increasing ties to nonfarm interests. During the Depression, the Farm Bureau became a powerful organization and one serving large-grower interests. The California Chamber of Commerce also emerged as favoring large agricultural interests. Many organizations have been formed to deal with grower concerns, especially labor, and marketing cooperatives have also become dominated by large growers. There has been stronger involvement by nonfarm interests in production. Concentration among processors, distributors and retailers has given these industries more economic power and they have a large interest in California agriculture. Some large conglomerates and nonfarm investors have become large owners and thus developed an interest in agricultural issues.

By the 1920s, it was apparent that private initiative could not provide what was needed in the way of irrigation development and the federal government became involved in several large projects. Large landowners were extremely interested in these projects and when it was recognized that the Federal Bureau of Reclamation's acreage restrictions were to be applicable, to both the Central and Imperial Valleys, they began to agitate for removal of these restrictions. Two strategies have been used: state development of water, and prevention/evasion of enforcement. The State Water Project is without acreage limitations and the high costs of water have been approximately halved for major agricultural users through use of surplus water. There are few examples of large holdings broken up by the

Bureau; the restrictions on federal projects have been successfully circumvented by large owners. In general, water prices have been kept low. The present structure of production, based on enormous acreages in low-value feed grains and pasture, has been maintained; the viability of large holdings has been assured.

The increasing importance of labor-intensive irrigated crops necessitated development of an adequate labor force and water supply. During the 1920s and 1930s growers were able to maintain conditions of labor oversupply and low wages. Through the 1930s the former was assured by allowing Mexicans to work in California fields. Then, refugees from the Midwest (Okies) flocked to California and augmented the Mexicans. Several organizations became involved with labor issues, including the Associated Farmers, an organization established by large growers and related interests. Worker organization was successfully stymied.

World War II resulted in many workers leaving agriculture for better paying jobs in the defense industries or to join the armed forces. Growers were able to maintain low wages and a good supply of labor through two federal programs: wage stabilization, and the Bracero program (which again brought Mexican workers into California fields). California growers were able to keep the Bracero program alive until 1964. Non-enforcement of laws against illegal aliens presently provides growers with a partial substitute for braceros.

Large landowners have continued to organize themselves to defeat labors' attempts to institute better working conditions. In earlier years, uncertain markets for labor-intensive crops made it necessary for labor to be poorly paid and oppressed in order for growers to profit. This has come to be less and less true as markets improve and as larger and larger producers enter the picture. These producers can afford higher wages and better working conditions. Nonetheless, the old goals of a lowly paid, docile labor force remain. Unionization has been resolutely opposed and the replacement of field workers by machines has become the contemporary version of the cheap, docile labor force.

Mechanization has been increasing since the 1940s. At first field crop harvests were mechanized and, beginning in the 1960s, some fruit and vegetable harvests. Labor needs have also been cut back by use of pesticides, herbicides, sprinkler systems and other nonharvest machinery.

General Summary of Landownership

Each chapter in this study has performed some magic with numbers to establish that concentration of landownership was increasing. On the face of it, this seems impossible since in 1872, 870 owners held approximately 11 million acres; in 1916/17, 892 owners held 11.4 million acres; in 1945, 77 owners possessed 6 million acres; and today, 757 owners possess 6.7 million acres. However, none of these surveys is strictly comparable with the others. The 1872 one was the most complete but it included all holdings, not just agricultural holdings. Similarly, the 1916/17 information included all holdings, but it was not as complete in its coverage. The 1945 information is extremely sketchy, being based on a survey of part of the Central Valley Project service area and whatever could be gleaned from the standard financial manuals. It includes several million nonagricultural acres owned by the railroad but most of the rest of the land is agricultural. The present survey is complete for only eleven counties and some care has been taken to exclude nonagricultural holdings.

Today we also see the result of more land in large holdings actually being used for production. In 1916/17 two owners, Miller and Lux and the railroad, held at least 5.75 million acres. Today the Miller and Lux holding no longer exists, the railroad holds some 2 million acres less, and only 194,000 acres of what it does own have been counted as agricultural. The breakup since 1918 of these largest holdings did not result in small holdings because, as has been established, large-scale irrigated production became increasingly attractive.

General Summary

One of the most striking things about landownership in California is that there has always been present a pool of large holdings being used extensively or being held for speculative reasons. Even today, the majority of land in large holdings is used extensively. The existence of these holdings has been responsible for the extreme concentration of landownership that has persisted over the years.

Although subdivision destroyed many large holdings in the pre-1918 period, California never became a state of small farms as occurred in the Midwest. In the post-World War I period concentration was becoming rampant in all areas of the economy. These tendencies were visible in agriculture; for example, the average farm size in the United States began an uninterrupted rise in 1925. Because California's agricultural production was already concentrated, these national tendencies were able to flourish and find their fullest expression here. The concentration that existed in extensive production was able to carry over into intensive production and today, large holdings dominate both aspects of production.

Appendix A

Description of the Study Used to Create Appendix B

There are no tablulations of present landownership, so I have made one myself. There are actually a number of sources of information, which are relatively easy, albeit astoundingly tedious, to use. I have relied on the following: the California AGRI-LAND maps produced by the Echoe Map Publishing Company, ASCS records and assessors' reports in the files of the California Institute for Rural Studies, the standard financial manuals, 10-K reports, and some miscellaneous articles.

The AGRI-LAND maps have been the mainstay of my study. These consist of books of plat maps (each plat consists of a single township) for a number of Central Valley counties. For each assessor's parcel the maps show its number, appraised value, size and owner. The maps I chose to use have an alphabetical index of owners which includes their address and indicates in which plats their land is located. Counties whose index did not include locational information were not chosen. Thus, I used the following maps:

Butte, 1979
Fresno East of Highway 99, 1978
Fresno West of Highway 99, 1978
Kern, 1980
Kings, 1979
Madero, 1979
Merced, 1979
San Joaquin, 1979
Solano, 1979
Yolo, 1980
Yuba-Sutter, 1979

My technique was to go through the index picking out all owners who might possess 2,000 or more acres. A single ownership unit was defined as all the land held by people listed at the same address. Often, this involved many members of a family, each of whom had some land in his or her name. There were, however, a number of instances in which very different names were located at the same address. The criteria for being a possible large landowner was either being mentioned as owning land in four or more plats or having a plus (+) after a plat location (a plus indicates that land is owned in more than one section in that plat). Possible large holdings were then checked on the maps to ascertain the exact amount of land, and if this was greater than 2,000 acres, I wrote down the name(s), address and, by plat and sections in that plat, the amount of land owned. I did not record the parcel number or its assessed value. I leave that task to hardier souls. After going through all of these maps, I then went back and double-checked all the ownerships on which I had collected information.

There are two main sources of error: those due to my own inaccuracy and those due to the maps. Because I double-checked all my work, I am confident that it is quite accurate. The largest possible source of error would be not matching names that have the same address. I made great efforts to keep track of this information and doubt that many such holdings were passed over. It should be added that no particular attempt was made to pick up small holdings that a large owner might have in other counties. Sometimes a name looked familiar and I noted down their holding but nothing systematic was done. This was regarded as too awesome a project.

The maps presented the major obstacle to accuracy. First, their accuracy has been impugned. Where comparisons have been made with assessors' records, AGRI-LAND has not always come out on top, sometimes giving incorrect parcel numbers, incorrect owners, or incorrect sizes. Nonetheless, it is my impression that the maps, while not totally accurate, are close to being so. The indices are also not above reproach. Names have been known to be left out and ownerships inaccurately recorded (i.e., locations and/or plus signs left out). Santa Fe Energy in Kern County is a particularly egregious example. They seem to have land in almost every plat, but in the index they are indicated as having one parcel in one plat. Because large ownerships are often located near each other, I was able to pick up many, if not most, of these holdings. The maps present other problems as well. The plus technique leaves room to miss a parcel. After a number of hours of looking at the maps this was bound to occur, which is why I went over all my work again. The names on the maps were not always complete. Owners with the same last name were not always distinguished by their initials. The most distressing case of this was the Twisselman family of Kern County. There are many Twisselmans, all at different addresses and all owning land near each other. By my rules they did not count as the same holding, yet the lack of initials made it impossible to separate out the holdings. Many thousands of acres were involved. A related difficulty is that thousands of acres are held in trusts by banks. The maps present no way to track down the true owner.

Information for other counties was obtained from the standard financial manuals, 10-K reports, and the files compiled by the California Institute for Rural Studies for their study of large farm operators, *Getting Bigger*. The latter included some miscellaneous information, some assessors' reports, and ASCS records covering land involved in ASCS programs farmed by operators of 2,000 or more acres. The records indicated which land the operator owned and who owned whatever was leased. There was some overlap between these sources and I established the following order of preference, based on my estimation of accuracy:

1) Assesor's reports
2) Financial manuals or 10-K reports
3) AGRI-LAND maps
4) ASCS reports

The ASCS records come last for several reasons. First of all, they represent a minimum on the amount of land in a given ownership unit. Like AGRI-LAND, they sometimes differ from assessors' reports, financial manuals, and 10-K reports. They also differ from AGRI-LAND. Although presumably minima, they will indicate larger holdings then AGRI-LAND. There are also ASCS records of large holdings not shown by the maps. Disagreement with the maps does not imply greater inaccuracy; however, I felt they were more likely to be inaccurate or contain misattributions of ownership because they are not, at bottom, based on assessors' information as the maps are. Thus, ASCS records were only used for counties not covered by the maps and the other sources were used instead of the maps when they overlapped.

Two other points should be made about the study. The first has to do with the date to which it applies. The AGRI-LAND maps refer to the the assesors' records for the year in the title. The ASCS information is based on visits made in 1978 or 1979 to the ASCS county offices. The information is not necessarily up-to-date for that year. Assessors' reports are for 1978 and other information ranges from 1977 to 1980, usually the last two years. Thus, the study refers to the late 1970s; further precision is not possible. The second point is that the land included is, as far as possible, only agricultural land. Land reported by the ASCS is clearly agricultural and only land holdings referred to as agricultural were taken from the financial manuals, 10-K reports, and miscellaneous sources.

Two problems arose in sequestering agricultural land. One problem was the Southern Pacific. I was not able to locate more recent information about the total holding than that in Fellmeth (1973) relating to 1971. He reported 2.4 million acres for the Southern Pacific, of which 400,000 were rights of way and so on. I think that the 198,000 acres I located in the Central and Imperial Valleys is the bulk of the railroads' agricultural land in California. The rest is either in the Mojave Desert or is timberland located in northern California. For this reason I have made no attempt to estimate the present size of the total holding for inclusion here. The second major problem lies with holdings found on the maps. Land owned by lumber companies has been excluded (for example, in Butte County both the holding of Diamond International (92,000 acres) and the holding of Louisiana Pacific (20,000 acres) were excluded), as has the land owned by Leslie Salt. Oil companies have been included. This probably has led to inclusion in their totals of some land not used agriculturally. I have also included nine doubtful holdings. These are:

1) Benicia Ind.
2) California Portland Cement
3) Cold Springs Granite
4) Dow Chemical Co.
5) Dynasonic
6) GWU and Great Western Cities
7) Lake Madera Country Estates
8) Monolith Portland Cement
9) U.S. Borax

California Portland, Monolith Portland and U.S. Borax are located in the eastern part of Kern county (It is the western part of the county, where the oil companies own land, that is irrigated and agriculturally productive). I am not clear that the land in those holdings is even valuable for grazing. Benicia Ind., Lake Madera County Estates, and Cold Springs Granite seem unlikely simply by name. GWU includes a depressingly large number of twenty-acre parcels because several thousand acres have been subdivided. Dynasonics is described in *Walker's Guide to Pacific Coast Securities* as being a holding company involved in land development and sales. Again, it is uncertain whether the land is being used agriculturally; it is not subdivided.

Overall, the study provides a lower bound on the number of large agricultural landholdings existing in California in the late 1970s. It is most accurate and complete for the twelve Central Valley counties for which the AGRI-LAND maps were used. Because efforts have been made to weed out nonagricultural land, the study should not be used as an indicator of the extent of total land concentration in California. The total amount of land in large agricultural landholdings is greater than that presented here and the total amount of land in large holdings is much greater than that presented here.

Appendix B

Large Landholdings in California—Late 1970s

The table below lists all owners of 2,000 or more acres of land in California discovered by the study described in Appendix A. All entries without a numbered footnote are derived from the AGRI-LAND maps. A lettered footnote indicates a map problem. The notes are at the end of the table. All names are as they were found in the sources; only punctuation has been added when neccessary.

Owner	Acreage	County
Abele, Mary	2,894	Yolo
Acme Associates	4,272	Madera
Adobe, A. C. & Mallad	2,004[3]	Glenn
Agrivest Inc.	2,079	Sutter
Ahart, Peter	2,428	Butte
Airway Farms	5,584.6	Fresno
AJ Ranch	15,413[1]	San Luis Obispo
Albitre, Dorothy	3,750	Kern
Albitre, R. O.	3,697	Kern
Alexander, Dorothy	2,359	Tulare
Alexander, W. B.	9,860[3]	Monterey
Allen, Carl	2,338	Kern
Allen, M. & R.	8,188	Fresno
Allustriarte, G. *et al.*	4,990	Solano
Altorfer and Alphens	2,375[3]	Glenn
Alturas Meadows	6,800[3]	Modoc
Am. Dev. Co.	8,020	Kern
Ama Vineyard	2,177	Merced
Amstar Corp.	2,845	

Owner	Acreage	County
	1,999	Fresno
	846	Yolo
Anchordoguy & Co.	8,596[1]	Tehama
Anderson, C. & Puryear, Kenneth	7,399	Kern
Anderson Clayton	2,518	Kings
Anderson Estate	4,635[3]	Glenn
Anderson, Claire	2,129	Solano
Anderson, Grant & Florence	3,470	Kern
Anderson, John	35,211.2	
	681.8[1]	Fresno
	4,496	Merced
	5,546	Sutter
	24,487.4	Yolo
Andreotti, A. & M.	5,607	
	3,342[3]	Colusa
	2,265[3]	Glenn
Andreson, N. & R.	2,749	Merced
Andrew, G. & G.	2,935	Madera
Ansberry Corp.	4,801[3]	Monterey
Ansin, Edmund & Martin Inv.	7,960	Kern
Apache Grove Land Co.	6,255	
	220	Fresno
	6,035	Madera
App, John et al.	3,341	Kern
Arbelbide, H.	5,705	Merced
Arburua, H. H.	10,396	Merced
Arburua, J. M.	13,379	Merced
Arnold, C. & Loftus, D	16,096[3]	San Luis Obispo
Arrosaray, P. & M.	3,509	Kings
Articrown Holding	2,056	Madera
Assoc. S. Calif. Inv. Co.	2,250	Fresno
Atlantic Richfield Co.	5,925	Kern
Augusta Bixler Farms	2,900	San Joaquin
Aurignac, Albert	2,032[3]	Monterey
Aurignac, Paul & Son	6,757[3]	Monterey
Avenal Land & Oil Co.	16,079	Kings
Avery, R. S.	7,102[3]	Monterey
Baldwin, Wm. R.	2,452[3]	Contra Costa
Balsdon & Balsdon	5,836[3]	Colusa
Bar Mtn. Ranch	2,956	Tulare
Barmby, Robt & Ada	2,411	San Joaquin
Barnes, Paul	2,700	Solano
Baroncini Brothers	6,828	Kern
Basham, Walter	7,577[3]	Monterey
Bayles, W. & M.	2,948	Butte
Bayse, George & Maywood, D. III	2,275	Solano

Owner	Acreage	County
BB Ltd.	2,572	Madera
Beard, John & Mary	2,511	Kern
Bechtel, Jon	5,017[a]	Butte
Beck, Nels & Sons	5,634[3]	San Luis Obispo
Becker, R. & B.	2,478	Fresno
Beckham, Marie	3,481	San Joaquin
Beechinor Cattle Feeding	4,272	Kern
Bellumoni, A. *et al.*	6,911	
	2,639	Fresno
	4,194	Kern
Benicia Ind.	2,760	Solano
Bennett, H.	2,168.5	Fresno
Benson, Eirwen	4,115	Solano
Bettencourt, F. & D.	3,087	Kings
Bevan, Ernest	2,747	Butte
Bidart Brothers	45,387.4	
	4,689[1]	Fresno
	7,883	Kern
	32,815.4[1]	Merced
Bidegary, V. & Sagardia, Ray	6,995.1	Fresno
Bigelow, J. E.	3,707	Madera
Birdwell, Carmel & K. P.	4,595	Fresno
Blackwell Land Co.	21,910	Kern
Blanc, Anne	3,259	Kern
Boccardo, James & Lorraine	2,778	Yuba
Bonanza Farms	2,874	Kern
Bonnifield, Floyd	2,798[3]	Placer
Borchard, John	6,339[3]	Imperial
Boswell, J. G.	183,222.99	
	22,004	Fresno
	22,180.01[1]	Kern
	93,410.76[1]	Kings
	41,376.22[1]	Tulare
Boswell, W. Jr.	4,513	Kings
Bouldin Farming	5,806[1]	San Joaquin
Bouris Ranches	11,397[3]	Riverside
Bowen, A. & A.	8,809	Kings
Bowen, Carver	28,141	
	20,183	Kern
	7,958	Tulare
Bowles, George	10,044	
	3,629	Kern
	6,415	Merced
Boyett, Barie	4,072	Kings
Braasham, Walter	7,577[3]	Monterey
Bradley Land Co.	2,419[3]	Santa Barbara
Brady, Howard,	6,377	Sutter
Brassfield, Jerry & Joann	3,395	Tulare
Brazelton, E. *et al.*	2,933	Solano

Owner	Acreage	County
Britton Co.	9,096.4	
	7,524.4	Fresno
	1,572	Madera
Britz Inc.	10,872.9	Fresno
Broome, John	25,093	
	23,650	Kern
	1,443[3]	Monterey
Brown, Fletcher	4,528[a]	Butte
Brown, Leslie & Dolores	2,738	Kings
Bryant, David & Gladys	2,730	Kern
Buchenau, Elsie & H. J.	16,436	Madera
Burnett, Leroy et al.	5,519	Fresno
Butte Creek Farms	2,712[3]	Colusa
Buttes Gas & Oil Co.	8,060[4]	
Buttonwillow Land & Cattle; Tracy Ranch Inc.	13,832	Kern
C. V. Ranch	2,536[3]	San Luis Obispo
Cahalan, H.	3,633	Fresno
Calarco Inc.	5,786	
	1,468	Fresno
	4,318	Tulare
Calhoun, Rick	2,837[3]	San Luis Obispo
Calhoun, R. L.	2,967[3]	Ventura
California Devco Inc.; Anglo Calif. Cons Inv.	8,867	Kern
California Land & Cattle Co.	34,363[3]	Monterey
California Portland Cement Co.	15,166	Kern
Call Family Ranch	3,840[3]	Sonoma
Calosso, Frank	3,212	San Joaquin
Calplans Agricultural Fund	10,308.7	
	1,928	Kern
	4,270[1]	Madera
	2,615[1]	Merced
	282.83[1]	Monterey
	198.15[1]	Sonoma
	1,014.72[1]	Fresno
Camp & Mebane Cattle Co.	24,646	
	22,746	Kern
	1,900	Tulare
Camp, W. B. & Son	2,674	Kern
Camsuzou, Madeline	5,340[3]	Monterey
Caratan, Anton et al.	2,955	Tulare
Carleton & Co.	5,799	Yolo
Carleton, A. V.	3,572	Fresno
Carmicheal, Francis	7,355[b]	Butte
Carrizo Ranch	24,770[3]	San Luis Obispo
Carter, Robt. S.	4,237	Yolo
Carver, C. & H.	2,642	Tulare
Casey, J. T.	6,400[3]	Shasta
Casillas Brothers	8,340[3]	San Benito

Owner	Acreage	County
Cattani, A. *et al.*	12,031	Kern
Chamberlain, S. Jr.	3,542	Tulare
Chance, J. & J.	4,886	Merced
Chandlers Gravel Co.	6,306	Kern
Chanslor Oil Company	2,596	Kings
Charter Brothers	3,317[3]	Colusa
Chatom Co.	2,169	Kings
Chevron Oil Company	261,441.6	
	77,134.6	Fresno
	61,895	Kings
	122,412	Kern
Chicca, (family)	2,140	Kern
Chingaza, S.	2,200[3]	Orange
Cholame Cattle Co.	15,028	
	12,142	Kern
	2,886[3]	San Luis Obispo
Choperena, C.	2,685	Merced
Chrisman, Ira & Charlotte	2,295	Tulare
Chrisman, Philip	4,116	Tulare
Christiana, Lillian	3,972	Madera
Christina Inv. N. V.	3,959	Kern
Church, Emery	2,255	Solano
Chy Co.	5,130	Yuba
Claasen, Arthur	5,445	Fresno
Clark, J. C.	2,389	Butte
Clayton, Vincent Inc.	18,065	Tulare
Cleary, R. & L.	2,512	Madera
Cloud, R. *et al.*	2,369	Madera
Coberly West Co.	2,222	Kern
Coehlo, Tony *et al.*	5,261	Fresno
Coit Ranch	17,977	
	2,264	Fresno
	15,713[1]	Santa Clara
Colby, P. & Glide, T.	17,906.2	
	3,398	Solano
	14,508.2	Yolo
Cold Springs Granite	2,497	Madera
Colpien Feed Yards Inc.	7,023	Tulare
Conn. Mutual Life Ins.	6,955	Merced
Connolly & Johnson	11,954	San Joaquin
Continental Vintners	2,500[3]	San Luis Obispo
Cook Land & Cattle Co.	9,856[3]	San Joaquin
Cook, Bill	2,000[3]	Sonoma
Cook, J. Micheal	4,209[3]	Imperial
Cook, Peter	2,202	Solano
Cooke, Jack	11,868	Kern
Cooper, Ella	2,955	Butte
Cooper, H. Alma	2,974	Tulare
Cornell, Edward & Barbara	4,576	Tulare

Owner	Acreage	County
Cornwall Brothers Estate	3,653[3]	Monterey
Correia, Joe & Elvira	3,458	Tulare
Costerisan Farms	3,325	Kern
Crabtree, Albin &	2,204[3]	Stanislaus
Enford, W. J.	[3]	
Crane, Bert & Nancy	5,585	Merced
Crane, Mary	6,981	Merced
Criss Brothers	6,520[3]	Siskiyou
Crook, John	7,800[3]	Lassen
Cummings Ranch Corp.	6,464	Kern
Curran, Yvonne	9,927	
	3,853	Madera
	2,946	Merced
Cuyama Farms	4,000[3]	San Luis Obispo
Dahl, Gary	2,840[3]	Lassen
Daley Ent.	17,352[3]	San Diego
Damon, Henry	2,182	Butte
Daulton, Clay	11,981	Madera
Davies, Kenneth	3,336[3]	San Luis Obispo
Davis Drier & Elevator	3,190.3	
	909.3	Fresno
	2,281	Merced
Davis Ranches	9,820[3]	Colusa
Davis, Claire W	2,674[3]	Tehama
Davis, Jean	3,520	Butte
Davis, Thomas Jr.	6,261	Tulare
Deep Violet Farms	2,289	Yuba
DeFrancesco, M. Jr. & Carolyn	4,419	Merced
Delta Properties	3,131[3]	Contra Costa
Den Hartog Cattle	3,421	Fresno
Dennis, Wilbur & Mary	8,721	Tulare
Deseret Farms	5,289	Yolo
Deterding, M. & F.	2,708	Solano
Deutsch, F. & P.	2,244	Kings
Deutsch, Lester	2,120[3]	Riverside
Dilday Land & Cattle	3,805	Madera
Doe Florence	3,935	Tulare
Dofflemyer & Kramer	2,552	Tulare
Dofflemyer, Robt. & Mary	6,323	Tulare
Dominick Ent. Ltd.	6,273.1	Fresno
Dompe Brothers Inc.	4,956[3]	Stanislaus
Douglas, W. & A.	13,503	Kern
Dow Chemical Co.	2,602	Solano
Dozier & Pressley	3,634	Solano
Dreyer, Peter	2,120.1	Fresno
Dryer, Tyrell	9,488	Fresno
Dudley Frank Farms	2,811	Kings
Dudley Ridge Oil Co.	2,962	Kings
Dudley, John	6,464	Tulare

Owner	Acreage	County
Durst, Melvin	3,883	Yolo
Durst, O.	3,616	Yolo
Dynasonics	5,054	Kern
Echenique, Lucia & Sons	7,685[3]	Monterey
Eddins, Ely	3,080[3]	Glenn
El Tejon Cattle Co.	2,314	Merced
Elliott Land & Cattle	21,417	Tulare
Elliott, R. *et al.*	11,636.1	
	9,581	Kern
	2,055.1	Yolo
Elmore, John (Estate)	5,392[3]	Imperial
E. M. Johansing Partnership	6,074[3]	San Luis Obispo
Emigh, Richard	3,300	Solano
Engelhardt, A. & C.	2,616	San Joaquin
Engvall, Barbara	4,479	Fresno
Ensher & Barsoom	3,837.1	
	1,930	San Joaquin
	1,907.1	Yolo
Erickson, C. E. & K	4,733	Kern
Erickson, C. E. & Thom, J. G.	6,329	Kern
Ernst Brothers	7,629[3]	San Luis Obispo
Erreca, B.	4,158	Merced
Estill, Jack	6,699[3]	Modoc
Etcheberria Brothers	6,712[3]	Orange
Etchegoinbery	2,227	Fresno
Etchelet, Anita	3,959	San Joaquin
Etcheverry, A.	3,788	Merced
Eyterabide	8,387	Kern
Farnsworth, Donna	2,276	Solano
Farnsworth, F. & Evelyn	3,213	Tulare
Fatjo, Mary	6,260	Merced
Faure & King	3,477	Tulare
Favier Brothers	16,852	
	3,716	Fresno
	13,136	Merced
Feeney, Bob	3,013[3]	Glenn
Fenn Land	2,076	Butte
Fenn, John & June	2,004	Sutter
Ferro, Thomas	4,794	Yolo
Fleming, (family)	4,200[2]	Imperial
Flournoy Brothers	4,069[3]	Tehama
Flournoy, Warren	8,893[3]	Modoc
Flying H Farms	3,156	Kern
Flynn & Menre	15,391	Tulare
Flynn, Elsie & Frank	7,734	Merced
Foley, Coleman	6,040	
	4,990[3]	Alameda
	1,050[3]	Contra Costa
Forbes, Ted *et al.*	5,696	Fresno

Owner	Acreage	County
Forster Cattle Co.	7,162[3]	Colusa
Forster	3,365	San Joaquin
Four Area;Three Area	2,784	Merced
Four Cty.;Merced 542 Lmtd.		
Freitas, Anna	5,896	Merced
French, C. M. (Estate)	19425[3]	Glenn
French, M. H.	8,854	Merced
Frick, Fred	2,358	Tulare
Froehlich, Ronald & Janice	2,444	Tulare
Frusetta Estate	11,905[3]	San Benito
Fulton, W. D. & B. E.	2,005	Madera
G. & M. Ranches	3,554	Butte
Gallatin, Malvena Estate	3,845[3]	Tehama
E. J. Gallo Co.	28,249	
	26,169	Merced
	1,120	San Joaquin
	960[3]	Stanislaus
Garner, Jay	2,738[a]	Butte
Getty Oil Co.	90,025.4	
	8,224.4	Fresno
	77,162	Kern
	2,299	Kings
	2,340	Yolo
Ghiglia, E. & D.	2,829	Fresno
Giffen, Micheal *et al.*	2,874	Fresno
Giffen, Price	8,032.5	
	2,650.5	Fresno
	5,382	Madera
Giguiere Ranch Inc.	2,558	Yolo
Gilkey Farms &	9,069	
Dan Riddle		
	5,219	Kings
	2,572	Tulare
Gill Brothers Feed Yard Inc.	15,437	Tulare
Gill, Velma	19,728	Tulare
Gill, Will & Sons	17,798	
	10,752	Madera
	7,046	Tulare
Gilmore Ranch	7,375	Fresno
Glenn Record Inc.	10,113	Kern
Glide, Lizzie	2,447	Kern
Golanka, J.	6,000[3]	Lassen
Gorrill Land Co.	3,159[a]	Butte
Gouldin, V. M.	3,383[3]	Tehama
Grace Ranches	23,204[3]	Modoc
Graciosa Co.	7,442[3]	Santa Barbara
Gragnani Brothers	10,232.2	Fresno
Grant, Sterling *et al.*	2,253	Tulare
Grisedale Ranch	5,542	Kern
Grune Brothers Ranch	3,930[3]	Modoc

Owner	Acreage	County
Guidici	2,593	Butte
Guimarra Brothers	9,577	
	7,576	Kern
	2,001	Tulare
Guisti Farms	3,365	Fresno
Gulf Oil Co.	2,919	Kern
Gumpert, Emil	2,351[3]	Alameda
Gunn, Leah	6,100	Butte
Gustine Land & Cattle Co.	2,211	Merced
Guthrie, John *et al.*	11,677	Tulare
Guy L. Godwin Co.	4,849[3]	San Luis Obispo
GWU & Great Western Cities	30,046	Kern
H. & R. Partnership	2,143	Tulare
Hage, E. W.	2,510[3]	PLUMAS
Hagemann, E. E. & Co.	2,100[3]	Stanislaus
Hahn Farms	2,000[3]	San Luis Obispo
Haire, Wesley	4,016[3]	Sonoma
Hall, W. A.	2,348[3]	Stanislaus
Hamblet, Elden	4,087	Yolo
Hambley, E.	2,634[3]	Monterey
Hammonds Ranch Inc.	8,158	Fresno
Hannon, Stafford	2,335[3]	Imperial
Hansen, Albert	16,992[3]	Monterey
Hansen, Homer & Tollenaere, Mary	23,303	Kern
Hansen, K. & M.	3,143[3]	San Luis Obispo
Hansen, Louis & Beulah	7,378	
	2,077	Kings
	5,301	Tulare
Hansen, M. & W.	3,483	Merced
Hansen, Marie	2,579	Kern
Harasta, C. & M.	4,106	Kern
Harp & Hansen	5,063	Kings
Harrell, Frieda	5,346	Tulare
Harrell, Harrell	4,859	Tulare
Harris Farms	30,458	Fresno
Harrison, F. E.	7,765	Merced
Hatch, Noel & Nola	2,896	Solano
Healy Enterprises Inc.	2,547[3]	Los Angeles
Hearst Corp.	115,074.69	
	497.8[1]	Butte
	13,231[1]	Monterey
	101,345.89[1]	San Luis Obispo
Heidrick, Fred *et al.*	3,831	Yolo
Heringer Ranch	3,604.8	Yolo
Hershey Land	2,783	Yolo
Hershey, John & Juanita	14,623	Tulare
Hewitson, R. & J.	2,879	Kings
Hilary Farms & Conway, Ray	3,834	Yuba

Owner	Acreage	County
Hill-Elliot Corp.	4,500[3]	Sonoma
Hillman, Bessie K	4,677[3]	San Luis Obispo
Hillman, C. D. & B.	6,824[3]	San Luis Obispo
Hofman, Frank & Emma	4,937	Yuba
Hollister, L. & C.	2,547	Merced
Holthouse, Leo	4,915[3]	Colusa
Homer, Forrest	5,625	Tulare
Honcut Creek Ranch	2,290	Yuba
Hooker Grain Co.	5,163[3]	Stanislaus
Houchin Brothers	6,268	Kern
Houghton, O. & R.	6,230	Fresno
Howard Properties	33,000[3]	Amador
Howe, R. & M. J.	6,725	Madera
Howell, Charles	3,977	Fresno
Hudson, Everett & John Jr.	11,407	Kern
Hultgren, E.	2,882	Merced
Hungerland, I.	6,866	Yolo
Hyde, C. B. & Richard	9,925	Tulare
Ichord, Robt.	3,228	Merced
Indian Creek Ranch	2,976	Kern
Inglin, Annie & Gus	2,417	Yolo
Irvine Co.	96,808	
	5,417[5]	Imperial
	86,928[3]	Orange
	4,463[3]	San Benito
J. & W. Farms Inc.	2,705[3]	Glenn
J. & J. Ranch	3,898[3]	Kern
Jackson & Reinert	8,346[3]	San Luis Obispo
Jackson, Don	3,018[3]	Fresno
Jameson Trust	3,987	Kern
Jamison, Betty & John	8,435	Madera
Jarmo Co.	2,932	San Joaquin
JB2H Ranch; Berrenda Mesa;JLH; Bonanza Acres;Callico Ranch	7,197	Kern
Jensen, R. *et al.*	3,534	Madera
Johnson, Cecil	3,535	Butte
Johnson, Frank & Norma	6,185	Fresno
Johnson, G. & O.	5,020	Fresno
Johnson, Wm.	3,299	Butte
Joughin, Ethel & William	5,029	Kern
Justeson, Doyle	4,333[3]	Butte
Justeson, M. J.	3,557	
	617	Butte
	2,940	Sutter
Kaiser Aetna	8,721[3]	Ventura
Kaplan & Niedemann	3,605[3]	Contra Costa
Keegan, M. J.	6,705[3]	Colusa
Keene Ranch	12,371	Kern

Owner	Acreage	County
Kelley, G. *et al.*	2,674	Merced
Kelsey, H. Jr.	5,411	Merced
Kern Property Corp.	3,720	Kern
Kings Cty. Devop.	6,810	Kings
Klein, B. D. Co.	3,227	San Joaquin
Klein, Lottie	5,980	Kern
Klein, Oscar	5,131	Tulare
Knaggs, Layton	9,979.8	Yolo
Knight Ranches	3,036[3]	Glenn
Knob Hill Mines &	4,737	Solano
Hastings Assoc.		
Koda, E. & T.	3,280.2	Fresno
Korda, Albert	7,454	Tulare
Kretzer, Lloyd	2,080	Kern
Kreyerhager Inc.	9,068[a]	Fresno
Kuhm, Fritz Jr.	7,062	Imperial
La Grande Farms	2,477[3]	Colusa
La Macchia, Mary (Estate)	3,480[3]	Monterey
Labarere, Joe (Estate)	5,372[3]	Monterey
Laborde, Jean	2,005	Yolo
Lackaff Cattle Corp.	3,110	Fresno
Lake Madera Ctry. Estates	2,807	Madera
Lake Cousins Prop.	3,855[3]	San Luis Obispo
Lakey, Andrew	5,000[3]	Lassen
LaMoine, Keith & Florence	2,530	Tulare
Lane, Hazel	2,160	Tulare
Lanigan, Roger (Estate)	2,019[3]	Monterey
Larson Ranch	2,320[3]	Los Angeles
Las Flores Ranch Ltd.	8,500[3]	San Bernardino
Lasgoity, John	7,140	Madera
Lassovitch, Farley	8,088	Fresno
Laupe, L. M.	2,302[3]	Sutter
Lavers, William & David	3,612	Kern
Lee Brothers	3,924	
	747[3]	Colusa
	2,187[3]	Glenn
Lesco Ltd. & Dilts, J. & L.	7,016	Tulare
Levinson, Albert & Lillian	11,867	Kern
Lewallen Land & Cattle	4,906	San Joaquin
Lewis Nixon Inc;	4,631	Solano
Islands Inc;Gladys Co		
Lindemann Farms	13,064	Merced
Liston, R. B.	3,994[3]	Colusa
Little San Juan Ranch	8,603[3]	San Luis Obispo
Lockhart Ranch Co.	2,792[3]	San Bernardino
Logan Land & Livestock Co.	6,166[3]	Glenn
Lopes, Zelinda	2,057	Solano
Los Cerritos Ranch Co.	4,035	Merced
Los Feliz Inv.	4,018	Tulare

Owner	Acreage	County
Lower Jones Co.	2,539	San Joaquin
LTM Prop.	3,624	Kern
Lund, Mattie & Parker, I. L.	4,969[c]	Butte
Lundblod Brothers	4,410	San Joaquin
Lyons, W. J.	7,820[3]	Stanislaus
Lyttle & Schneider	2,439	Fresno
M. & T. Inc.	18,547	
	9,408	Butte
	9,139[1]	San Joaquin
Machado, A. A.	2,010	Merced
Madera Investors	4,313	Madera
Magoon Brothers	3,154	Sutter
Marchini Brothers	3,503	Fresno
Marshburn Farms	6,545[3]	Riverside
Martel Co.	2,560	San Joaquin
Martin, Julia & Benton	2,245	Kern
Martin, L. R. Inc.	4,429	Madera
Martinus, P. H. *et al.*	5,486[3]	Monterey
McCarthy Brothers	40,812.06	
	5,139.03[1]	Colusa
	3,693.12[1]	Fresno
	10,914[1]	Kern
	21,065.91[1]	Kings
McConnell, Irene	2,742[3]	Monterey
McCormack, D.;	3,222	Solano
Lumberson *et al.*		
McCormack, D.	5,336.7	
	2,459	Solano
	2,877.7	Yolo
McCullough, M. *et al.*	2,090	Yolo
McCune, H. E. Co.	2,114	Solano
McDonald, Mark	5,923	San Joaquin
McDougald, E. & J.	3,642	Madera
McDowell, Charles M.	3,378[3]	Tehama
McGlashan, J. H. Estate Co.	3,397	Kings
McGowan, Bob & Harry	5,207[3]	Glenn
McGrew, John	5,071	Yolo
McKee, Edna	4,312	Tulare
McKenzie, Richard	2,442	Fresno
McKinney, Edith	2,509	Madera
McKinney, J. E. & M	3,128	Madera
McNally, John & Pauline	3,497	Kern
McPherrin, Calvert	4,061	Sutter
McWilliams Land & Cattle Co.	3,214	San Joaquin
Mebane, Kenneth	3,244	Kern
Mednick, Sam *et al.*	2,400	Kern
Meline, Jack & Rabo, Fred	4,972	Butte
Mendiburu, Joe & G.	24,254	Kern
Menefree Ranch	9,162	Merced

Owner	Acreage	County
Merrill Farms	2,235[3]	Monterey
Merritt Brothers	2,224[3]	Monterey
Merritt, E. W. Farms	17,500	Tulare
Merritt, L. E.	4,829	Yolo
Meyer, Horace	3,220	Merced
Mill Creek Land & Cattle Co.	7,696	Fresno
Miltrol Inc.	5,300[2]	San Joaquin
Missouri SCR Ranch & Co. KG	13,897	
	7,958	Kern
	5,939[2]	San Luis Obispo
Mobil Oil Co.	16,809	Kern
Monolith Portland Cement Co.	11,331	Kern
Montgomery Equipment	18,908	Tulare
Moody, D. W.	2,723	Madera
Moore Brothers	2,702[3]	Placer
Moore, D. & M.	2,717	Fresno
Moore, G. E. et al.	2,558	Fresno
Moresco, Louis et al.	6,082	Solano
Mormon Church	2,305[1]	Stanislaus
Morris, Boyd & Velma	2,608	Kings
Moulton, Mathes Tr.	16,115[3]	Colusa
Mouren Farming Co.	10,186	Kings
Mouren, W. J.	7,286.29	
	1,761	Kern
	5,525.29[1]	Kings
Mouren, Wm. & Doris et al.	2,984	Kern
Myers, John	4,404	Merced
Naftzger, Roy	6,340	San Joaquin
Naraghi, H.	7,187[3]	
	2,012	Merced
	5,175[3]	Stanislaus
Narducci, Olinti	2,296	San Joaquin
National Distillers & Chemicals	5,877.14[1]	San Benito
Neufeld Farms	3,461	Tulare
Nevada Rice Ranches Inc.	4,572	Yuba
Nevis Industries Inc.	10,100.05	
	6,333	Butte
	1,800[3]	Modoc
	1,967.05[1]	Tehama
Newhall Land & Farming Co.	124,600	
	4,902	Butte
	1,800[4]	Contra Costa
	3,966.8	Fresno
	38,750[4]	Los Angeles Ventura
	13,700[4]	Madera
	15,168	Merced
	38,300[4]	Santa Barbara San Luis Obispo

Owner	Acreage	County
	4,611	Sutter
Newton Brothers	3,108	Kings
Nichelmann, Fred	2,110	Madera
Nichol, D. L.	9,227[3]	Tehama
Nickel Enterprises	12,338	
	10,675	Kern
	1,663	Merced
Noble Land & Cattle Co.	24,581[3]	Monterey
Noble, Contra Costa	2,305	Madera
Noble, P. G.	5,000[3]	Plumas
Norden Farms Inc.	2,088[3]	Sacramento
North Shore #1;	4,409	Madera
Sharon Farms #1		
Norton, J. III	8,399	Merced
Novy, Lowell L.	2,548[3]	Siskiyou
O'Brien, R. & N.	2,422	Yuba
O'Connell, Fenton	2,600[3]	San Benito
O'Neill Livestock	6,102	Fresno
O'Sullivan Ranch	5,317[3]	Colusa
Oji Brothers	2,166	Sutter
Oliverra, T. T. Corp.	2,461	Kings
One Market St. Properties	3,544	
	2,085	Madera
	1,459	Solano
Orchard, Joseph	9,406	
	3,582	Kern
	5,824	Kings
Osgood, Jose	3,808	Butte
Otterson, Bert	2,614[3]	Glenn
Oviatt, Kim	3,548	Tulare
Jim Owens Cattle Co.	11,783[3]	Colusa
Owens, Ronald	2,738	Butte
Owens, Roy Estate	17,106[3]	Tehama
Owens, Wm. R.	8,754[3]	Glenn
Pacheco, T. et al.	4,480	Tulare
Pacific Agri Land Inc.	8,426[3]	Modoc
Palla, Livio & Rose	2,046	Kern
Palla	2,131	Kern
Palm Island Farms	2,469[3]	Contra Costa
Paloma Farms	5,952.64[1]	Kern
Pappas Land Co.	3,753	Fresno
Par Realty	2,436	Kern
Paramount Citrus	2,014	Kern
Parker, R. R. &	11,420	Kern
Beard, Alice &		
Rankin, Walker		
Parrott Ranch	38,296	
	6,179	Butte
	18,710[3]	Glenn

Owner	Acreage	County
	13,407[3]	Tehama
Patterson Const. Co.	2,748	San Joaquin
Pearson & Pearson	6,121[3]	Colusa
Pellkoper, E. & P.	2,939	Madera
Perez, Thomas	3,990	Fresno
Perkins Estate Ranch	7,600[3]	Ventura
Perkins, S.	2,495	Fresno
Peterson Ranch	5,715	Solano
Peterson, H. E.	2,503	Solano
Peterson, Peter	2,115	Butte
Pfeiffer, F.	12,600	Merced
Pic Realty Corp.	2,915.9	Fresno
Pilibos Sales Inc.	2,686	Fresno
Plaugher, Wilbur *et al.*	2,880	Fresno
Pleasants Ranch	3,595	Solano
Pleasants, Thomas	8,498.8	Yolo
Pope G. A. & G. A. Jr.	15,544	Madera
Porter Estate Co.	11,522	.
	1,400[3]	Contra Costa
	10,122[3]	Monterey
Porterfield Ranch	11,484[3]	Siskiyou
Prudential Ins.	2,189	Madera
Ralls, Lawrence & Carrie	4,217	Kern
Ranchita Cattle Co.	10,322[3]	San Luis Obispo
Rancho California	85,541[3]	Riverside
Rancho Gavilan Corp.	3,679[2]	San Benito
Rancho Granada	3,828[3]	Imperial
Rancho Mission Viejo	50,127[3]	Orange
Rankin, Helen & Julie	27,060	Kern
Reclaimed Islands Co.	2,328	San Joaquin
Red Rock Farms	2,136	Merced
Redfern Ranches	3,223.1	Fresno
Reece, H. C.	2,715	Fresno
Reed, Burrell	4,546	Kern
Rehse Brothers	10,103	
	603[3]	Glenn
	9,500[3]	Tehama
Reimann, Frank	3,400[3]	Glenn
Renz, Wm. Jr.	4,816[3]	San Benito
Resnick, S. & M.	2,923	Merced
Rexroth, Clara & Tafjen, V	6,649	Kern
Reynolds Land & Cattle Co.	6,895[3]	Monterey
Reynolds, R. *et al.*	2,653	Kern
Richards Land & Cattle Co.	5,138	Yuba
Ritter, Loren	3,317	Kern
River Garden Farms	14,714.92	
	1,549.82[1]	Colusa
	13,165.1[1]	Yolo
River Inv. Co.	3,359	San Joaquin

Owner	Acreage	County
Roberts Farms;	33,868	
Roberts Syndication;		
Kern Lake		
	32,036	Kern
	1,832	Tulare
Roberts, C. & N.	6,204	Fresno
Robidart, M. J.	3,381	San Joaquin
Robinson, Donald	4,697	Merced
Robinson, G.	3,015	Merced
Robinson, Ray	3,756	Merced
Roblee Inc.	4,119	Sutter
Roche, Joseph	2,500	Sonoma
Rocky Hill Inc.	10,290	
	2,838	Kern
	7,452	Tulare
Rodden, R. L. Estate	2,870	San Joaquin
Rodgerdts, H.	2,432	Yolo
Roduner Cattle & Farming Co.	10,440	
	3,017	Madera
	7,423	Merced
Rolston, R. T. & Reynolds, T.	4,411	Kern
Root, L. & D.	5,885	Fresno
Rosasco, E.	2,184	Merced
Rosasco, J. & M.	3,912	Merced
Rowan, R. A. Co;	6,724	
South Boston Co.		
	2,380	Fresno
	4,344	Kings
Rudnick, Milton & Diane	13,628	Kern
Rudnick, Oscar *et al.*	77,616	Kern
Rumbley, Wm.	2,867	Tulare
Runitz, Jeanette	2,689[3]	San Luis Obispo
Russell Bros. Ranches	2,107[3]	San Bernardino
Ruston, J. A.	3,104	San Joaquin
Ruth, Clarisa & Lloyd	2,978	Yuba
Rutherford, E. C.	16,262[1]	San Diego
Safford Ent.	6,823	Butte
Sallaberry, Mary	5,433	Madera
Salyer Land Co.;	50,048	
Basin Farms		
	45,072	Kings
	4,976	Tulare
Salyer, E. C. & Nichols, V.	6,938[1]	San Joaquin
San Benito Co.	10,404.67[1]	San Benito
San Bernardo Rancho	2,838[3]	Monterey
San Felipe Ranch	11,331	Merced
Santa Ana & Fresno Land Co.	2,849	Fresno
Santos, Anthony	2,126[3]	Alameda
Scarborough, Robinson	8,028	Merced
Schader, Richard	4,162[3]	Siskiyou

Owner	Acreage	County
Schang, Eugene	3,937	Yolo
Schohr, Elna	8,192	Butte
Schramm Ranch	4,329.3	Fresno
Schwabacher, May	3,204	Madera
Scott, W. B.	2,510[3]	Los Angeles
Seagram & Sons Inc.	5,200[4]	
Seegers, R. R.	2,383	San Joaquin
Seeley	2,870	Madera
Seeno Const. Co.	2,109	Solano
Selby, Carl & Dorothea	2,351	Yuba
Sequoia Ranch	8,577	Tulare
Sexton, A *et al.*	14,314[3]	Glenn
Shamrock Farms	2,535	Tulare
Shannon, Jack	2,720	Tulare
Shannon, Reuben	6,002	Tulare
Sheen, Celia, Ben & Sons	2,243	Madera
	9,663	Fresno
Shell Oil Co.	60,099	
	9,663	Fresno
	50,436	Kern
Shimizu Brothers	6,242[c]	Butte
Shintaffer Farms	2,613	Yuba
Shoemaker, A. C.	7,897[3]	Stanislaus
Siller Brothers	19,444	
	4,058[c]	Butte
	4,436	Sutter
	10,950	Yuba
Sinarle Corp.	3,710	Tulare
Smith, Kenneth	2,835	Madera
Smith, M. B.	11,725	Madera
Smith, R. F.	6,758	Madera
Smith, Wm	5,231	Solano
Snedden	8,979	Kern
Somavia, Ramon Jr.	9,527	Merced
South Lake Farms	53,848.1	
	14,302.1	Fresno
	4,777	Kern
	23,388	Kings
	10,858	Tulare
Southern Pacific Railroad	197,229	
	4,949	Butte
	77,705	Fresno
	4,457[5]	Imperial
	69,205	Kern
	32,293	Kings
	345	Madera
	5,229	Merced
	813	San Joaquin
	596	Solano
	1,637	Yuba

Owner	Acreage	County
Sprague Ranches	7,446	Kern
Squire, Grant	6,624	Fresno
Squire, J. E. & M	3,655	Fresno
St. Agnes Vineyards	2,171	Tulare
Steele, T. R. *et al.*	3,038[3]	Glenn
Steffan, Alban	2,233	San Joaquin
Steidlmayer, A. & Sons	4,982[3]	Colusa
Steidlmayer, J. P.	3,245	Sutter
Stevinson, J. J. Corp. & Kelley, G. *et al.*	9,510	Merced
Still, E. & Rodden E. & W.	14,205	Kern
Stivers, H. C.	11,487	Madera
Stockton, Jacobs, Armstrong *et al.*	7,184	Kern
Stone Enterprises	4,164	Madera
J. G. Stone Land Co.	6,583	Kings
Stone, Martha	2,033	Kern
Studhorse Creek	2,346	Kern
SUG Farms	2,740	Kern
Summit Line Co.	5,649	Kern
Sumner Peck Ranches	12,650.8	
	4,292.8	Fresno
	8,358	Kern
Sumner, Howard (Estate)	2,372	Kern
Sundance Ranches Inc.	4,048	Kern
Sunland Vineyard Co.	3,160[3]	San Bernardino
Sunshine Farms	2,357	Fresno
Superior Oil Co.;	37,941	
Superior Farming Co.	1,214	Fresno
	35,481	Kern
	1,246	Madera
Sutfin, O. L. & Sons	6,153[3]	Tehama
Sutfin, Roy	3,845[3]	Tehama
Sutter Basin	2,785	Sutter
Swearington	3,351	Fresno
Swett, Kenneth	3,397	Solano
Synanon	4,800[3]	Marin
Talbot, Elena & J. A.	2,043	Merced
Taylor, Ann	3,114	Kern
Tejon Ranch Co.	270,000[4]	
Telles Ranch Carr;Dicks; Silver Creek	11,992.3	Fresno
Telles, J. F. *et al.*	12,574	
	7,960.3	Fresno
	4,614	Tulare
Tenneco West Inc.	260,710[4]	
	1,316	Madera
	2,728	Merced

Owner	Acreage	County
Terhel Farms Inc.	13,958[3]	Colusa
Texaco Oil Co.	10,057	
	2,320	Fresno
	7,737	Kern
Texas Meat Brokers Inc.	2,283[3]	Contra Costa
Thomas, H. B. & Deutschman, R. E.	3,053	Fresno
Thomas, Sherman & Cordelia	8,717	
	5,022	Fresno
	3,695	Madera
Tikal, Micheal	2,417	Kern
Timm, Ollin	2,526	Solano
Title Insurance Co.	11,446	
	3,400	Madera
	4,073	Solano
	3,973	Tulare
Tobias, Quentin	11,745	
	10,000[3]	San Benito
	1,745[3]	Siskiyou
Tolle, James & Mary	3,098	Fresno
Tompkins, Mabel	3,716	Yolo
Tooby Farms	3,644.8	
	2,201	Solano
	1,443.8	Yolo
Tooby, Gladys et al.	3,186	Solano
Topaz Land	2,329	Kern
Topping, L.	2,196	Madera
Tow, Henrietta Benson	2,355[3]	Imperial
Traction Ranch & Loundy, Mason Tr.	7,113	Fresno
Tracy Land & Water Co.	2,797	San Joaquin
Trans America Dev Co.	5,300[3]	Los Angeles
Transco Prod Inc.	2,233[3]	San Luis Obispo
Trescony	5,600[2]	Monterey
Triangle T Ranch	14,361	Madera
Triple Jay Ranch	3,096	San Joaquin
Tripp, L. & Dinapoli, E.	2,865	Yuba
Tryon, Lorin H. Jr.	6,105	
	3,531	Fresno
	2,574	Merced
Tsakopaulous, G. & D.	4,516	Yolo
Tulare Lake Representives	19,174.4[1]	Kings
Tuley, D. L. & SL	5,601	Merced
Turri, Wm. R.	6,239[3]	Tehama
Union Oil Co.	12,064.2	
	1,520.2	Fresno
	10,544	Kern
Union Properties;Sonol Sec.	4,110	San Joaquin
Upham Ranch	3,000[3]	Sacramento
Upper Swanston Ranch Inc.	2,584	Yolo

Owner	Acreage	County
Urratia, L.& G.	6,795	Merced
Urrutia, Wm.	7,445.32[1]	Madera
U.S. Borax & Chemical Corp.	20,639	Kern
VAB Assoc.	2,230[3]	San Luis Obispo
Valersin, Pio	5,000[3]	Sacramento
Valley Nitrogen Producers	3,619.7	Fresno
Van Deventer, Ida	3,641	Tulare
Van Dyke, C. & V.	5,156	Fresno
Van Horn, Philip	5,807	Kern
Van Vleet	3,065	Fresno
Vaquero Farms Inc.	6,122[3]	Contra Costa
Varalen, M. A.	2,598	Madera
Veater, E.	6,368	Madera
Vierra, M. G.	5,511	San Joaquin
Vignol, C. J. & R.J.	2,444	Kern
Villard, Jules & Leona	12,261	Kern
Visbeek, Roy	9,115.7	
	2,875	Merced
	6,240.7	Yolo
Vista Livestock Co.	3,364	Merced
Vitree Farms	3,180	Madera
Wahl, Ida	6,997[3]	Tehama
Wallace Properties	14,973	San Luis Obispo
Wallace, Allen	3,984[3]	Monterey
Wallace, E. L. *et al.*	11,481.3	Yolo
Weisenberger, N. *et al.*	4,427	Tulare
Weldon Cattle Co.	4,092	Fresno
West, Ethel	9,223	Kern
Westhaven Farms	11,051	Kings
Westlake Farms	27,324	Kings
White, Douglas	31,724.41[1]	San Benito
Wiggin, Asa	2,601[3]	Colusa
Wilbur, Roger & Jeanne	2,053	Sutter
Wildo Inc.	2,086	Fresno
Willey & Sons	2,697	Sutter
Williams, D. L.	3,327[3]	Tehama
Wilmarth, *et al.*	5,836[3]	Colusa
Wilson Brothers	2,931	Yuba
Windswept Ranch Co.	6,102[3]	Tehama
Wofford, John	5,456	Kern
Wofford, Meders, Russell, Snedden, *et al.*	5,237	Kern
Wolfenberger, R&B	2,099	Fresno
Wolfsen Brothers;	102,470.4	
Romero Ranch; Hoyt, G.;	9,165.4	Fresno
Simon Newman;	45,988	Merced
Turner Island	47,317[1]	Stanislaus

Owner	Acreage	County
Woodland Farms Ltd.	18,462	Yolo
Woody, Robt.	5,379	Kern
Woolstenhulme, M.	11,132	Merced
Work, George *et al.*	10,455[3]	Monterey
Wyle, Frank	7,562	Madera
York, Dorman	3,524[3]	Siskiyou
Yoshuba Farms	2,203	Sutter
Yparraguirre, A. M.	4,235	Fresno
Yuba Goldfields	9,199	Yuba
Zaninovich & Sons	3,595	Tulare
Zuckerman, J.	2,117	San Joaquin
Zuckerman-Mandeville Inc.	7,478	San Joaquin
Zumwalt Farms Inc.	21,512	
	18,848[3]	Colusa
	2,664[3]	Glenn
Zwang, Darrell	10,655	
	7,516	Fresno
	3,139	Kings

Notes
[1] Assessor's Reports.
[2] Miscellaneous information in the files of the California Institute for Rural Studies.
[3] ASCS reports.
[4] Financial manuals or 10-K reports.
[5] United States Senate, Committee on Energy and Natural Resources (1978), p. 436.
[a] Size of one parcel was not stated on the map.
[b] Sizes of two parcels were not stated on the map.
[c] Sizes of three parcels were not stated on the map.

Bibliography

Adams, Frank. *Irrigation Districts in California.* Sacramento: California Department of Public Works Bulletin #21, 1929.
——. "Memo: Re Mexican Land Grants in California Still intact in 1943." Typewritten. Berkeley: Bancroft Library, July 1944.
——. "The Historical Background of California Agriculture." In *California Agriculture,* edited by Claude B. Hutchison, pp. 1-50. Berkeley: University of California Press, 1946.
Adams, R. L. *Seasonal Labor Requirements for California Crops.* Berkeley: University of California, Agricultural Experiment Station Bulletin #623, July 1938.
Adams, R. L. and Smith, William H. Jr. *Farm Tenancy in California and Methods of Leasing.* Berkeley: University of California, Agricultural Experiment Station Bulletin #655, October 1941.
AGRI-LAND Butte County, 1979. Echoe Map Publishing Company.
AGRI-LAND Fresno E99 County, 1978. Echoe Map Publishing Company.
AGRI-LAND Fresno W99 County, 1978. Echoe Map Publishing Company.
AGRI-LAND Kern County, 1980. Echoe Map Publishing Company.
AGRI-LAND Kings County, 1979. Echoe Map Publishing Company.
AGRI-LAND Madera County, 1979. Echoe Map Publishing Company.
AGRI-LAND Merced County, 1979. Echoe Map Publishing Company.
AGRI-LAND San Joaquin County, 1979. Echoe Map Publishing Company.
AGRI-LAND Solano County, 1979. Echoe Map Publishing Company.
AGRI-LAND Tulare County, 1980. Echoe Map Publishing Company.
AGRI-LAND Yolo County, 1980. Echoe Map Publishing Company.
AGRI-LAND Yuba-Sutter County, 1979. Echoe Map Publishing Company.
Allen, R. H. "The Influence of Spanish and Mexican Land Grants in the Agricultural History of California." Typewritten. Berkeley: Giannini Foundation Library, 1932.
——. "Economic History of Agriculture in Monterey County, California During the American Period." Ph.D. dissertation, University of California, Berkeley, 1934.
——. "The Spanish Land Grant System as an Influence in the Agricultural Development of California." *Agricultural History* 9 (July 1935): 127-142.
American Cooperation, 1942-1945. Philadelphia: American Institute of Cooperatives, 1945.
American Cooperation, 1979-1980. Washington, D.C.: American Institute of Cooperatives, July 1980.
Bailey, Warren R. *Economics of Sugar-Beet Mechanization.* USDA Circular #907, August 1952.

Bain, Joe S.; Caves, Richard E.; and Margolis, Julian. *Northern California's Water Industry*. Baltimore: Johns Hopkins Press, 1966.

Bainer, Roy. "Science and Technology in Western Agriculture." *Agricultural History* 49 (January 1975): 56-72.

Baker, George L. "Land is Power: The Kingdom of the Railroads." *Nation* 216 (March 12, 1978): 334-349.

Ballard, Patricia Louise. ". . . And Conflict Shall Prevail." Master's thesis, University of California, Los Angeles, 1980.

Bancroft, Hubert Howe. *The Works of Hubert Howe Bancroft*. Santa Barbara: Wallace Hebbard, 1970.

Bangor Punta Corporation. *10-K Form* for the year 1979.

Barnett, Paul; Bertolucci, Katherine; Villarejo, Don; and Weaver, Regan. *Labor's Dwindling Harvest*. Davis: California Institute for Rural Studies, 1978.

Beck, Warren A. and Haase, Ynez D. *Historical Atlas of California*. Norman, Ok.: University of Oklahoma Press, 1974.

Beebe, Lucius. *The Central Pacific and the Southern Pacific Railroads*. Berkeley: Howell-North, 1963.

Benedict, Murray R. *Farm Policies of the United States, 1790-1950*. New York: The Twentieth Century Fund, 1953.

―――. *Can We Solve the Farm Problem*. New York: The Twentieth Century Fund, 1955.

Berg, Norman. *A History of the Kern County Land Company*. Kern County Historical Society, 1971.

Bratten, Marsha. "Federal Land Grants Benefiting the University of California." Master's thesis, University of California, Berkeley, 1967.

Brown, William S. and Shaw, S. B. *California Rural Land Use and Management*. USDA Forest Service California Region, 1944.

Burcham, L. T. *California Range Land*. Sacramento: Division of Forestry, State Department of Natural Resources, 1957.

California. *Hearings on Farm Labor*. Co-Sponsored by Edmund G. Brown, Governor and John F. Henning, Under Secretary of the U.S. Department of Labor. March 13, 1964.

California Assembly. "Central Valley Project: Federal or State." *Assembly Interim Committee Reports, 1953-1955* 13 (May 1955).

California Assembly, Special Committee on Land Monopoly. *Report, 1876*. Sacramento, 1877.

California's Central Valley Project. California State Chamber of Commerce, September 1943.

California Crop and Livestock Reporting Service. *1979 California Fruit and Nut Acreage*. Sacramento, June 1980.

―――. *California Annual Livestock Report, 1947*. Sacramento, January 1947.

―――. *California Annual Livestock Report Summary for 1947*. Sacramento, April 5, 1948.

―――. *California Annual Vegetable Summary, 1979 Preliminary*. Sacramento, January 1980.

―――. *California Field Crop Statistics, 1866-1946*. Sacramento, July 1947.

―――. *California Field Crop Statistics, 1944-1952*. Sacramento, May 1953.

―――. *California Field Crop Statistics, 1955-1964*. Sacramento, June 1965.

―――. *California Fruit and Nut Statistics, 1954-1967*. Sacramento, June 1968.

―――. *California Fruit and Nut Statistics, 1965-1977*. Sacramento, April 1978.

―――. *California Fruit and Nut Statistics, 1978-1979*. Sacramento, January 1980.

―――. *California Livestock Statistics, 1943-1957*. Sacramento, January 1957.

―――. *California Livestock Statistics, 1955-1967*. Sacramento, January 1968.

―――. *California Livestock Statistics, 1974*. Sacramento, June 1975.

―――. *California Livestock Statistics, 1979*. Sacramento, June 1980.

―――. *California Principal Crop and Livestock Commodities 1979*. Sacramento, June

1980.
———. *California Vegetable Crops, 1959-1967.* Sacramento, August 1968.
———. *California Vegetable Crops, 1968-1969.* Sacramento, August 1970.
———. *California Vegetable Crops, 1969-1977.* Sacramento, July 1978.
———. *California Vegetable Crops, 1977-1978.* Sacramento, August 1979.
———. *California Vegetable Crops, 1978-1979.* Sacramento, July 1980.
———. *Field Crop Statistics, California 1962-1971.* Sacramento, June 1972.
———. *Field Crop Statistics, California 1967-1976.* Sacramento, June 1977.
———. *Field Crop Statistics, California 1977-1978.* Sacramento, July 1979.
———. *Prices Received by California Producers for Farm Commodities, 1909-1950.* Sacramento, 1951.
California Commission of Immigration and Housing. *A Report on Large Landholdings in Southern California.* Sacramento, 1919.
California Department of Agriculture. *California Livestock and Poultry: A Statistical Summary, 1867-1942.* Special Publication #193. Sacramento, March 1943.
California Department of Employment. *California Annual Farm Labor Report* for the years 1952-1966. Sacramento, 1952-1966.
California Department of Rural Resources, Division of Mines. *Geologic Formations and the Economic Development of the Oil and Gas Fields of California.* Bulletin #118. Sacramento, April 1943.
California Department of Water Resources. *The California State Water Project, 1976: Activities and Future Management Plans.* Bulletin 132-77. Sacramento, November 1977.
———. *The California State Water Project, 1979: Activities and Future Management Plans.* Bulletin 132-80. Sacramento, November 1980.
California Employment Development Department. *Midmonth Estimate of Agricultural Employment by Type of Worker, Report 881W.* September 15, 1980.
———. "Peak Employment on California Farms by Type of Worker, 1966-1979." n.d.
California Legislature, Joint Committee on Public and State Lands. *Report, 1871.* Sacramento, 1872.
California Legislature, Joint Committee on Swamp and Overflowed Lands and Land Monopoly. *Report, 1874.* Sacramento, 1875.
California State Agricultural Society. *Transactions.* Sacramento, 1859.
———. *Transactions.* Sacramento, 1869.
California State Board of Agriculture. *Statistical Report, 1911.* Sacramento, 1912.
———. *Statistical Report, 1918.* Sacramento, 1919.
———. *Statistical Report, 1921.* Sacramento, 1922.
California State Board of Control. *California and the Oriental.* Sacramento, 1922.
California State Board of Equalization. *Annual Report, 1872-1873.* Sacramento, 1874.
California State Bureau of Labor Statistics. *Second Biennial Report for the years 1885 and 1886.* Sacramento, 1887.
California State Land Commission. *Third Report, 1875-1876.* Sacramento, 1877.
California State Mexican Fact-Finding Committee. *Mexicans in California.* San Francisco, 1930.
California State Reconstruction and Reemployment Committee. *Suggested Agricultural Policies for California.* Sacramento, June 1947.
California State Surveyor General. *Annual Report* for the years 1855, 1856, 1860, 1862. Sacramento.
———. *Biennial Report* for the years 1865-1867 through 1877-1879, 1880-1882 through 1902-1904. Sacramento.
California State Tax Commission. *Report, 1917.* Sacramento, 1917.
California Westside Farmers. "Fact Sheet." , 1977.
Carman, Hoy F. "Tax Loss Agricultural Investments Before and After Tax Reform." *American Journal of Agricultural Economics* 54 (November 1972): 627-34.
———. "Tax Shelter Investment in Agriculture, Some Economic Issues."

Mimeographed. Berkeley: Giannini Foundation Library, 1976.

———. "Tax Loss Farming: A Perennial Problem." *California Agriculture* 32 (December 1978): 12-13.

Carr, Ezra S. *The Patrons of Husbandry on the Pacific Coast.* San Francisco: A. L. Bancroft and Company, 1875.

Caughey, John W. *California.* Englewood Cliffs: Prentice Hall Inc., 1953.

Chambers, Clarke A. *California Farm Organizations.* Berkeley: University of California Press, 1952.

Chiu, Ping. *Chinese Labor in California.* Madison: State Historical Society of Wisconsin, 1963.

Cleland, Robert Glass. *The Cattle on a Thousand Hills.* San Marino, Ca.: Huntington Library, 1941.

———. *The Irvine Ranch of Orange County.* San Marino, Ca.: Huntington Library, 1952.

Cochrane, Willard W. and Ryan, Mary E. *American Farm Policy, 1948-1973.* Minneapolis: University of Minnesota Press, 1976.

"Concerning California's Horticultural Industry." *Orchard and Farm* 2 (January 1904): 16.

Cone, Victor. *Irrigation in the San Joaquin Valley, California.* USDA Office of Experiment Stations Bulletin #239, 1911.

Cook, Sherburne F. *The Conflict Between the California Indian and White Civilization.* Berkeley: University of California Press, 1976.

Coolidge, Mary Roberts. *Chinese Immigration.* New York: Henry Holt and Company, 1909.

Cooper, Margaret. "Land, Water and Settlement in Kern County, California 1850-1890." Master's thesis, University of California, Berkeley, 1954.

Cooperative Digest Yearbook and Directory of Farmer Cooperatives, 1st Edition. Ithaca, New York: Roy H. Paul Inc., 1947.

Cothern, James H. *The Cattle Feeding Industry, Past, Present, Future.* University of California, Agricultural Extension Service AXT-379, July 1973.

Cox, Edwin E. "Farm Tenantry in California." *Transactions of the Commonwealth Club* 11 (December 1916): 444-56.

Craig, Richard B. *The Bracero Program.* Austin: University of Texas Press, 1971.

Crouch, Winston A. and McHenry, Dean E. *California Government.* Berkeley: University of California Press, 1949.

Crow, Carl. "A New Eight Million Dollar Crop." *The Country Gentleman* 82 (October 13, 1917): 10-11, 25.

Crowe, Earle. *Men of El Tejon.* Los Angeles: Ward Ritchie Press, 1957.

The Daily Californian. Berkeley.

Dale, Edward Everett. *The Range Cattle Industry.* Norman: University of Oklahoma Press, 1930.

Dana, Samuel Trask and Krueger, Myron. *California Lands.* Washington: American Forestry Association, 1958.

Dangerfield, Jeanne. "Sowing the Till." *Congressional Record* 119 (May 16, 1973): S9247-S9255.

Davis, Horace. "California Breadstuffs." *Journal of Political Economy* 2 (1894): 517-35, 600-08.

Dixon Tribune. Dixon.

Dumke, Glenn S. *The Boom of the Eighties in Southern California.* San Marino, Ca.: Huntington Library, 1963.

Eldridge, Zoeth Skinner. *History of California.* New York: The Century History Company, nd.

Erdman, H. E. "The Development and Significance of California Cooperatives, 1900-1915." *Agriculture History* 32 (July 1958): 179-85.

Faustman, Stanley Paul. "Pressure Groups and the California State Relief Administration." Master's thesis, University of California, Berkeley, 1942.

Fellmeth, Robert G. *Ralph Nader's Study Group Report on Land in California*. New York: Grossman Publishers, 1973.

Fisher, Lloyd H. *The Harvest Labor Market in California*. Cambridge: Harvard University Press, 1953.

French, Ben C.; Tamini, Niniv; and Nuckton, Carole Frank. *Marketing Order Program Alternatives: Use and Importance in California, 1949-1975*. University of California, Agricultural Experiment Station Bulletin #1890, May 1978.

Fridley, R. B. and Adrian, P. A. *Mechanical Harvesting Equipment for Deciduous Tree Fruits*. University of California, Agricultural Experiment Station Bulletin #825, July 1966.

Friedland, William H. and Barton, Amy E. "Tomato Technology." *Society* 13 (Sept./Oct. 1976): 1-17.

Friedland, William H.; Barton, Amy E.; and Thomas, Robert J. *Manufacturing Green Gold*. University of California, Davis, July 1978.

Froberg, John. "The Land Grant to the Southern Pacific Railroad." Typewritten. Berkeley: Bancroft Library, 1917.

Fuller, Levi Varden. "The Supply of Agricultural Labor as a Factor in the Evolution of Farm Organization in California." Ph.D. dissertation, University of California, Berkeley, 1934.

Galarza, Ernesto. *Merchants of Labor*. Charlotte: McNally and Loftin, 1964.

Gates, Paul W. "California's Agricultural College Lands." *Pacific Historical Review* 30 (May 1961): 103-23.

————. *California Ranchos and Farms: 1846-1862*. Madison: State Historical Society of Wisconsin, 1967.

————. *History of Public Land Law Development*. Washington: Government Printing Office, 1968.

————. "Public Land Disposal in California." *Agricultural History* 49 (January 1975): 159-78.

George, Henry. *Our Land and Land Policy*. San Francisco: White and Bauer, 1871.

Golzé, Alfred R. *Reclamation in the United States*. Caldwell, Idaho: Caxton Printers, Ltd., 1961.

The Great San Joaquin and Sacramento Valleys of California-an Irrigation Scheme. 1873.

Harding, S. T. *Water In California*. Palo Alto: n-p Publishers, 1960.

Hedges, Trimble R. and Bailey, Warren R. *Economics of Mechanical Cotton Harvesting*. University of California, Agricultural Experiment Station Bulletin #743, April 1954.

Higgins, F. Hal. "John M. Horner and the Development of the Combined Harvester." *Agriculture History* 32 (January 1958): 14-24.

Holmaas, Arthur J. *Agricultural Wage Stabilization in World War II*. Washington: USDA Bureau of Agricultural Economics Agricultural Monograph Number 1, 1950.

Hundley, Norris Jr. *Water and the West*. Berkeley: University of California Press, 1975.

Hutchinson, William H. *Oil, Land and Politics: The California Career of Thomas Robert Bard*. Norman, Ok.: University of Oklahoma Press, 1965.

Irrigation in California, the San Joaquin and Tulare Plains. Sacramento: Record Stream Books and Job Printing Company, 1873.

James, Marquis, and Rowland, Bessie. *Biography of a Bank*. New York: Harper Brothers, 1954.

Jamieson, Stuart Marshall. "Labor Unionism in American Agriculture." Ph.D. dissertation, University of California, Berkeley, 1943.

Johnston, W.E. and Dean, G.W. *California Crop Trends: Yields Acreages and Production Areas*. University of California, Agricultural Experiment Station Circular #551, November 1969.

Kahrl, William L., ed. *The California Water Atlas*. Sacramento: Governor's Office of Planning and Research, 1978.

Key, Leon Goodwin. "The History of the Policies in Disposing of the Public Lands in California, 1769-1900." Master's thesis, University of California, Berkeley, 1938.

Kincaid, E. A. "The Federal Land Grants of the Central Pacific Railroad." Ph.D. dissertation, University of California, Berkeley, 1922.

King, G. A.; Fitz, J. C.; Warner, C. M.; and Bywater, A. C. *Trends In California Livestock and Poultry Production, Consumption and Feed Use: 1961-1978.* University of California, Division of Agricultural Sciences Bulletin 1899, November 1980.

Kraemer, Erich and Erdman, H. E. *History of Cooperation in the Marketing of California Fresh Deciduous Fruits.* Berkeley: University of California, Agricultural Experiment Station Bulletin #557, 1933.

Krebs, A. V. "Profile of California Agribusiness." In United States Senate, Committee on Labor and Public Welfare, 92nd Congress, 1st and 2nd Sessions, *Hearings before the Subcommittee on Migratory Labor, Farm Workers in Rural America,* pp. 3055-3136. Washington, D.C.: Government Printing Office, 1972.

Kumar, Ramesh; Chancellor, William; and Garrett, Roger. "Estimates of the Impact of Agricultural Mechanization Developments on In-field Labor Requirements for California Crops." In *Technological Change, Farm Mechanization and Agricultural Employment,* University of California, Division of Agricultural Sciences Priced Publication #4085, July 1975.

Kyle, Leonard R.; Sundquist, W.B.; and Gulther, Harold D. "Who Controls Agriculture Now?." In *Who Will Control U.S. Agriculture?,* pp. 3-12. Urbana: University of Illinois, College of Agriculture Cooperative Extension Service Special Publication #27, August 1972.

Land, Alan E. "Unraveling the Rurban Fringe." *Hastings Law Journal* 19 (January 1968): 421-53.

Lantis, David W.; Steiner, Rodney; and Karinen, Arthur. *California, Land of Contrast.* Dubuque: Kendall/Hunt Publishing Co., 1977.

"The Latest Threat to Chavez: Mechanization." *Business Week* (January 30, 1978): 69.

Latta, F. F. *Black Gold in the San Joaquin.* Caldwell, Idaho: Caxton Printers, Ltd., 1949.

Lawrence, William D. "Henry Miller and the San Joaquin Valley." Master's thesis, University of California, Berkeley, 1933.

London, Joan and Anderson, Henry. *So Shall Ye Reap.* New York: Thomas Y. Crowell Co., 1970.

"Look Into Prorate." *Rural Observer* 1 (February 1939): 1.

MacCurdy, Rahno Mabel. *The History of the California Fruit Growers Exchange.* Los Angeles: G. Rice & Sons, 1925.

McAllister, Walter Alexander. "A Survey of Railroad Land-Grant Disposals in California." Ph.D. dissertation, University of Southern California, 1939.

McGowan, Joseph A. *History of the Sacramento Valley.* New York: Lewis Historical Publishing Company, 1961.

McGroaty, John Steiner, ed. *History of Los Angeles County.* Chicago: American Historical Society Inc., 1923.

McKay, A. W. *The Organization and Development of a Cooperative Citrus Fruit Marketing Agency.* Washington: USDA Department Bulletin #1237, 1924.

McWilliams, Carey. *Factories in the Fields.* Santa Barbara: Peregrine Press, 1971.

Mead, Elwood. *Report of Irrigation Investigations in California.* USDA Office of Experiment Stations Bulletin #100, 1901.

————. "Colonization in California." *Transactions of the Commonwealth Club* 11 (December 1916): 397-414.

Metzler, William H. *Operation of the Wage Ceiling on Picking Cotton California, 1943.* Berkeley: USDA, Bureau of Agricultural Economics, July 1944.

————. *Two Years of Farm Wage Stabilization in California.* Berkeley: USDA, Bureau of Agricultural Economics, February 1946.

Montgomery, Mary and Clawson, Marion. *History of Legislation and Policy Formation of the Central Valley Project.* USDA, Bureau of Agricultural Economics, March 1946.

Moody's Manual of Investments: Industrial Securities, 1947. New York: Moody's

Investors Service, 1947.

Moody's Manual of Investments: Railroad Securities, 1946. New York: Moody's Investors Service, 1946.

Morrison, Earnest Merrill. "An Economic Analysis of Farmers' Cooperative Activity in California During 1936." Master's thesis, University of California, Berkeley, 1939.

Murray, William G. *Agricultural Finance.* Ames, Iowa: Iowa State College Press, 1953.

Nash, Gerald D. *State Government and Economic Development: A History of Administrative Policies in California, 1849- 1933.* Berkeley: University of California Press, 1964.

Nelson, Howard J.; Loesser, Cornelius; McMullean, Eugene; Reeves, Richard; Scott, Frank; and Zierer, Paul. "Remnants of Ranchos in the Urban Pattern of Los Angeles." *California Geographer* 5 (1964): 1-11.

Newhall, Ruth Waldo. *The Story of the Newhall Land and Farming Company.* San Marino, Ca.: Huntington Library, 1958.

Newhall Land and Farming Company. *10-K Form* for the year 1980.

No Hands Touch the Land. Davis: California Agrarian Action Project, February 1979.

Nordhoff, Charles. *California for Travellers and Settlers.* Berkeley: Ten Speed Press, 1973.

————. *Northern California, Oregon and the Sandwich Islands.* Berkeley: Ten Speed Press, 1974.

Official Map of the County of Fresno, California 1907. Frank C. McIntire, 1907.

Ogden, Gerald R. *The Excess Lands Provisions of Federal Reclamation Law: A Bibliography.* Davis: Institute of Governmental Affairs Agricultural History Center of University of California, July 1980.

Older, Fremont. *George Hearst, California Pioneer.* Los Angeles: Westernlore, 1966.

Oppenheimer Industries. *10-K Form* for the year 1980.

Paul, Rodman W. "The Wheat Trade Between California and the United Kingdom." *Mississippi Valley Historical Review* 45 (December 1958): 391-412.

Poor's Manual of Railroads, 1888. New York: Poor's Manual Co., 1888.

Puter, S. A. D. *Looters of the Public Domain.* New York: De Capo Press, 1972.

Rasmussen, Wayne D. *A History of the Emergency Farm Labor Supply Program, 1943-1947.* Washington D.C.: USDA Bureau of Agricultural Economics, Agriculture Monograph #13, September 1951.

Reich, William. "The Struggle for the Central Valley Project." *Farm Labor* 5 (Autumn-Winter 1967).

Requa, M. L. and Cory, H. J. *The California Irrigated Farm Problem.* Washington, D.C., March 1919.

Rhodes, Benjamin Franklin Jr. "The Thirsty Land." Ph.D. dissertation, University of California, Berkeley, 1943.

Robbins, Roy M. *Our Landed Heritage.* Princeton: Princeton University Press, 1942.

Robinson, W. T. *Land in California.* Berkeley: University of California Press, 1948.

Rochin, Rufugio I. "Illegal Mexican Aliens in California Agriculture: Courses and Implications." Mimeographed. Davis: University of California, Department of Agricultural Economics, 1977.

Roeding, F. W. *Irrigation In California.* USDA Office of Experiment Stations Bulletin #237, 1911.

Rogin, Leo. *The Introduction of Farm Machinery and its Relation to the Productivity of Labor in the Agriculture of the United States During the 19th Century.* Berkeley: University of California Press, 1931.

Sacramento Daily Union. Sacramento.

San Francisco Chronicle. San Francisco.

Schwartz, Harry. *Seasonal Farm Labor in the United States.* New York: Columbia University Press, 1945.

Seasonal Labor in California Agriculture. University of California, Division of Agricultural Sciences, 1963.

Smith, Roy James. "An Economic Analysis of the California State Land Settlements at Durham and Delhi." Ph.D. dissertation, University of California, Berkeley, 1938.

Smith, Wallace. *Garden in the Sun*. Los Angeles: Lyman House, 1939.

————. "The Development of the San Joaquin Valley, 1772-1882." Ph.D. dissertation, University of California, Berkeley, 1932.

Standard and Poor's Register of Corporations, Directors and Executives, 1981. New York: Standard and Poor's Corp., 1981.

Staniford, Edward. *The Pattern of California History*. San Francisco: Canfield Press, 1975.

"Statement Before a Hearing of the United States Department of Labor, December 7, 1964." Citizens for Farm Labor: *Farm Labor* 2 (December 1964): 22-28.

Stein, Walter J. *California and the Dust Bowl Migration*. Westport, Conn.: Greenwood Press, 1973.

Steiner, Rodney. "The Largest Private Landholdings in the Los Angeles Area." Unpublished list obtained from the author, 1964.

Strahorn, A. T.; Nelson, J. W.; Holmes, L. C.; and Eckmann, E. C. *Soil Survey of the Fresno Area*. USDA Bureau of Soils Survey, 1914.

Street, John M. "Large Landholdings in California." Typewritten. Berkeley: Giannini Foundation Library, January 1955.

Tait, C. E. *The Use of Underground Water for Irrigation at Pomona, California*. USDA Office of Experiment Stations Bulletin #236, 1912.

Taylor, Paul S. "The Excess Land Law: Pressure vs Principle." *California Law Review* 47 (1959): 499-541.

————. "The Excess Land Law: Secretary's Decision." *UCLA Law Review* 9 (1962): 1-43.

————. "The Excess Land Law: Calculated Circumvention." *California Law Review* 52 (1964): 978-1014.

————. "Water, Land and People in the Great Valley." *The American West* 5 (March 1968): 24-8.

————. "Water, Land and Environment." *Natural Resources Journal* 13 (January 1973): 1-35.

Tejon Ranch Incorporated. *10-K Form* for the year 1979.

Tenneco Incorporated. *10-K Form* for the year 1979.

Tetreau, E. D. *The Objectives and Activities of the California Farm Bureau*. Berkeley: University of California Agricultural Experiment Station Bulletin #563, November 1933.

Thickens, Virginia. "Pioneer Colonies of Fresno County." *California Historical Society Quarterly* 25 (March 1946): 17-39.

Thompson, John. "The Settlement Geography of the Sacramento-San Joaquin Delta, California." Ph.D. dissertation, Stanford University, 1957.

Thompson, Thomas H. *Historical Atlas Map of Fresno County*. Tulare: Thomas H. Thompson, 1891.

————. *Official Historical Atlas Map of Tulare County*. Tulare: Thomas H. Thompson, 1892.

Thompson, Thomas H. and West, Albert Augustus. *History of Santa Barbara and Ventura Counties*. Berkeley: Howell- North, 1961.

Tompkins, Walter A. *Santa Barbara's Royal Rancho*. Berkeley: Howell-North, 1960.

Treadwell, Edward F. *The Cattle King*. Boston: Christopher Publishing House, 1950.

Tweeten, Luther. *Federal Farm Policy*. Lincoln, Nebr.: University of Nebraska Press, 1970.

United States Bureau of the Census. *14th Census of the United States: Volume VII Irrigation and Drainage*. Washington, D.C.: Government Printing Office, 1922.

————. *16th Census of the United States, 1940: Irrigation of Agricultural Land*. Washington, D.C.: Government Printing Office, 1942.

————. *United States Census of Agriculture, 1950: Volume III Irrigation of Agricultural Lands*. Washington, D.C.: Government Printing Office, 1952.

————. *United States Census of Agriculture, 1959: Volume 1 Counties, Part 48 California.* Washington, D.C.: Government Printing Office, 1961.

————. *1974 Census of Agriculture Volume 1 Part 5 California State and County Data.* Washington, D.C.: Government Printing Office, April 1972.

United States Bureau of Reclamation. *Comprehensive Plan for Water Resources Development of the Central Valley Basin: Department of the Interior Project Planning Report No. 2-4.0-3.* Washington, D.C.: Government Printing Office, November 1945.

————. *Landownership Survey on Federal Reclamation Projects.* Washington, D.C.: Government Printing Office, 1946.

United States Comptroller General. *Marketing Order Program—An Assessment of its Effects on Selected Commodities.* Washington, D.C.: Government Printing Office, April 23, 1976.

United States Department of Agriculture. *Crops and Markets.* Washington, D.C.: Governement Printing Office, 1942-1945.

————. *Major Statistical Series of the USDA.* Agricultural Handbook #118. Washington, D.C.: Government Printing Office, 1958.

United States Department of Agriculture, Agricultural Stabilization and Conservation Service. *Annual Report, California* for the years 1971-1979. California State ASCS Office, 1971-1979.

United States Department of Agriculture, Bureau of Agricultural Economics. *Agricultural Finance Review.* Vol. 1-9, 1938-1946. Washington, D.C.: Government Printing Office.

————. *Farm Mortgage Recordings, California, 1917-1938.* Washington, D.C., 1939a.

————. *The Migrants, Migration to the Pacific Northwest.* Washington, D.C., 1941a.

United States Federal Trade Commission. *Report of the Federal Trade Commission on Agricultural Income Inquiry, Part II - Fruits, Vegetables and Grapes.* Washington, D.C.: Government Printing Office, 1938.

United States General Accounting Office. *Congress Should Re- evaluate the 160-acre limitation on Land Eligible to Receive Water from Federal Water Resources Projects.* Washington, D.C., November 30, 1972.

United States General Land Office. *Report* for the years 1870-1920. Washington, D.C.: Government Printing Office.

United States House of Representatives, Committee on Interior and Insular Affairs. *Central Valley Project Documents, Part One: Authorizing Documents.* House Document #416, 84th Congress, 2nd Session. Washington, D.C.: Government Printing Office, 1956.

————. *Central Valley Project Documents: Part Two, Operating Documents.* House Document #246, 85th Congress, 1st Session. Washington, D.C.: Government Printing Office, 1957.

United States Immigration Commission. *Immigrants in Industries, Part 25.* Senate Document #633, 61st Congress, 2nd Session. Washington, D.C.: Government Printing Office, 1911a.

————. *Summary Report on Immigrants in Industries in the Pacific Coast and Rocky Mountain States.* Washington, D.C.: Government Printing Office, 1911b.

United States Interagency Task Force. *Price Impacts of Federal Marketing Order Programs.* USDA Farmer Cooperative Service, Special Report #12. Washington, D.C.: Government Printing Office, January 7, 1975.

United States President's Commission on Migratory Labor. *Migratory Labor in American Agriculture: Report of the President's Commission on Migratory Labor.* Washington, D.C., 1951.

United States Senate, Committee on Education and Labor. *Hearings before a Subcommittee to Investigate Violations of the Right of Free Speech and Assembly and Interference with the Right of Labor to Organize and Bargain Collectively.* 74th Congress, 3rd Session. Washington, D.C.: Government Printing Office, 1940.

————. *Employer's Associations and Collective Bargaining in California, Parts I-IV.*

Senate Report #1150, 77th Congress, 2nd Session. Washington, D.C.: Government Printing Office, 1941.

———. *Employer's Associations and Collective Bargaining in California, Part V.* Senate Report #398, 78th Congress, 1st Session. Washington, D.C.: Government Printing Office, 1943.

United States Senate, Committee on Energy and Natural Resources. *Hearings before the Subcommittee on Public Lands and Resources, Acreage Limitation on Bureau of Reclamation Projects.* Publication #95-67, 95th Congress, 2nd Session. Washington, D.C.: Government Printing Office, 1978.

———. *Hearings before the Subcommittee on Energy Research and Development, Reclamation Reform Act of 1979.* Publication #96-39, 96th Congress, 1st Session. Washington, D.C.: Government Printing Office, 1979.

United States Senate, Committee on Labor and Human Resources. *Hearings, Farmworkers Collective Bargaining.* 96th Congress, 1st Session. Washington, D.C.: Government Printing Office, 1979.

United States Senate, Committee on Labor and Public Welfare. *1966 Report of the Subcommittee on Migratory Labor, The Migratory Labor Problem in the United States.* Senate Report #1549. Washington, D.C.: Government Printing Office, 1966a.

———. *Hearings Before the Subcommittee on Migratory Labor, Amending Migratory Labor Laws.* 89th Congress, 1st and 2nd Sessions. Washington, D.C.: Government Printing Office, 1966b.

———. *Hearings Before the Subcommittee on Migratory Labor, Farmworkers in Rural America.* 92nd Congress, 1st and 2nd Sessions. Washington, D.C.: Government Printing Office, 1972.

United States Senate, Committee on Public Lands. *Hearings before a Subcommittee, Exemption of Certain Projects from Land Limitation Provisions of Federal Reclamation Laws.* 80th Congress, 1st Session. Washington, D.C.: Government Printing Office, 1947.

United States Senate, Joint Special Committee to Investigate Chinese Immigration. *Report.* Senate Report #689, 44th Congress, 2nd Session. Washington, D.C.: Government Printing Office, 1877.

United States Water and Power Resources Service. *Federal Reclamation Projects: Water and Land Resource Accomplishments.* Washington, D.C., 1978.

United States of America, Congress. *Congressional Record* 105 (1959), 86th Congress, 1st Session. Washington, D.C.: Government Printing Office.

———. *Congressional Record* 123 (1977), 95th Congress, 1st Session. Washington, D.C.: Government Printing Office.

Upton, Don. "Interior Department Attacks Farmers, Oilmen." *American Oil & Gas Reporter* 21 (September 1978): 1-3.

Vandor, Paul E. *History of Fresno County.* Los Angeles: Historic Record Company, 1919.

Vatter, Ethel. "The California Canning Industry, 1910-1935." Master's thesis, University of California, Berkeley, 1952.

Villarejo, Don. *Getting Bigger.* Davis: California Institute for Rural Studies, Inc., March 1980.

Walker's Manual of Pacific Coast Securities for the years 1918, 1920, 1925, 1930, 1935, 1940, 1945, 1946, 1978. San Francisco: Walker's Manual Inc.

Walker, Ben R. *Fresno County Blue Book.* Fresno: Arthur H. Cawston, 1941.

Webber, Herbert John; Reuther, Walter; and Lauten, Harry W. "History and Development of the Citrus Industry." In *The Citrus Industry,* edited by Walter Reuther, pp. 1-40. Berkeley: University of California Press, 1967.

White, Gerald T. *Formative Years in the West.* New York: Appleton-Century-Crofts Inc., 1962.

White, Jerry. *Number of Farms in the Westlands Water District by Size.* One page sheet obtained from the author.

Whiteside, Thomas. "Onward and Upward with the Arts (Book Publishers-Part III)."

The New Yorker (October 13, 1980): 52-143.

Wickson, E. J. *Rural California*. New York: MacMillan Company, 1923.

Wilcox, Walter W. *The Farmer in the Second World War*. Ames, Iowa: Iowa State College Press, 1947.

Williams, E. W. *Frozen Foods, Biography of an Industry*. Boston: Cahners Publishing Co., 1970.

Williamson, John C. *The Bracero Program and its Aftermath*. Paper prepared for the use of the Assembly Committee in Agriculture, April 1, 1965.

Williamson, Paul Garland. "Labor in the California Citrus Industry." Master's thesis University of California, Berkeley, 1940.

Wills, Harry W. "Large Scale Farm Operations in the Upper San Joaquin Valley." Master's thesis, University of California, Los Angeles, 1953.

Wilson, Edwin E. and Clawson, Marion. *Agricultural Land Ownership in the Southern San Joaquin Valley*. Berkeley: USDA, Bureau of Agricultural Economics, 1945.

Winchell, Lilibourne Alsip. *History of Fresno County and the San Joaquin Valley*. Fresno: Arthur H. Cawston, 1933.

Index

Adams, Frank, 9
Advertising, 58, 59, 141, 179
Agribusiness, 144-47, 181
Agricultural Adjustment Act (1938), 102
Agricultural Adjustment Administration (AAA), 101-3
Agricultural Experiment Station, 119, 168, 181
Agricultural Extension Service, 119, 168, 181
Agricultural Labor Relations Act (1975), 167
Agricultural Marketing Act (1937), 102, 141
Agricultural Producers Labor Committee, 116-17
Agricultural Workers Industrial League (AWIL), 113-14
Agricultural Workers Organizational Congress (AWOL), 166
Agriculture Act (1973), 138
Agriculture Act (1977), 138
Alfalfa, 62, 88, 119, 133
Alien Land Act (1913), 66
Allen, R. H., 9
American Federation of Labor (AFL), 114, 162
Anderson, John, 142, 146, 169
Anderson Clayton Inc., 90, 138
Asparagus, 91, 112, 117, 164, 165
Associated Farmers (AF), 114-16, 124, 182

Bankhead Act (1934), 102
Bankhead-Jones Act (1937), 96

Bank of America, 96-97, 115, 147
Barley, 16, 48, 50, 88
Beale, Edward, 15, 23, 45, 70
Beans, 49, 50, 119, 164-165
Bidwell, J., 16, 47
Bixby, Flint and Company, 14, 15, 23
Boswell, J. G., 137, 138, 151
Boulder Canyon Project Dam (Hoover Dam), 109, 123, 159, 181
Bowles, Henry, 137
Bracero program, 110, 117-19, 124, 130, 160-68, 181, 182
Brier, William, 63, 65
Brody, Ralph, 156

California farm policies: about labor, 114, 116, 167; about marketing and prices, 103, 123; about mechanization research, 167; about urban encroachment, 132-33; about water, 61, 148-51, 173, 181
California and Oregon Railroad, 36-41; merger with Southern Pacific Railroad, 37
California Agricultural Society, 18
California Asparagus Growers Association, 117
California Citrus Union, 58
California Commission of Immigration and Housing, 75-76
California Farm Bureau Federation, 99-101, 103, 112, 123, 181
California Fruit Agency, 58, 59
California Fruit Distributors, 59
California Fruit Exchange, 59, 100
California Fruit Growers and Dealers

Association, 57, 58, 100, 111, 123, 144
California Fruit Union, 57
California Lands Inc., 97
California Marketing Act (1937), 141
California Prorate Act (1933), 103, 123
California Raisin Growers Association, 59
California State Chamber of Commerce, 99, 115-16, 123, 181
Calpak Corporation (California Packing Corp.), 56, 92, 115, 144, 166
Cannery and Agricultural Workers Industrial Union (CAWIU), 114-16
Carey Act (1897), 60
Cattle (see Livestock industries)
Central Pacific Railroad, 36-41; land sales, 67, 68, 69; merger with Southern Pacific Railroad, 37
Central Valley, 2, 113, 131, 132, 170, 178 (see also Sacramento Valley, San Joaquin Valley)
Central Valley Project, 105-9, 123, 130, 147, 148, 151-57, 159, 181, 183
Chambers, Clarke, 100
Chapman, William, 35, 68
Chavez, César, 166
Chinese as farm laborers, 18-19, 26, 63-66, 80-81, 112, 179
Coachella Valley, 109, 110
Coblentz, William, 146, 147
Colorado River Compact, 109-110
Commodity Credit Corporation (CCC), 101-3, 136
Communist Party, 113, 114
Confederación de Uniones Obreras Mexicanas (CUOM), 113
Congress of Industrial Organizations (CIO), 114
Cooper, Margaret, 70, 71
Corporations, 86; and agribusiness, 144-47, 181; foreign, 146-47; processors and shippers, 90, 91, 123, 125; oil, 94, 97, 145 (see also specific corporations)
Cotton, 88-90, 122, 136-38, 141; ASCS payments for, 137; dominance of processors in production, 90; federal policies concerning, 102, 136-37; irrigation and, 88, 180; large landholdings and, 89, 90, 136, 137; mechanization and, 168, 169
Credit: in land sales 21-22, 31, 33; large corporations vs. small farmers and, 146-47; long-term real estate, 94-98; short-term agricultural, 94, 101-2, 136

Criminal Syndicalism Act, 114

Dairying, 86, 87, 88, 133-34
Dams: in the Central Valley Project, 151, 155; Hoover, 109, 123, 159, 181; in the State Water Project, 148
Delta, Sacramento-San Joaquin: 49-51, 91, 179; large landholdings, 50, 97; leasing land, 50-51
Depression: federal action due to low prices during, 101-103, 136, 180; foreclosures during, 95-98; labor situation during, 110-117
Desert Land Act (1877), 33, 70
Di Giorgio, 92, 144, 157, 162, 166, 167
Drought: of 1863 to 1864, 14, 18; of 1876 to 1877, 14-15
Dry-farming, 80
Dudley, xi

Earl Fruit Company, 56 (see also Di Giorgio)
East Indian laborers, 66
Emergency Farm Mortgage Act (1933), 96
Emergency Price Control Act (1942), 102
Engle, Clair, 156
Enlarged Homestead Act (1909), 32

Farm Bureau (see California Farm Bureau Federation)
Farm Land Bank loans, 96-98
Farm organizations: general, 99-100, 103; for labor, 114-16, 124, 184; for marketing, 57-59, 98, 123, 144, 179; for water, 108, 156-57; 98-100, 124 (see also specific organizations)
Farm Placement Service, 162
Farm Workers Association (FWA), 166
Faustman, Stanley, 116
Federal farm policies: about credit, 95-96; about labor, 116, 117-19, 124, 130, 160-68, 181; about marketing and prices, 101-3, 136-39, 141; about taxes, 134-35, 143-44; about water, 105-10, 123, 130, 147, 148, 151-57, 159, 181, 182
Federal Emergency Relief Administration (FERA), 116
Federal Farm Board, 101
Federal Farm Mortgage Corporation, 96
Federal Land Bank System, 96
Federal-State Water Resources Commission, 105
Federal Surplus Commodities

Corporation, 101
Federal Surplus Relief Corporation,
101-2
Federated Agricultural Labor
Association (FALA), 115
Field crops, 46-51, 88-91, 101-3, 136-40;
and irrigation, 62, 88, 89, 134, 159;
price and production programs, 101-
103, 136-40 (see also Alfalfa, Barley,
Cotton, Rice, Sugar beets, Wheat)
Filipino laborers, 112, 113, 115
First Deficiency Act (1936), 105
Forest Homestead Act (1906), 32
Forest Lieu Land Act (1897), 34-36
Forest Reserve Act (1891), 34
Forkner, J. C., 55
Foster, John, 15, 23
Fresno County: cotton in, 89;
subdivision in 53; Westlands area of,
146, 154, 156-57, 159
Friedlander, Issac, 23, 35, 68
Frozen foods, 91, 130
Fruits, 7, 17, 18, 51-54, 91, 92 140-44,
179, 180-81; conversion costs for
production of, 55-56; dominance of
shippers and processors in production,
91-2, 100, 130, 144-47, 181; labor
and, 63, 65, 111, 164, 166; large
orchards and vineyards, 51-53, 92,
122, 142-43, 180; marketing of, 56-
59, 103, 141; mechanization and,
167-69; and tax laws, 143-44
Fuller, Varden, 51, 113

Galarza, Ernesto, 162
Gallo Brothers, 92, 93, 98, 135, 166,
167
Gates, Paul, 12
Geary Act (1888), 65
General Revision Act (1891), 33
George, Henry, 13, 23, 24n., 26
Graduation Act (1854), 31, 32
Guildford-Miller decision (1887), 41

Haggin, Ben Ali, 33, 70-71, 71n.
Hayes, Ed, 162
Hearst: George, 44, Corporation, 134,
135
Homestead Acts: Enlarged Homestead
Act (1909), 32; Forest Homestead
Act (1906), 32; Homestead Act
(1862), 32; Stockraising Homestead
Act (1916), 32
Hoosac Mills decision, 102
Hoover Dam, 109, 123, 159, 181
Humboldt County: land fraud in, 31,

34; oil in, 71

Illegal farm workers, 161, 163-164, 181
Immigration and Naturalization Service
(INS), 161, 164
Imperial Valley 2, 91, 93; irrigation in,
109-110, 123, 124, 158;
landownership, 109, 158; Mexican
labor in, 111-12; 160-acre limitation
and, 109, 124, 158; strike of 1928 in,
113
Indians: as farm laborers, 8, 18, 26, 63,
177-79; land tenure system, 6
Irrigation, 60-62, 104-10, 147-59, 179,
180-82; acreage irrigated, 60, 104,
159, 180; Central Valley Project, 104-
9, 123, 130, 147, 148, 151-57, 159,
181, 183; cotton and, 88, 180; crops
irrigated, 53-54, 62, 86, 88, 89, 123,
134, 159, 179, 180; and Desert Land
Act, 33; for fruit production, 53-55;
groundwater, 62, 104; in Imperial
Valley, 109-110, 123, 124, 158;
increase in use of, 130; irrigation
districts, 61; in production of animal
feed, 134; productivity increase due
to, 86-87; rice and, 88, 180; under
Spanish control, 7; State Water
Project, 148-51, 173, 181; subdivision
and, 53-55; subsidies for, 158-59;
water costs, 123, 150, 151, 159; water
rights and 60, 124; wells, 89-90, 102,
122
Irvine: James, 14, 43, 49; Ranch (or
Company), 53, 56, 92, 121, 133, 135,
158

Japanese laborers, 65-66, 80-81, 179

Kern County: early land concentration,
23; petroleum land, 35, 36; State
Water Project, 148, 151-51, 152 (see
also Kern County Land Company,
Miller and Lux Company, Tejon
Ranch, Oil companies)
Kern County Land Company, 23, 145;
ASCS payments, 103; irrigation and,
62; land acquisition from railroads,
70-71; oil and, 35, 36, 88 (see also
Tenneco)
Kern County Water Agency (KCWA),
150-51; large landholdings in, 152
Kings River Canal and Irrigation
Company, 70

Labor, 18-19, 63-67, 110-19, 124-25,

160-69, 179, 180, 181; Bracero
program, 110, 117-19, 124, 130, 160-
68, 181, 182; Chinese, 18-19, 26, 63-
66, 80-81, 112, 179; decline in use of
since World War II, 130; East Indian,
66; Filipino, 112, 113, 115; grower
activity in 1920s and 1930s, 115-117;
Indian, 8, 18, 26, 63, 177-79; increase
in need for in 1920s and 1930s, 86-87;
Japanese, 65-66, 80-81, 179;
mechanization and, 19, 119, 130,
167-69; Mexican, 63-64, 66-67, 111-
12, 118, 124, 160-68, 179, 182; in
ranchos, 8; under Spanish control, 7;
wages of farm, 18, 64, 66, 110-11,
112, 161, 163, 165, 166; worker
activity, 66, 113-15, 124, 166-67;
during World War II, 110, 117-19,
124, 182
Labor Management Relations Act
(1947), 161, 167
Labor unions: Chavez, César, 166;
CUOM, 114; employer groups and,
115-17; FALA, 115; UCAPAWA,
114-15; in the 1920s and 1930s, 113-
15; UFWOC, 164, 166, 167
La Follette Committee, 98, 98n, 99,
116, 119
Land Bank Commission, 96
Land concentration, 23-24, 73-79, 119-
122, 169-171, 172, 178, 182-83;
agribusiness and, 144-47; in the delta,
50, 97; farm size change and, 130-31;
federal land disposal and, 30-42; grain
production and, 45-48, 178-79; in the
Imperial Valley, 109, 158; livestock
and, 43-48, 178; ranchos and, 7-8,
177-78; in the Sacramento Valley, 24,
77-79, 172; in the San Joaquin Valley,
24, 77-79, 172; in southern California,
24, 43, 44, 78, 172; speculation and,
23-24; state land disposal and, 22, 23;
subdivision and, 51-56, 179; sugar
beets and, 48-49, 88 (see also Large
landholdings)
Land disposal, California, 20-24, 26, 30,
178
Land disposal, federal, 13, 20, 30-42,
178; cash sales, 20-21; Desert Land
Act (1877), 33, 70; Homestead Acts,
32; mineral lands, 35-36; railroads,
36-42; scrip and lieu, 34-35; Timber
Culture Act (1873), 36; timberlands,
34
Land investment, 67-73; by foreign
corporations, 146-47; oil and, 71-73,

81; railroads and, 67-71, 81 (see also
Speculation, land)
Land leasing, 49-51, 93, 157, 180
Land monopoly (see Land
concentration)
Large landholdings (by name): for
cotton, 90, 138; in delta in 1918, 50;
for field crops in general, 88; in
Imperial Valley, 158; in Kern County
Water Agency, 152; largest in 1871,
23; for livestock, 15, 43-45, 87-88,
134-35; in late 1970s, 188-208; in
1945/46, 120-21; oil companies, 73,
94, 145; orchards and vineyards, 51-
52, 92, 142-43; for rice, 48, 139; in
Sacramento Water Contractors
Association, 155; southern California
in 1917, 43, 44; sugar companies, 48,
88, 140; Tulare Lake area, 47, 137;
used for wheat, 19, 46, 47 (see also
specific names of holdings)
Lettuce, 91, 93, 112, 142, 145, 165, 168
Livestock industries, 13-15, 26, 43-45,
87-88, 131, 133-136, 177; dairying,
86-88, 133-34; feedlots and feed grain
production,, 134-35; large
landholdings and, 15, 43-45, 87-88,
134-35, 178; origins, 12, 14; on
ranchos, 8, 14-15, 26, 177-78; tax
shelters for, 134-35

McCarren-Walter Act (PL414), 163
McCreary Act (1893), 65
McLaughlin, Charles, 23, 68
McNary-Haughen Plan, 101
Marketing associations, 57-59, 98, 123,
144, 179; advertising by, 58, 59;
drying and canning by, 59, 144;
railroads and, 56-57
Marshall, Robert, 104
Matt vs. *Union Pacific* (1879), 42
Maudlin, B. M., 22
Mechanization, 19, 46, 119, 130, 167-
69, 173, 182; of cotton, 168, 169; of
fruits, 167-69; productivity and, 142-
43, 178; of vegetables, 142, 168-69
Metropolitan Water District of southern
California (MWD), 149, 150-51
Mexican Farm Labor Agreement, 118
Mexicans: as farm laborers, 63, 66-67,
110-13, 118, 124, 160-68, 179, 182;
labor unions of, 113
Miller, Henry, 70
Miller and Lux Company, 23, 35, 44-45,
71, 76, 178, 183; irrigation and, 62;
liquidation of, 87-88, 97

Mission system, 6-7, 26, 177
Morrill Act (1862), 21, 22, 35
Mullen and Hyde, 22

National Agricultural Workers Union
    (NAWU), 162, 166
National Farm Labor Union (NFLU),
    162
National Land for People vs. *Bureau of
    Reclamation*, 152
National Recovery Act (1933), 109
Newhall Land and Farming Company
    (same as Newhall Land Company and
    Newhall Land and Cattle Company),
    12, 43, 53, 56, 121, 133, 144, 147; oil
    production and, 88, 93
Nickel, George, 137
Nordhoff, Charles, 47, 63, 112
Nuts, 91, 141-43, 169

Oil, 35-36, 71-73, 81, 88, 93-94, 145
Omnibus Adjustment Act (1926), 107,
    157
Onions, mechanization and, 169
Orange Growers Protection Union, 57
Orland Project, 109
Ostrich Industry, 45
Our Land and Land Policy (George), 13,
    23

Pacific Gas & Electric Company (PG &
    E), 105, 115
Placer Mining Act (1870), 34, 35
Pomeroy, Harold, 116
Potatoes, 50
Preemption Act (1841), 31, 32, 34
Presidios, 6
Pueblos, 6-7
Puter, S. A. D., 31, 34

Railroad Land Grant Forfeiture Act
    (1890), 41
Railroads, 16; Chinese laborers and,
    18-19, 26, 63-66, 80-81, 112, 179;
    federal land grants for, 36-42; grain
    production and, 19-20; land
    ownership by, 122, 156-58, 169-70,
    183; land sales by, 67-71; land
    speculation and, 67-71, 81; oil on
    lands of, 73; rates and marketing of
    produce, 56-57; in the San Joaquin
    Valley, 19-20, 37, 42; southern
    California land boom and, 53
Ralston, William C., 70
Ranchos, breakup in southern
    California, 79; establishment of; 7-8,

177-78; grain cultivation and, 19;
    influence of, 8-13, 26, 178; livestock
    and, 8, 14-15, 26, 43, 177-78
Reclamation Project Act (1939), 106
Revenue Act (1942), 143
Rice, 48, 119, 139-40; irrigation and, 88,
    180; large landholdings and, 88, 139
Rivers and Harbors Act (1937), 105
Rivers and Harbors Act (1939), 151,
    154

Sacramento Valley, 2, 7, 17, 131, 132;
    dry-farming in, 80; field crop
    production in, 88; fruits and
    vegetables in, 91; land concentration
    in, 24, 77-79, 172; land subdivision
    in, 54; natural gas in, 93; Orland
    Project, 109 railroads and, 19; rice in,
    139-40; Sacramento Water Contractors
    Association, 155 wheat in, 47;
Sacramento Water Contractors
    Association, 155
Sales of land: cash, 31-32; credit in, 21-
    22, 32, 33; by railroads, 67-71
Salinas Valley: Filipino laborers in, 112;
    sugar beets in, 48-49; Mexican labor
    in, 111-12; vegetables and, 93; wheat
    and, 46
San Benito Valley, 46
San Fernando Valley, land subdivision
    in, 54
San Joaquin Valley, 7, 16, 51, 131, 132;
    Central Valley Project in, 105-9, 123,
    130, 147, 148, 151-57, 159, 181, 183;
    cotton in, 89-90, 122; fruits and
    vegetables in, 51, 91; land
    concentration in, 24, 77-79, 172;
    livestock in, 43, 131; Miller and Lux
    holdings in, 44-45; oil in, 71-73;
    railroads and, 19-20, 37, 42; rice in,
    139; sugar beets in, 140; wheat
    production in, 46, 47
San Luis Act (1960), 156
San Luis project, 156
Sargent, A. A., 33, 65
Schulenberg vs. *Harrison* (1874), 41
Scott, Tom, 72, 73
Secularization of missions, 7-8
Sheep (*see* Livestock industries)
Silliman, Benjamin, 71-72
Simon J. Lubin Society, 103
Sioux Indian scrip, 35
Soil Bank program, 136
Soil Conservation and Domestic
    Allotment Act (1936), 102
South Lake Farms, 137, 138, 146

Southern California, 2, 132; fruit in, 54; land boom, 53-54; oil in, 71, 72, 93 land concentration in, 43-44, 78, 172; oil in, 71, 72, 93
Southern California Fruit Exchange, 58
Southern California Fruit Growers Exchange, 59
Southern Pacific Railroad: forefeiture of land, 42; landholdings, 76, 121, 138, 156-57, 158; land leasing, 90; land sales, 67, 69, 73, 109; merger with other railroads, 37; oil lands, 73, 90 (see also Railroads)
Spanish period, 6-13, 177-78
Specialty crops (see Fruits, Vegetables)
Speculation, land, 20, 178-79; in conversion to fruit orchards, 55; land concentration and, 23-24; railroads and, 67-71, 81; state Surveyor-Generals and, 22 (see also Land investment)
Spreckels Sugar Company, 48, 88, 140
Standard Oil Company, 73, 90, 94, 145
Stanford, Leland, 68
State Board of Equalization, 24, 24n.; Report of 1872, 23, 24, 25, 74-75
State Emergency Relief Administration (SERA), 114, 116
State Relief Administration (SRA), 116
State Water Project, 148-51, 173, 181
Stockraising Homestead Act (1916), 32
Strangers in Our Fields (Galarza), 162
Strawberries, 165
Subdivision of large holdings, 51-56, 79-80, 179, 183; Kern County Land Company, 71; post-World War I, 87
Subsidies, for irrigation, 158-59
Sugar Act (1937), 102
Sugar beets, 88, 119, 140, 165; large landholdings and, 48-49, 88, 140; mechanizing harvest of, 167-69 price and production controls, 102, 140
Surveyor-General, state land disposal and, 21-22
Swamp lands, disposal of, 20-24, 49

Taxes: livestock tax shelters and, 134-35; for orchard and vineyard development, 143-44; relief from, 132-33
Tax Reform Act of 1969, 134, 143
Tax Reform Act of 1976, 143
Taylor, Paul, 150
Tejon Ranch, 15, 45, 146, 170; fruit production by, 53; oil and, 88; Tejon Land Company, 133

Tenant farming, 48-51, 66, 179-80
Tenneco Inc., 133, 134, 145, 151, 170 (see also Kern County Land Company)
Tevis, Lloyd, 35, 70-71
Timber and Stone Act (1878), 34
Timberlands, 34
Tomatoes, 142, 143, 164, 168, 169,
Trade Union Unity League (TUUL), 113-14
Transamerica Corporation, 97
Treaty of Guadalupe-Hidalgo, 8, 12
Trespass Act (1850), 16, 43
Tulare Lake area, 47, 62, 89, 137, 154

Union Pacific Railroad Act (1862), 37
United Cannery, Agricultural, Packing, and Allied Workers of America (UCAPAWA), 114-15
United Farm Workers Organizing Committee (UFWOC), 164, 166, 167
United States Corps of Engineers, 151, 154-55, 157
United States Bureau of Reclamation, 94, 105-6, 108-10, 147-59, 167, 173, 181-82; 160-acre limitation and, 107-109, 137-38, 147, 152-58, 181 (see also Boulder Canyon Project; Central Valley Project)
United States Census of Agriculture, 2-3, 104
United States vs. Tulare Lake Canal, 154
Urbanization, 132, 171

Valentine scrip, 35
Vegetables, 18, 49, 51, 52, 62, 91-93, 141-143, 180; dominance of shippers and processors in production, 90, 100, 130, 144-47, 181; effects of Bracero program on production of, 164-65; mechanization and, 142, 168-69 (see also specific crops)

Wages of farm laborers, 18, 64, 66, 110-111, 112, 161, 163, 165, 166, 182
Wage Stabilization Program, 124, 182
War Food Administration, 117
Water (see Irrigation)
Water rights, irrigation and, 60, 124, 179
Western Pacific Railroad, 36-41; land sales, 67; merger with Southern Pacific Railroad, 37
Westlands Water District, 146, 154, 156-57, 159
Wheat, 16-19, 45-48, 178-79; export of,

16-17, 46; large landholdings and, 19,
  46, 47, 178-79; mechanization and, 46
Wheatland Riots of 1913, 66
Wickson, E. J., 12
Williamson Act (Land Conservation
  Act), 132-33; effect on large
  landholdings, 133
Wolfskill, W., 57
World War II: labor situation during,
  110, 117-19, 124, 182; mechanization
  during, 167-68
Wright-Bridgeford Act (1897), 61
Wright District Act (1887), 61

Yellen vs. *Hickel*, 157

About the Author

Ellen Liebman holds a Ph.D. in geography from the University of California at Berkeley.